DATE DUE

MINNESOTA STUDIES IN THE PHILOSOPHY OF SCIENCE

Minnesota Studies in the
PHILOSOPHY OF SCIENCE

VOLUME I

*The Foundations of Science and the Concepts
of Psychology and Psychoanalysis*

EDITED BY

HERBERT FEIGL AND MICHAEL SCRIVEN

FOR THE MINNESOTA CENTER FOR PHILOSOPHY OF SCIENCE

UNIVERSITY OF MINNESOTA PRESS, MINNEAPOLIS

PRINTED IN THE UNITED STATES OF AMERICA

Fifth Printing 1964

Library of Congress Catalog Card Number: 56-11610

PUBLISHED IN GREAT BRITAIN, INDIA, AND PAKISTAN BY
GEOFFREY CUMBERLEGE: OXFORD UNIVERSITY PRESS, LONDON, BOMBAY, AND KARACHI

Preface

This first volume of *Minnesota Studies in the Philosophy of Science* presents some of the relatively more consolidated research of the Minnesota Center for the Philosophy of Science and its collaborators. Established in the autumn of 1953 by a generous grant from the Hill Family Foundation, the Center has so far been devoted largely, but not exclusively, to the philosophical, logical, and methodological problems of psychology. Some papers in the present volume are concerned with the broader philosophical foundations, others with more specific problems of method or interpretation.

All but one * of the papers included here have in some measure either grown out of Center discussions or been modified by them. As one would expect, in a group of ten contributors, there are some significant disagreements on issues of importance. Nevertheless, a substantial common core in the views represented here—amounting in the case of the Center staff virtually to unanimity—will not escape the reader. An important example is our view regarding the meaning of theoretical concepts as defined by their locus in the "nomological net," and the related rejection of the reductionist forms of operationism and positivism.

The core of the Center's staff during the first three years of operation was drawn from the University of Minnesota's faculty and consisted of Paul E. Meehl (Chairman, Psychology Department), Wilfrid S. Sellars (Chairman, Philosophy Department), Michael Scriven (Philosophy Department; Center Research Fellow), and Herbert Feigl (Philosophy Department; Director of the Center). For various periods at various times, consistent with its original intentions, the Center added to its

* Professor Skinner's paper was originally presented at a symposium involving two members of the Center staff, and it is discussed in such detail in one of the papers in this volume that we considered it advisable to reproduce it in full.

Preface

staff and enjoyed the collaboration of Kenneth MacCorquodale (Psychology Department, University of Minnesota), Antony Flew (University College of North Staffordshire, England), and Arthur Pap (Philosophy Department, Yale University). We benefited greatly by conferences that we arranged with H. G. Bohnert (University of California at Los Angeles), C. D. Broad (Cambridge University), R. C. Buck (Duke University), Robert Bush (Harvard University), Rudolf Carnap (University of California at Los Angeles), L. J. Cronbach (University of Illinois), Albert Ellis (New York City), Else Frenkel-Brunswik (University of California, Berkeley), Starke R. Hathaway (University of Minnesota), C. G. Hempel (Princeton University), Abraham Kaplan (University of California at Los Angeles), Howard Kendler (New York University), Sigmund Koch (Duke University), Gardner Lindzey (Harvard University), Henry Margenau (Yale University), Ernest Nagel (Columbia University), C. S. Pepper (University of California, Berkeley), Hilary Putnam (Princeton University), John R. Reid (University of Maryland), B. F. Ritchie (University of California, Berkeley), Gilbert Ryle (Oxford University), B. F. Skinner (Harvard University), K. W. Spence (University of Iowa), P. F. Strawson (Oxford University), Donald Thistlethwaite (University of Illinois), L. L. Whyte (London), and Karl Zener (Duke University). To all these scholars, we wish to express our sincere appreciation for the help and stimulation the Center has obtained from them.

Apart from the papers included in this and the subsequent volumes, members of the Center staff have produced a great deal of less complete material. Most of our local discussions, especially those with outside visitors, were tape-recorded; the core staff and several of our collaborators have written hundreds of pages of memoranda, and longer papers not deemed suitable for reproduction; these materials have been—and we hope will continue to be—utilized by students and faculty; the conferences we have arranged have made possible a large number of public lectures of a more general nature which reached a wide audience at the University of Minnesota; and the individual teaching and research of the Center's staff has of course benefited from our joint discussions. We hope that any judgment of the Center's activities will take into account the full range of these activities.

We set out with the hope and in the belief that intensive investigations in the logical foundations of the sciences would more or less

Preface

directly aid in substantive scientific research. It must be left to the judgment of our readers in what measure the present analyses contribute to the clarification of issues in psychological theory and indirectly to research practice. A second volume, currently in preparation, will also concentrate on the foundations of psychology, and will contain an extended comparison of the methods of definition and explanation in various sciences. Our current plans for the near future include research in the philosophy of physics and will perhaps later expand into other fields of the philosophy of science.

Research in the Center has been an exciting intellectual adventure. We are profoundly grateful to the Louis W. and Maud Hill Family Foundation as well as to the administration of the University of Minnesota for affording us the splendid opportunities that made our concerted efforts possible. Our particular thanks are due to the friendly and efficient assistance of our secretaries, Betty Jacobsen and Betty Unger; to Grover E. Maxwell, who helped prepare the index; and to the staff of the University of Minnesota Press.

Herbert Feigl, *Director*
Michael Scriven, *Research Associate*
MINNESOTA CENTER FOR PHILOSOPHY OF SCIENCE

June 1956

Synopsis

It may be useful to indicate very briefly the content of the papers in this volume, which is in some cases very inadequately conveyed by their titles. The volume begins with a paper of general philosophical interest.

1. *Some Major Issues and Developments in the Philosophy of Science of Logical Empiricism:* HERBERT FEIGL. After a brief introductory survey of current trends in the philosophy of science, the author selects for more detailed discussion the following three issues: the attempt to distinguish the formal from the factual sciences in terms of the distinction between analytic and synthetic statements; the attempt to provide a criterion for factual meaningfulness and the difficulties with the operationist account; and the view that science requires metaphysical presuppositions, particularly those invoked for the justification of induction.

The second paper deals with one of these themes more fully and precisely.

2. *The Methodological Character of Theoretical Concepts:* RUDOLF CARNAP. The author attempts a clarification of the relations of theoretical to observational terms in the scientific language. It contains a new formulation of the (empiricist) criterion of factual meaningfulness for theoretical concepts—here worked out with considerable precision. A further critique of the operationist view of dispositional concepts and an analysis of theoretical concepts as determined by postulates is applied toward a better understanding of psychological concepts.

After this paper on the general logic of theoretical concepts, there follows a series of specific discussions of important theoretical concepts employed in psychology, beginning with the concepts of psychoanalysis.

3. *Critique of Psychoanalytic Concepts and Theories:* B. F. SKINNER. The author sets out very briefly some of his objections to Freudian concepts on the joint grounds of superfluity and adverse heuristic effect, and indicates the approach he prefers—that of radical behaviorism.

Synopsis

4. *A Study of Radical Behaviorism*: MICHAEL SCRIVEN. The author undertakes an extensive analysis of Skinner's reasons for criticizing Freudian theory, and of Skinner's own approach. The argument is that (a) Skinner's approach violates his own methodological principles; (b) these principles cannot be defended on Skinner's grounds; and (c) in the modified form in which they can be defended, they justify a much more thorough and effective behavioristic analysis of psychological concepts than Skinner gives, but relatively few of his more striking conclusions.

5. *An Operational Reformulation of Some of the Basic Principles of Psychoanalysis*: ALBERT ELLIS. In this paper the author attempts to provide an account of behavior genesis and psychotherapy, which is less radical than Skinner's and less highly abstract and metaphorical than Freud's.

6. *Motives and the Unconscious*: ANTONY FLEW. The author, a philosopher, attempts to provide a logical analysis of certain concepts in Freud, and includes new comments on the long discussion of psychoanalytic explanation in the pages of *Analysis*.

7. *Construct Validity in Psychological Tests*: L. J. CRONBACH and P. E. MEEHL. The authors present a detailed analysis of the concept "the validity of a test," arguing for a clearer recognition of four quite different but related sub-types, and show how the procedures used to establish what they call "construct validity" are special cases of the general scientific methods for giving inductive support to regions of a theoretical network.

8. *Problems in the Actuarial Characterization of a Person*: P. E. MEEHL. The author extends his consideration of the empirical studies demonstrating the superiority of mathematical over subjective prediction methods to a new domain, that of the descriptive and dynamic characterization of a single personality. He offers tentative suggestions, based upon theoretical analysis of the clinical process, as to which areas of behavior prediction can be expected to yield similar results, and which will probably not.

9. *On the Logic of General Behavior Systems Theory*: R. C. BUCK. In this paper the author points out some profound logical difficulties and inadequacies of the currently popular approach to psychology via General Systems Theory.

In the ensuing two papers, the approach is carried into the borderlands of psychology and philosophy.

Synopsis

10. *The Concept of Emergence:* P. E. MEEHL and WILFRID SELLARS. Re-examining the fundamental paper on emergence * published by S. C. Pepper thirty years ago, the authors criticize his attempted proof that emergents must necessarily be epiphenomenal. They try to show that the notion of genuine emergence (e.g., raw feels of color) does not involve any contradictions within the scientific framework; and, in particular, that such emergents might possess efficient-causal properties without doing violence to the usual scientific conceptions of causality and explanation.

11. *Empiricism and the Philosophy of Mind (The University of London Special Lectures in Philosophy for 1955–56):* WILFRID SELLARS. The paper works up to an account of the logic of private episodes (thoughts; immediate experiences) by an argument the earlier stages of which constitute a sustained attack on what the author calls "the myth of the given." It begins with a critique of sense-datum theories (both classical and heterodox) but emphasizes that the myth is not limited to the sense-datum form. In addition to the concluding discussion of private episodes (Parts XV and XVI), the constructive steps of the argument include an analysis of facts of the form x *looks red to* S (Part II, Secs. 10–18), an interpretation of Locke, Berkeley, and Hume on the nature of *ideas* and *impressions* (Part VI, Secs. 26–29), a defence of an empiricist version of a 'coherence theory of meaning' (Part III, Sec. 20; Part VIII, Secs. 35–38), some remarks on the logic of semantical statements (Part VII, Sec. 31), and a discussion of the methodology of theory construction in psychology (Parts XII and XIV).

12. *A Possible Distinction between Traditional Scientific Disciplines and the Study of Human Behavior:* MICHAEL SCRIVEN. In this brief note, an attempt is made to provide what the author believes to be a more natural balance to our assessment of the comparative achievements and methods of the traditionally termed "natural" and "social" sciences.

* The idea that when physical systems (e.g., developing animal organisms) reach a certain complexity they acquire properties of an essentially new kind (e.g., life or consciousness).

Contents

Contents

xiv

MINNESOTA STUDIES IN THE PHILOSOPHY OF SCIENCE

Some Major Issues and Developments in the Philosophy of Science of Logical Empiricism

ABOUT twenty-five years ago a small group of philosophically minded scientists and scientifically trained philosophers in Vienna formulated their declaration of independence from traditional philosophy. The pamphlet *Wissenschaftliche Weltauffassung: Der Wiener Kreis* (1929) contained the first succinct statement of the outlook which soon after became known as "logical positivism." In the first flush of enthusiasm we Viennese felt we had attained a philosophy to end all philosophies. Schlick spoke of a "Wende der Philosophie" (a decisive turning point of philosophy). Neurath and Frank declared "school philosophy" as obsolete and even suggested that our outlook drop the word "philosophy" altogether, and replace it by "Einheitswissenschaft" or by "scientific empiricism." The notable impact of Alfred Ayer's first book in England, and my own efforts toward a propagation of Logical Positivism in the United States during the early thirties, and then the immigration of Carnap, Frank, von Mises, Reichenbach, Hempel and Bergmann created a powerful movement, but it elicited also sharp opposition and criticism. Through the discussions within the movement and its own production and progressive work, as well as in response to the

NOTE: This essay is a revised and considerably expanded version of a lecture given in plenary session at the International Congress for Philosophy of Science, Zurich, August 25, 1954. It was first published in *Proceedings of the Second International Congress of the International Union for the Philosophy of Science* (Neuchatel, Switzerland, 1955). In the cordial letter of invitation I received from Professor Ferdinand Gonseth, president of the Congress, he asked me to discuss "l'empirisme logique,—ce qu'il fut, et ce qu'il est devenu." Much as I appreciated the honor of this ambitious assignment, I realized of course that the limitations of time would permit me to deal only with some selected topics within this larger frame. I have had to omit almost entirely all detailed references to the history of logical positivism, the Unity of Science Movement and the present world-wide representation of logical empiricism, and to related movements such as those of criticisms that were leveled against it from without, many important changes and modifications have occurred and are still occurring.

The movement resembles the philosophical development of Bertrand Russell, who in many ways is the prime progenitor of logical empiricism, in that the vitality of our outlook is based upon, and demonstrated by, its flexibility and capacity for growth and adaptation. There is nothing dogmatic or ritualistic in our movement. It is *not* a religion. Quite to the contrary, it is a reaction against and an emancipation from the bondage of metaphysical dogma and speculation. The spirit of the Enlightenment of the eighteenth century and of the *Encyclopedistes* has been revived and been brought to bear upon the foundations of the scientific outlook of the twentieth century. In this it was immensely aided by the tools of modern logic and of logical analysis.

As I see it, logical empiricism has made its most important and constructive contributions in the logic and methodology of the sciences. The foundations of logic, mathematics, physics, biology, psychology and of the social sciences have been penetrated in an unprecedented manner by the work of Schlick, Carnap, Reichenbach, Wittgenstein, Frank, von Mises, F. Kaufmann, Hempel, Woodger, Brunswik, Zilsel, Popper, Nagel, Kaplan, Braithwaite, Pap and many others. It would take many hours merely to outline the most important achievements in these fields. I have reluctantly decided to restrict this paper to a few selected points of basic and general philosophical interest.

As the movement of logical empiricism attained its world-wide scope, we may clearly discern three major trends differing amongst each other more in their method of procedure than in their basic outlook. There is first the trend exemplified most typically by the work of Philipp Frank (and to some extent also by the earlier work of Neurath and von Mises), which combines informal *logical* analyses of the sciences with a vivid

American or Italian operationism, the Signifies Movement of the Netherlands, the contributions of the Polish logicians, or of the various trends in British analytic philosophy. (Recent excellent studies, (30) and (28), have given a well-rounded account of the history of logical empiricism.) Instead, I propose to deal with just a few fundamental points in the epistemology and methodology of the empirical sciences. This enables me to sketch, at least in outline, some of the more important changes and developments in the outlook of logical empiricism. I also attempt to reply to some criticisms which have been made against our position. The present report will unavoidably reflect my own interests and predilections. But this will be compensated by the fact that my own views have developed partly through repeated personal discussions in various periods of the last thirty years with most of the leaders of logical empiricism and of related movements.

awareness of *psychological* and *social-cultural* factors operating in the selection of problems and in the acceptance or rejection of hypotheses and which contribute to the shaping of certain styles of scientific theorizing. In a sense, this is a genuine sequel to the work of Ernst Mach. There is, secondly, the trend characterized variously as "analytic philosophy," "therapeutic positivism," or "casuistic logical analysis," originally introduced by G. E. Moore in England and most strikingly developed and modified by Wittgenstein. Nowadays Cambridge and Oxford, the second even more strongly than the first, are among the chief centers of this type of philosophizing. Here we find the Socratic method applied with extreme subtlety to the peculiarities (ambiguities and vaguenesses, strata and open horizons, implicit rules) of *natural* languages. To be sure, extreme preoccupation with this approach has led to some excesses which were stigmatized as "futilitarian" (the phrase is Gustav Bergmann's). Nevertheless, this informal but often very brilliant method is fundamentally not as different as it may appear from either the older (first mentioned) positivistic-pragmatist approach, or the more rigorous logical reconstruction method. This last and third method is best exemplified in the work of Carnap and Reichenbach, and in that of their students. It is also pursued in the work of Woodger and Braithwaite as well as in the work of Tarski, Mehlberg and others among the Polish logicians and methodologists.

Awareness of meaning and of logical structure can indeed be attained by the informal analyses of the Wittgensteinian type as well as by the special construction of artificial languages in which the cognitively significant features of the natural or the scientific languages are subjected to a more rigorous and systematic scrutiny. It was Wittgenstein's basic insight that the meaning of terms must be found in the rules of their usage. Pointing up this usage in various contexts, eliminating ambiguities and other pitfalls of ordinary language, will always remain at least the first and indispensable step in the business of clarification. And whether, beyond this, strict and systematic explication in terms of a constructed language is necessary or advisable clearly depends on the nature of the problem concerned and on the degree of precision desired in the logical penetration of its structure. It seems fairly obvious that the clarification of the logic of science is greatly aided by the construction of syntactical and semantical metalanguages. As practiced by Carnap, this method of analysis is much more flexible than is realized

5

Herbert Feigl

by its opponents, especially those who support the British natural-language approach. Carnap has pointed out repeatedly * that exact rational reconstruction or explication by means of artificial languages (or language-schemata) may be achieved in various alternative manners, and that the respective advantages and disadvantages of these alternatives have to be weighed against one another. Perhaps only the total set of useful alternative reconstructions can give us anything like a satisfactory analysis of meaning. This corresponds closely to the current British point of view (inspired by the later work of Wittgenstein) with its attention to families of concepts, strata of language, "slippery slopes," tacit presuppositions, and so on.

One of the controversial issues, which I am confident may be resolved by proper attention to the distinction between natural and constructed languages, concerns the division of all statements into *analytic* and *synthetic* ones. As is well known, this dichotomy forms one of the cornerstones of modern logical empiricism, just as it did already—in a different nomenclature—in the classical empiricism of Hume. At least, according to the view held in common by Schlick, Carnap, Reichenbach and many others, this provides the basis for an adequate account of the difference between the formal sciences (logic and pure mathematics) and the factual or empirical sciences. One of the greatest logicians of our time (I shall for special reasons leave his name unmentioned) shocked me considerably when in a conversation many years ago he branded the sharp distinction between analytic and synthetic as *the* metaphysical prejudice in logical empiricism. And only a few years ago another outstanding logician, W. V. Quine (of Harvard University) published an article, "Two Dogmas of Empiricism," (35) † contending that our distinction is an indefensible dogma. Similar criticisms of the analytic-synthetic dichotomy have been made by various British writers.

I shall present my reply to Quine's (and related) criticisms in the extremely compressed form of a few theses and very brief arguments. I shall be concerned to point out in which regards the logical empiricists may maintain the *status quo* and in which other regards important changes of their outlook have become imperative.

1. *The sharp distinction between analytic and synthetic statements is not only fruitful but indispensable.*

---

* See (8), especially p. 204; also (9), especially p. 40.
† See also, however, the incisive critique by Benson Mates (33).

6

No matter what a more sophisticated syntactical, semantical, or pragmatical analysis may finally contribute toward a definitive clarification and characterization of the difference between purely logical truths and factual truths; no matter whether we formulate the distinction in terms of analytic and synthetic, or in terms of true (or false) by virtue of presupposed definitions, designation rules, etc.—the distinction itself is indispensable, if for nothing else, then certainly for the sake of mere clarity of thought. The most obvious and most convincing case can be made out for statements which depend for their truth (*logical* truth in this case) upon presupposed definitions of the purely explicit, abbreviatory, or notational kind. The statement, "If this room is 60 feet long, then it has a length of 20 yards," may serve as an obvious and trivial example. More generally, metrical scales which differ only in the conventional choice of a unit (as, e.g., kilogram vs. pound; Fahrenheit vs. Centigrade; etc., etc.) are analytically equivalent, or logically translatable into one another.

Along similar lines we may say that any sentence, which upon logical analysis reveals itself as a substitution instance of a logical truth, is analytical or tautological. If I say that the weather will either stay the same or change, I have not managed to express an empirical (or synthetic) statement. Clearly we have here a substitution instance of the law of the excluded middle. In Quine's own felicitous formulation, the descriptive terms in such sentences occur only "vacuously."

Besides purely explicit definitions, ordinary contextual definitions (definitions in use) and recursive definitions furnish the bases of undeniably analytic statements. Definitions of these three kinds may be construed either as rules of synonymy (or equivalence), or else as analytic statements in either a syntactical or a semantical metalanguage. Given the context of pure syntax or semantics and given a full-fledged specification of the object-language on hand, definitions may in the second alternative be construed as analytic statements in the respective metalanguage.

I cannot here argue (which, I think, would be laboring the obvious) that the sharp dichotomy of the analytic and the synthetic is indispensable for the logic and methodology of science in that it, and only it, enables us to explicate the difference between necessary and problematic inference, in other words between *deduction* and *induction*.

2. *The revolt against the dualism of the analytic and the synthetic*

7

Herbert Feigl

rests on a confusion of the logical analysis of (artificially fixed) languages with the historical investigation of (growing, shifting natural) languages.

Quine's protestations to the contrary notwithstanding, I am yet to be convinced that this is not the main source of his erroneous repudiation of the fundamental distinction. Even in the historical or descriptively semantic study of languages, we cannot possibly do without specifying the meanings of terms, since they depend upon culture, period, speaker, writer, listener, reader, practical context, etc. Granting all the ambiguities, relativities, vaguenesses and shifts of meaning as they occur in the natural languages,* we cannot fail to notice the rule-governed aspects of linguistic behavior that establish synonymies of terms and consequently the analyticity of certain statements. Once the historical type of investigation is supplanted by the logico-analytical type of reconstruction, we deliberately decide upon certain rules and definitions. This may be done informally by the usual techniques of the Socratic (casuistic, dialectical) procedure or by the systematic elaboration of a language in terms of its vocabulary and its syntactic, semantic, and pragmatic rules. No one will deny the artificial and sometimes even procrustean character, especially of the latter procedure. But, if the simple illustrations given under my first thesis are remembered, could it be seriously maintained that we know what we mean by our assertions unless—at least implicitly and in the given context—the game of language is played according to specifiable and definite rules?

Intelligible and responsible communication is impossible without adherence to rules of inference which presuppose, at least, contextually and temporarily fixed meanings, i.e., synonymies and logical equivalences. Must I tell the logicians that their business would be of no use if these conditions could not be fulfilled?

3. It must be admitted that many empiricists have traditionally tended to misclassify certain rather basic synthetic statements as "really analytic." But reference to this mistake does not justify the repudiation of the basic distinction.

Anxious to avoid the taboo of the synthetic a priori, empiricists have frequently declared that such fundamental statements as those of the transitivity of temporal succession, or of the principle of causality (sometimes even some of the general laws of physics) are analytic—i.e., dis-

---

* Copiously illustrated in a series of articles by Friedrich Waismann (49).

guised definitions, conventions, ultimately tautologies. This must be recognized as a mistake to be charged against those empiricists who commit it. Logically, the mistake boils down to a confusion of what is customarily, but perhaps somewhat misleadingly called "implicit definition" (or "definition by postulates") with explicit definition. The mistake occurs when, e.g., it is said, "we would not call an event A 'earlier' than B; and B 'earlier' than C unless A is also earlier than C"; this is said in (false) analogy to "we would not call Z a 'vertebrate' unless it had a spinal column"; or: "we would not call U an 'uncle' unless it (he) were of the male sex." The applicability of a certain formal structure such as transitivity to a set of empirically given facts is clearly a matter for synthetic statements. And although it might be said that Newtonian time is analytically transitive, or that Euclidean equilateral triangles are analytically equiangular, it cannot be claimed that the transitivity of experienced (or physically measured) time is a matter of analytic truth. Nor can it be said that it is logically true that a physical triangle *empirically* determined as equilateral must therefore also be equiangular. Similarly any formulations which express the principle of causality as an analytic truth simply do not render adequately its ordinarily understood meaning, be that the homely "same causes, same effects," or any of the more sophisticated formulations of nineteenth-century field physics. This meaning can be construed only by means of a synthetic statement. Surely, there are statements which are true by virtue of the meaning of certain terms they contain, and are nevertheless not analytic but genuinely synthetic. But in this case the meaning of the terms in question is not specifiable by explicit definition.

Wherever the meaning of scientific terms is determined by postulates (implicit definitions), statements formulating such meaning may be said to be both synthetic and necessary. But "necessary" does not mean the same as "a priori" in the Kantian sense. "Necessity" here amounts to no more than causal connection as formulated in syntactical P-transformation rules (45) or else in a modal logic. This is perfectly compatible with the empiricist outlook, although it does represent a certain emendation of Hume's analysis of causality. But since in scientific research we can never be sure of the laws of nature, and thus really never know where to apply the accent of modal connection, the problem of induction remains precisely where Hume (or better, perhaps, Reichenbach) left it. All this, however, does not in the least tend to blur the distinc-

9

tion of the analytic and the synthetic. Quite to the contrary, a sharp differentiation between the analytic and the synthetic is needed.

4.*The fact that a given string of signs (a sentence, a formula, etc.) may be the vehicle for either an analytic or a synthetic statement neither blurs the distinction nor introduces a neutral third category of statements. The neutral third thing is nothing more than the series of signs.*

This elementary insight which many of us are at pains to hammer home to our freshman and sophomore students scarcely needs elaboration here. But since several important writers in recent decades have espoused the notion of *functional analyticity* or of a *pragmatic a priori*, it may be useful to scrutinize these ideas, especially inasmuch as they are applied to the logical reconstruction of scientific theorizing.

Is Newton's second law a definition of force; or is it a law of nature that enables us to predict the acceleration of given mass under the influence of a given force? Or is it neither the one nor the other? Is the first law of thermodynamics a definition of "energy" (kinetic and/or potential) or is it a genuine law that tells us that certain measurable quantities are invariant with respect to a whole class of transformations? Is the constancy of the speed of light a matter of definition or of empirical fact? I shall not pause to restate the excellent criticisms (by Mach, Planck, Enriques, Schlick, Reichenbach, or Kraft) that have exposed the weakness of the more exaggerated aspects of Poincaré's, Dingler's, and Eddington's versions of conventionalism. My own tentative resolution of the problem, however, differs from those of the radical empiricists. As I view the matter, I urge that we must recognize the essentially network-like character of scientific theories. A given formula or sentence which somehow relates two or more concepts in the network may be construed as either analytic (definitional) or synthetic (factual) depending on the interpretation of the rest of the system. Since scientists, as a matter of obvious record, shift from one interpretation to another, depending on the context of inquiry (often without being fully aware of this), the only adequate reconstruction would be in terms of a whole set of alternatives. This of course makes the meaning of given symbols systematically ambiguous, but in each single one of the alternative reconstructions the meaning of the symbols is completely fixed. In a sense I am merely applying the Socratic method on the level of the methodology of scientific theorizing. If a physicist tells me—or better still, if he reveals by his very procedures—that he uses Newton's formula, $F =$

M.A, as a means of prediction or explanation, then I know that he must have independent operational access to the three magnitudes M, A, and F. (In that case either Newton's third "law"—here misnamed a "law"—or perhaps Hooke's "law"—equally misnamed—will serve as a definition of force.) Similarly, I would question the customary conventionalistic interpretation of the constancy of c. Surely we cannot interpret both the constancy of c and statements about simultaneity (of spatially distant events) as factual assertions. But a closer analysis of the inductive implications of the results of Michelson and Morley, and especially of de Sitter's observations, suggests that the invariance * of c can be empirically justified, even without recourse to any determination of simultaneity at a distance.

If these conclusions are correct, then one must seriously doubt that "functional analyticity" or the "pragmatic a priori" as applied to specific scientific sentences (formulae) constitutes a genuine third category of statements. If anywhere at all, then these terms had better be used for the very frame-conventions † of the total cognitive enterprise. Parenthetically, I might suggest that some of those frame-conventions might be explicated as P-formation rules of the language of science. For example, it seems plausible that the three-dimensional character of physical space (in ordinary contexts an unquestioned but by no means unquestionable presupposition of science) could be construed as a syntactical feature that determines the form of singular descriptions in science. The rule that a functor like temperature is to be used as a prefix for a triple of coordinates x, y, z; or for a quadruple of coordinates x, y, z, t; reflects a certain basic feature of reality and may thus be construed as a synthetic characterization of our world.

Be that as it may, I have been concerned in the present context merely to point out that the idea of the systematic interchangeability of the analytic and the synthetic character of formulae in theoretical networks may furnish a more adequate reconstruction than *functional analyticity*. According to the interpretation here proposed, *functional analyticity* is a hybrid notion which, when properly analyzed, comes down to either ordinary analyticity (definitional truth), or else to synthetic factuality assumed with the customary inductive confidence and credit bestowed upon well-confirmed hypotheses.

* I.e., the equality of the speed of light in its motion toward and from a reflector.
† Such as the principle of induction; or the realistic outlook. See (18).

5. *Independent testability of logically independent postulates of a scientific theory is a practical requirement of the actual methodology of the empirical sciences.*

It is significant that Pierre Duhem's view of the impossibility of crucial experiments has been reiterated and re-emphasized primarily by mathematicians and logicians (such as Poincaré and Quine). Indeed, from a purely formal point of view it must be admitted that adjustments in any part of the theoretical network may result in a better empirical "fit." But, this does scant justice to the actual practice of science. Moreover, it presupposes the shifting of interpretation from one alternative to another. The successive confirmation of logically independent hypotheses is, after all, one of the most striking features of the scientific enterprise. The search for independent, even if indirect, evidence, the search for converging *lines* of independent evidence, is the major concern of all the experimental ingenuity of modern science.

Permit me to remark somewhat *ad hominem* that logicians would look askance at any scientific theory which presented itself with the claim, "Take me or leave me, but you can't pick out any parts." If I recall correctly, that is precisely what Freud once said about psychoanalytic theory and its "monolithic" character. But Freud himself has repeatedly modified parts of his theory—presumably on the basis of clinical evidence. Science would be in a sorry condition if its theories could not be stated in terms of logically independent postulates. It is precisely for the sake of systematic examination through empirical testing that we must unravel the knowledge claims of a theory into a maximal number of independently confirmable postulates. For example, only after disentangling the various components in the principles of special relativity can we say which experiments confirm which laws. The experiments of Michelson and Morley (Trouton and Noble) confirm one component, the observations on double stars by de Sitter another; and for the confirmation of auxiliary hypotheses, the measurements of aberration and the experiment of Fizeau are equally indispensable.

A view that maintains that the whole body of a scientific theory (if not of all science) confronts experience and that modifications may be required in any part of the system if it does not "fit" obscures dangerously what is of the greatest importance for the progress of science: the successive testing and securing of parts of science—at least in the sense of an approximation. Naturally, no part can be considered as established with finality; but this insight, which impresses the pure logician, should not blind him to the recognition of the method of successive confirmation. It is curious that it should be the logicians who first undermine their own enterprise by a denial of the sharp distinction between the empirical and the logical (because here they are struck with the vagueness of ordinary discourse and of scientific methodology), and then proceed to blur the methodology of science beyond recognition (because from a purely formal point of view a theory is in principle adjustable in any one of its parts). I suggest that if our logical analyses and reconstructions of the scientific enterprise are thus far unable to do justice to its most important and indispensable criteria (of confirmability and of confirmation), we must look for better analyses and reconstructions instead of giving a distorted picture of scientific method.

6. *There is no convincing instance of the alleged need to change the laws of logic in order to achieve better conformity of theory and fact.*

I realize fully that this is a highly controversial and, besides, a very large issue. So permit me here merely to register my serious doubts concerning the role of alternative (three-valued, or many-valued) "logics" as a solvent of scientific problems. Naturally, I expect to be called "conservative," if not "reactionary"; I expect to be reminded of the fate of those who considered Euclidean geometry as unique and as eternally true (or at least of those who were convinced that it will always be more economical to use Euclidean geometry for physical space). I cannot here specify the reasons why I consider the two-valued logic the only one that deserves to be considered a theory of deduction. Nor can I here furnish convincing arguments that neither von Neumann's nor Reichenbach's alterations of logic are required or even helpful in the axiomatization of quantum mechanics. I shall only say that the yes-or-no character of the logic, the only one that can rightfully be claimed to provide the canons of deductive inference, stems from the most basic feature of language: the semantic rules which govern the univocality of the application of terms to items or aspects of experience.

I turn now to one of the most fundamental and notoriously controversial issues: *the empiricist criterion of meaning.* It is not surprising that this has aroused so much dispute. Occam's razor is apt to mobilize the castration complex of the metaphysicians. But psychoanalytic jokes aside, there are, as it were, three blades to Occam's razor, and careful distinctions between them will help toward a more adequate understanding of the import of the meaning-criterion. I shall again proceed by means of concise theses and their elucidation and justification.

1. *The criterion of factual meaningfulness must be distinguished from the principle of formal simplicity and from the principle of inductive simplicity (or factual parsimony).*

Whenever the factual content of two cognitive systems is invariant relative to purely analytic transformations, preference of one system of conceptual representation over another can be justified only on the basis of a principle of formal simplicity or of logico-mathematical expediency. The preference for the kinematics of the heliocentric over against that of the geocentric system is a case in point. If, however, two theories differ in factual content, if the assumptions made in the one theory are more numerous than in the other, then a decision may be made in favor of the factually simpler one. This is merely part of the policy of normal inductive or hypothetico-deductive procedures. The excess cut away by this (second) blade of Occam's razor consists in (presumably) superfluous but meaningful hypotheses. This is the principle of parsimony, the methodological core of Newton's first *regula philosophandi.*

The empiricist criterion of factual meaningfulness, in contrast to the two principles of simplicity just mentioned, is directed exclusively against hypotheses which are absolutely proof against disproof. Such unconfirmability-in-principle may be due to the employment of concepts which are completely isolated from the observation basis of science; this in turn may result from assumptions or stipulations especially made in order to protect some favored hypothesis from refutation. The history of scientific thought contains many examples of this sort. An hypothesis which in its original conception had confirmable consequences is rendered absolutely unconfirmable by special provisions. Absolute space and time, the phlogiston, the caloric, the ether, vital forces or entelechies, etc., at least in the final stages of their most desperate defense, were equipped with properties which made even indirect or incomplete confirmation (or discomfirmation) a *logical* (and not just a practical) impossibility.

2. *In the more liberal formulation of the meaning criterion, considerable progress has been made beyond the narrow position of the earlier logical positivism.*

Direct and complete verifiability—if not explicitly demanded—seemed implied by the position as taken by Carnap, Wittgenstein, and Schlick up to about 1930. But, as Reichenbach had then urged already, a much more liberal meaning criterion is needed in order to do justice to the inferential (inductive) character of practically all our knowledge claims. Carnap, in his epoch-making article, "Testability and Meaning" (6), and Reichenbach, in his important book, *Experience and Prediction* (36), have explicitly formulated the broader new meaning criterion. Further modifications and refinements have been under discussion ever since. Paul Marhenke (32), C. G. Hempel (26), and others have expressed serious doubts as to the adequacy of all thus far suggested, or even as to any conceivable formulations of the meaning criterion.

I admit that an all-around satisfactory and fully precise explication is difficult, but I am confident that confirmability-in-principle (for statements) or logical connectibility with the terms of a suitably chosen observation basis (for concepts) is the explicandum of at least a *necessary* condition for factual meaningfulness. Understood in this way, the meaning criterion still provides a sharp delimitation between sense and nonsense. The suggestion that meaningfulness is a matter of degree seems to me to rest on a confusion between meaningfulness and *degree of specification of meaning.* There are many concepts at the growing edge of scientific theorizing whose meaning may be only very incompletely determined or only very sketchily outlined. In this regard there is indeed no sharp line of demarcation between science and *inductive* metaphysics (or even "natural" theology). The objections to inductive metaphysics or theology should be formulated in terms of the principle of parsimony (inductive simplicity, Occam's razor—second blade) rather than in terms of the meaning criterion (third blade). The meaning criterion applies exclusively to *transcendent* metaphysics or theology, i.e., to doctrines which are immune against tests of even the most indirect sort.

3. *The criterion of factual meaningfulness is to be understood as a proposal and not as a proposition.*

Hence the criterion does not fall under its own jurisdiction. Its adoption can be justified only practically; it cannot be validated, except in the trivial sense that languages of a certain syntactical-semantical-pragmatic structure can analytically be shown to exclude the asking and the answering of empirically unanswerable questions. The criterion is still a powerful instrument for discriminating between sentences with factual meaning and sentences which have only purely formal meaning (such as tautologies or contradictions) and/or those which carry exclusively emotive (i.e. pictorial, emotional, or motivative) appeals. Whether one

Herbert Feigl

considers the distinction thus achieved as the delimitation of science
from metaphysics seems to me mainly an issue of terminology.

4. *Adoption of the more liberal meaning criterion permits the abandonment of phenomenalism and of radical operationism in favor of a
genuinely critical empirical realism.*

The *Aufbau* or logical-construction phase of the early work of Carnap
is now completely superseded by an epistemology and philosophy of
science which has greater affinity with critical realism than with phenomenalistic positivism. This new phase may be regarded as a semioti-
cally more sophisticated and logically more secure form of the empirical
realism which Schlick had so forcefully expounded in his *Allgemeine
Erkenntnislehre* of 1918 (second edition, 1925).* Knowledge, both on
the level of common sense and on that of science, is now being regarded
as a network of concepts and propositions tied only in a few places to
the data of immediate experience, and for the rest a matter of "free
construction." The construction, however, is not that of the *Aufbau*,
which was inspired by Russell's doctrine of abstraction and his hierarchy
of types. It is rather the free but tentative positing of a language, some
of whose particulars and universals correspond to data and features of
direct experience, the vast remainder of which, however, designate unobservables. Einstein, in repeated pronouncements (see especially 15),
embraced precisely this point of view after the abandonment of his
earlier phenomenalistic or more radically empiricist position which he
owed largely to Hume and Mach. To be sure, phenomenalists have
always tried to distinguish their position from subjective idealism, but
the result was never quite convincing. It was a hypocritical realism
essentially designed to counteract the speculative excesses of the transcendent forms of realism. I contend that this hypocritical realism of
phenomenalism must be supplanted by a hypercritical realism (see especially 19, 20, 21, and 44).

5. *The new empirical realism insists on the distinction of the evidential basis and the factual reference of knowledge claims.*

* Credit should here be given also to the independent contributions to a similar
semiotic-realistic epistemology by Richard Gätschenberger. His book, *Symbola* (G.
Braun, Karlsruhe, 1920), which was completed in 1915, contains striking anticipa-
tions of the ideas of Schlick, Wittgenstein and Carnap. The work of the German
epistemologists, Günther Jacoby and Curt Weinschenk, and of some of the American
critical realists, especially of A. O. Lovejoy and Roy W. Sellars, deserves mention in
the same connection. The semiotic aspects of the reality problem had, however, been
largely neglected by this group of thinkers.

The traditional doctrine of radical empiricism, positivism, operationism, and phenomenalism identified the meaning of a statement variously with its verifying evidence, the method of its verification, the observational or experimental operations of verification, or with the verifying data of immediate experience. In keeping with the terminology common to Wittgenstein and the point of view of semantics, these ideas were often formulated also in the slogan, "The meaning of a statement consists in its truth conditions." But in typically phenomenalistic manner, "truth conditions" was invariably understood in the sense of "verifying data."

Critical realists have consistently objected to this myopic identification. It is perfectly clear that existential hypotheses (involving theoretical constructs, illata) cannot be logically translated into statements about evidential data. Obvious examples are as follows: statements about past events; hypotheses of modern physics regarding such unobservables as electro-magnetic fields, atomic and subatomic particles, photons, etc. Positivistic-phenomenalistic attempts at "reduction" of these concepts must now be regarded as complete failures. According to the network analysis of scientific concepts and laws, the verifying evidence is to be viewed as causally related to the *evidenced* "theoretical" entities. If this be metaphysics, make the most of it! But surely it is not the sort of metaphysics that will generate unanswerable problems or unsolvable riddles of the universe. The realism here suggested allows for hypotheses only if they are at least indirectly confirmable, and for theoretical constructs only if they are part of the network which connects them with terms designating data of direct observation.

6. *The meaning of theoretical constructs is best explicated in terms of their locus in the nomological network, i.e., by means of postulates.*

This insight was clearly formulated by Schlick, especially in his doctrine of implicit definition (as formulated especially in the 1925 edition of the *Allgemeine Erkenntnislehre*). Strangely enough, neither Schlick himself nor Carnap utilized this insight in the subsequent development of the late twenties and the early thirties. As I interpret it, Schlick was overwhelmed by the then predominantly phenomenalistic tendencies of Carnap's and Wittgenstein's outlook. But Carnap (and perhaps even Wittgenstein—though I am still not quite clear about his later development) abandoned phenomenalism by stages and came to embrace an epistemology of decisively realistic outlook. In "Testability and Meaning," and the particular form of physicalism advocated there, the constructs of science were analyzed in terms of their introduction through reduction sentences. "Electric charge," "magnetic strength," "elasticity," and countless other dispositional concepts of physics, chemistry, biology, psychology, and the social sciences were analyzed by means of test condition $\rightarrow$ test result conditionals. But more recently it became increasingly clear that the conditionals cannot be construed as material implications. Subjunctive and contrary-to-fact conditionals demand interpretations in terms of some sort of modal (causal) implication.

With this insight the pivotal place of laws in the formation and in the very meaning of concepts was realized. Wilfrid Sellars (43, 45, 46, 47) more prominently than anyone else, at this crucial juncture in the history of ideas, emphasized and demonstrated convincingly that "concepts involve laws and are inconceivable without them." This is the idea which Schlick had rather informally and casually anticipated by realizing the role of postulates in the determination of the meaning of concepts. Positivists of an earlier period were blinded by what they conceived as the power of explicit and of ostensive definitions. But explicit definitions presuppose meanings, i.e., the meanings of the definientia. And the so-called ostensive definitions are not definitions at all, but at best a way of learning to associate certain labels with certain items or aspects of experience. To be sure, if our language is to have extralinguistic reference, some terms must be related by an ostensive step to the data of experience. But this does not suffice as an analysis of the meaning of terms. Wittgenstein and his disciples have for a long time insisted that the meaning of terms consists in the rules according to which they are used. If we decide to fix these rules (at least temporarily) in order to study whatever *definite* meanings there may be, and if we codify these rules in some formal manner, then we discern immediately that it is the interrelations of the symbols in a language that are essential to meaning. These rules of usage may be represented as rules of inference in a syntactical metalanguage. The illusion that the meaning of concepts can be distilled by mere abstraction out of the raw material of experience or direct acquaintance is thereby effectively removed. Wilfrid Sellars' incisive critique of "concept empiricism" (i.e., the doctrine according to which the meaning of concepts is ultimately reducible to the elements of direct acquaintance) applies, as he has amply and emphatically argued, not only to the concepts of scientific theories but also to the concepts of common sense and everyday life. Through adjustments and readjustments the terms of ordinary language have come to be used according to rules, which—fully articulated—amount to implicit definitions. This is epistemologically of the greatest significance in that the customary sharp distinction between observation language and theoretical language is thereby called into serious question, if not entirely eliminated. The predicates and relations even of natural language attain their meanings through a process reminiscent of Darwinian selection, i.e., by a process which is ultimately biopsychological in character. Various networks of concepts (or laws) are subjected to trial, and those which "fit" best are adopted—until further notice.

7. *The new (semiotic) empirical realism requires a revision of the thesis of the unity of science and allows for a monistic (double language) interpretation of the relation of the mental to the physical.*

Carnap's views on the unity of science dated from his constructionistic periods—first phenomenalistic, later physicalistic. It was a thesis of the reducibility of the language of all sciences to a unitary basis (experiential or physicalistic, respectively). But even during the early period of the physicalistic reducibility view, there was the belief that in some way all statements of the sciences were nothing more than convenient *façons de parler* about the data of actual and possible observations. I know, from many conversations with him in recent years, that Carnap has now completely abandoned this last remnant of phenomenalistic positivism. Of course, he is still an empiricist in that he insists that the concepts and statements of the factual sciences must be *related* to concepts designating data of experience. The thesis of the unity of science, if it is to be readapted, must now be formulated as a program of unification rather than as an achievement of unity. The unification of the sciences is progressing most auspiciously on the level of scientific theory. Many originally separate disciplines within physics and chemistry were welded into coherent conceptual structures through the development of the theory of relativity and of the theories of atomic structure and quantum dynamics. Similarly, the progress of biophysics, biochemistry, psychophysiology, etc., especially aided by such interdisciplinary developments as cybernetics, promises higher degrees of coherence for the future. These developments, together with the results of the epistemology sketched earlier, enhance the plausibility of a new monistic solution of the old puzzle regarding the relations of the mental and the physical. While

19

the evidential bases of introspective, behavioral, and neurophysiological studies of human organisms are disjoint, it is quite plausible that some of the concepts formed on these respective bases refer to one and the same set of events. "Mind" and "body" may thus be revealed as hopelessly clumsy and singularly unenlightening categories of an earlier epoch in the history of thought.*

8. *Two quite different forms of logical reconstruction of empirical science, each with its respective advantages and disadvantages, must be distinguished.*

The idea of a unitary nomological net is, as was just pointed out, the projection of an ideal science which can at present be sketched only in a very incomplete outline. Nevertheless, such a schematic reconstruction of the network of concepts and laws can be helpful and illuminating. Only in such an idealized schema are the concepts designating observables connected with the concepts designating unobservables by lawful connections. (Whether these lawful connections are conceived as essentially deterministic or, as present-day physics strongly suggests, as statistical is an important question in its own right, but not vital for the point of the present remarks. Only the future advance of science can show whether something like the determinism of classical physics will be justifiable on a more fundamental level of experimental or theoretical analysis. If the question is raised in the "absolute" sense—i.e., as to the deterministic or statistical character of the "groundlevel" of nature—it is bound to be unanswerable. It reveals itself a pseudo problem because of the complete lack of criteria which would identify the "absolute groundlevel." The question makes sense only when the level of analysis is specified by reference to the variables occurring in the laws and descriptions on that level.)

While the ideal aim of a unitary science is reflected in the sort of reconstruction just suggested, the actual progress of unfinished, *growing* science is more adequately reconstructed by an analysis which sharply distinguishes between theoretical and observation language. The customary reconstruction (5, 13, 27, 2) in terms of partially interpreted postulate systems makes use of the idea of coordinating definitions, or semantic designation-rules (Campbell's "dictionary") which connect the

---

* See my article (25). Another, more elaborate, essay on "The 'Mental' and the 'Physical,' " together with critical discussions by some of my collaborators in the Center is being prepared for a later volume of our publications.

(undefined primitive or defined complex) concepts of the erstwhile uninterpreted postulate system with the concepts of the observation language. The meanings of the observation terms are either taken for granted as they are found in the natural language of common life, or else introduced on the basis of such meanings by explicit or by conditional (operational, reduction-sentence) definitions. The one-to-one correspondence, implied in the idea of coordinating definitions and especially encouraged by the well-known philosophical accounts of physical geometry, is however quite problematic. No matter whether the observation terms are concepts of the physicalistic thing-language or of a phenomenal language, there is at best some sort of probabilistic or confirmatory relation between them and corresponding terms of the theoretical language. This is due, in part, to the usually rather complex causal (or statistical) relations between the theoretically posited magnitudes and the indicator variables of the instruments of observation or measurement. In practically all these situations—from astrophysics to the dynamic psychology of personality—there are obfuscating or "nuisance" variables which interfere with the direct assessment of the theoretical laws (relating basic variables). Then there is also the complexity and/or the (possibly only) statistical character of the relations between the physical situations (stimulus-patterns) of the extradermal world, the central processes, and the ensuing responses of the observer. As long as the obfuscating variables in these domains are neither adequately known, nor sufficiently controllable, the confirmation of theories proceeds implicitly (here pointed out explicitly) with such promissory notes as this: "We are going to account for these anomalies, irregularities, or apparent exceptions at some later date when we know more about all this."

I have used the phrase "promissory note" on previous occasions mainly to emphasize the sketchy character theoretical concepts often have when first introduced. Witness, for example, the progressive enrichment of the concepts of atomic physics during the last century; or, in psychophysiology, the transition from rather barren outline-concepts like memory trace to more fully specified neurophysiological structures and processes. But there are also those other promissory notes at the confirmation base of theories. Once sufficient evidence encourages us to postulate theoretical assumptions (nomological or existential), we disregard baffling anomalies in other domains of evidence and thus feel justified in postponing their explanation as "disturbances" until experimental research has succeeded in disentangling them. An adequate logic of the confirmation of theories will therefore have to differ radically from the logic of primary (simple enumerative) induction. In what follows I shall discuss the contributions of Carnap and Reichenbach toward a theory of inductive probability. I shall begin with a logical-empiricist critique of the widely current view which asserts that scientific method rests upon unconfirmable presuppositions.*

1. *There are no philosophical postulates of science, i.e., that the scientific method can be explicated and justified without metaphysical presuppositions about the order or structure of nature.*

My positivistic or logical empiricist background, I must admit, may have made me somewhat allergic to the term "metaphysics." I realize full well that there are uses of this word that cover quite respectable or at least semirespectable endeavors. If "metaphysics" designates the examination and explication of the basic concepts, methods, and assumptions of the quest for knowledge, then, surely, logical empiricists are metaphysicians—only they prefer to label this sort of study "logical analysis," "theory of knowledge," or "philosophy of science." The term "metaphysics" is sometimes used also for the highly extrapolative—and in this sense precariously speculative—pursuits of the synthesis of a well-rounded world view. "Inductive metaphysics" is perhaps a good label for this type of endeavor. But metaphysics in this sense is continuous with science. It is merely the most venturesome part of scientific theorizing. Modern cosmological theories in physics and astronomy furnish a good example of this sort of speculation. Generally, it seems that scientists are much more competent than professional philosophers to judge to what extent, if any, hypotheses of this more sweeping sort are warranted by the empirical evidence on hand.

I shall refrain from discussing other meanings of the badly ambiguous term "metaphysics," such as the alleged intuitive or dialectical methods of arriving at ultimate truths concerning the nature of existence.

The two senses in which the term "metaphysics" covers enterprises that seem objectionable to the logical empiricist are of course (1) transcendent, i.e., in principle untestable, assertions, and (2) the belief in factual truths that could be validated a priori, i.e., in complete independence of the data of observation.

* This last part of the present paper is reprinted, with minor alterations, from (24).

The history of modern and recent physics provides a long series of devastating object lessons in both respects. From Galileo down to our days of the theory of relativity and of quantum mechanics, physicists have become poignantly aware of the futility of untestable assumptions and of the questionability of erstwhile unquestioned a priori postulates or presuppositions. In an impressive sequence of incisive changes the very postulates of physical theory have undergone profound revisions. The impact of these developments upon philosophy has quite generally tended to diminish, if not to abolish, the traditional prepossessions of of Rationalism. Little, if anything, is left of the veritées éternelles of Leibniz or of the Kantian synthetic a priori and other principles of this sort, formerly considered as self-evident, indubitable, or as the preconditions for the very possibility of scientific knowledge.

The discovery of the non-Euclidean geometries more than a hundred years ago, and especially their utilization in present-day physical and astronomical theories, shattered the rationalistic and absolutistic conceptions of space and time. The electrodynamic, quantum, and wave-mechanical theories of matter have transformed the time-honored idea of substance beyond recognition, if they have not indeed made it completely obsolete. In this connection the ancient dogma of continuity, one of Leibniz' basic truths of pure reason, had to give way to the conception of the discontinuous interaction between matter and radiation. Connected with the transition to discontinuity was the even more fundamental critique of the deterministic conception of causality. The principles of sufficient (or of insufficient!) reason, as well as the closely related symmetry principles used in many demonstrations of classical and statistical physical theory, have long been exposed as only speciously a priori. Ever since the critique by Ernst Mach of Archimedes' proof of the law of the lever, and Richard von Mises' critique of the principle of indifference (e.g., in Keynes' theory of probability), we have recognized that the correspondence of physical with geometrical symmetries is a matter of empirical fact. Indeed, one would wish to know what the rationalists have to say on the geometrical relation of electric and magnetic field vectors, for this basic asymmetry in our universe should certainly shatter anyone's faith in a priori discernible laws of nature.

But to continue with more recent revolutions in our concept of nature, neither the idea of particles that remain self-identical and indestructible nor the idea of the strict predictability of micro-processes can be maintained any longer with confidence. A large mass of experimental evidence militates relentlessly against practically each and every one of the alleged truths of pure reason held inviolable for so long by countless philosophers. Adding insult to injury, recent physical theories (introducing advanced potentials) seem to upset completely all classical notions concerning the temporal structure of causal relations, and recent cosmological theories have called into doubt even the dictum ex *nihilo nihil fit*—and blithely assume the possibility of spontaneous generation of matter, along with assorted doctrines of expanding or oscillating finite but unbounded universes.

Even if some of these developments need not be taken too seriously, their total trend and significance is indisputable. The mere fact that some of the allegedly indubitable first principles have been called into doubt, indicates that they cannot be indispensable presuppositions of science. The great conservation principles (of energy and of momentum), for example, were for a while (around 1924) under suspicion of being merely statistical macro-laws—along with so many other such manifestations of the "law of large numbers." But the detailed studies of the Compton effect reassured the physicists that these basic laws still hold good in a strictly deterministic fashion, even for micro-processes. I shall not tire my readers with the narration of further instances. The a priori in physical theory is either of the analytic, purely definitional sort or it is nonexistent. Of course, if one wishes to speak of a *relative* or *pragmatic a priori*—in the sense of C. I. Lewis, Victor Lenzen, Arthur Pap, or of Wilfrid Sellars—this is another matter. This sort of a priori is different from the classical rationalistic one (especially from the Kantian) in that it is ultimately under the jurisdiction of experience. This conception of the a priori connotes only universality and necessity, the latter in the sense in which even synthetic propositions can be true by virtue of the meaning of the terms they contain. I shall return to this later.

The upshot of our discussion thus far is simply this: Any proposed assertion concerning the order and structure of our universe, no matter how fundamental its role or pervasive its scope, must be regarded as tentative and may be held only until further notice; such notice being given by data of experience which may conceivably motivate us to modify, if not to abandon, the assumption at issue. In other words, any assertion regarding nature, if it is to be scientifically meaningful, must in principle be confirmable or disconfirmable.

24

2. *Assumptions about the uniformity of nature are neither necessary nor effective for the justification of inductive probability.*

In an interesting recent article (4) A. W. Burks argues the necessity of unconfirmable presuppositions for the very confirmation of any scientific laws (be they causal or statistical) and of any scientific hypothesis or theory. Along lines fairly familiar since J. S. Mill and Jevons, and elaborated in various ways in more recent decades by Edgar Zilsel, W. E. Johnson, C. D. Broad, J. M. Keynes, J. Nicod, Bertrand Russell, and others, he asks what assumptions regarding the uniformity of nature are required in order to account for the probability of inductive generalizations. Burks claims he does not intend to furnish a justification of the inductive leap. This, he recognizes (3), is an insoluble problem precisely because—at least in its traditional setting—any proposed solution involves either a self-contradiction or a *petitio principii*. This has of course been known ever since Hume's incisive critique of causality and induction. If we attempt to transform induction into deduction, we require premises whose validity cannot be anything but *inductive*. And if we try to demonstrate the (certain or even only the probable) success of inductive inference on the basis of its success to date, then we assume the very principle we propose to prove.

What, then, is the function of the sort of presuppositions that Burks deems indispensable? He tells us that they are required in order to *explain* induction. This seems to mean that these presuppositions are needed as premises from which the assumed or actual success of the inductive methods can be *deduced*. Unfortunately Burks gives no more than a hint as to precisely what presuppositions he has in mind. He suggests that they are of the type of Keynes' principle of limited variety, or, more generally, that they are assumptions concerning the uniformity of nature.

I fail to see the philosophical importance of any attempt in this direction. If it were the success of human adaptive learning and theorizing behavior that was to be accounted for, I would be the first to admit that this is a genuinely meaningful question—but surely a question of science, not of philosophy. This question can indeed be answered. And the answer is clearly along the lines of the biology and psychology of knowledge. It is the same sort of question that can be asked on a more lowly level in regard to the learning and generalizing behavior of that pet of our psychologists, the white rat. Given the rat's equipment of

Herbert Feigl

learning capacities, how complicated a maze will it be able to master, in how many trials, under what conditions of previous training, etc.? While it is a long way from the orientation of rats in a maze to the intellectual adaptations (if I may be forgiven the irreverent comparison) of the Newtons, Maxwells, and Einsteins in their theoretical constructions of the physical universe, the nature of the problem is the same: What type and degree of uniformity must the universe possess in order to be successfully predictable by means of the inductive and hypothetico-deductive procedures of modern science? I think the answer to this question is very obvious. The universe must have precisely the type and degree of uniformity which the successfully confirmed laws and theories ascribe to it (or rather, to some of its aspects).

Burks, however, does not propose this sort of conception of presuppositions or premises for the explanation of induction. He states explicitly and emphatically that the presuppositions of induction are in principle unconfirmable. They result in the choice of a definition of initial probabilities (or of a concept of degree of confirmation) which, once adopted, bestows certainty upon its own presuppositions, and a probability of zero to any alternative presupposition. This trivial and tautological confirmation of the presuppositions of all inductive inferences whose probabilities are determined by the respective choice of a definition of degree of confirmation can indeed not be regarded as a genuine appraisal on the basis of empirical evidence. The three inductive methods which Burks outlines are according to his claim altogether immune to the testimony of experience. Yet, Burks indicates, in a world of completely random character one method (Mr. "Dagger's"), would yield results superior to those of the standard or *normal* procedure of inductive extrapolation (Mr. "Star's" method; best adapted to a uniform world). The third method, finally (i.e., Mr. "Diamond's"), would serve most effectively in a universe of such diabolically perverse structure that what for the normal method is the most probable, would in that universe be the least probable predictions or hypotheses (and vice versa).

Without wishing to go into technical details of Burks' comparison of the three methods, I should like to raise a more fundamental question: What is the point of the presuppositional analysis if only an omniscient being could decide which presupposition actually applies to this universe of ours in which limited human beings grope for reliable knowledge? If finite, limited empirical evidence has no relevance for the preference of one presupposition as against another and if limited empirical evidence is the only sort of evidence that human beings will ever be able to marshal, then what, in Burks' opinion, justifies us in clinging to the standard method and in considering the other two as "perverse"?

Of the many traditionally proposed solutions of the problem of induction, which one is relevant or helpful in deciding this issue? The psychologistic, or "animal faith," doctrine of Hume and Santayana merely restates what the human animal as a matter of stark propensities and of habituation believes so strongly anyway. It furnishes no objective reason for a preference. The Kantian theory of knowledge in its anthropological version yields an equally psychologistic, but implausible doctrine of forms inevitably impressed upon the contents of raw experience—and thus depends for its plausibility and effectiveness on the assumption of the constancy of the forms of pure reason. But this is clearly an inductive assumption and thus ineffective in resolving our problem. The presuppositional interpretation of Kant's critique is of course the one to which Burks (along with many other modern thinkers) appeals but it does not enable him to ground the preference for the standard inductive method. Probabilistic solutions of the problem of induction, such as that of D. C. Williams are equally unavailable because they too endorse the standard method by presupposing (D. C. Williams' protestations to the contrary notwithstanding) uniformity. The commonsense school of philosophy (mostly the disciples of Moore and Wittgenstein) reminds us that the very meaning of "rationality" and "reasonableness" includes besides formal consistency especially the normal method of profiting from experience, i.e., standard induction. But since no reasons are given why this standard method should be dignified with the honorific label "reasonable," we are, despite the helpful reminder, left in the dark as far as our problem is concerned.

It should scarcely be necessary to explode the illusion that the presupposition of uniformity is an ultimate postulate. "Postulate" in modern science, especially in mathematics, means an assumption which serves as a premise for deduction. In contradistinction to the term "axiom," it does not carry the traditional connotation of self-evident truth or indubitability. In keeping with its etymology, a postulate is a demand, a requirement. But the mere fact that we require or demand uniformity does not make it sure or even only likely that nature will be good enough to conform with such demands.

Herbert Feigl

3. *Carnap's and Reichenbach's theories of induction involve pragmatic vindication rather than theoretical justification.*

I shall forgo the discussion of intuitionistic, metaphysical, and other clearly ineffective approaches to the problem of induction. Instead I shall more fruitfully turn to a brief discussion and comparison of two outstanding contributions by logical empiricists, i.e., those of Carnap and Reichenbach. Since it would take much more space than is available here, I shall have to assume some familiarity with the basic features of these two theories. It is clear that the normal method of induction (or at least something very close to it) is here absorbed in Carnap's definition of a logical concept of probability. Like J. M. Keynes' concept of probability, Carnap's degree of confirmation is relational in that it determines the degree to which some given evidence supports an inductive conclusion. Reichenbach, though an avowed proponent of the frequency conception of probability, defines a concept of *weight* for singular predictive inferences as well as for the probability of hypotheses. Since the supporting evidence in Carnap's conception consists in observed frequency ratios, and since Reichenbach's concept of weight is similarly defined in terms of the relative frequency of a certain type of event in a properly chosen reference class, these two theories of probability are perhaps not as irreconcilably different as might appear at first glance. It is true, Carnap's concept of null-confirmation (i.e., a degree of probability on the basis of no evidence whatever) allows for a qualified use of a principle of indifference and thus seems objectionable to Reichenbach, the stanch empiricist. But Carnap's "a priori" probability (if I may label it in this perhaps somewhat misleading manner) is rendered fairly innocuous by the qualification that in his theory the reliability of assertions of degrees of confirmation on scant evidence is extremely low. This corresponds to the absence of appraised posits in the so-called "primitive induction" according to Reichenbach's theory. And this means that numerically specified weights for predictions and hypotheses can be justified only after certain basic frequency ratios have been posited without assignable weight. Furthermore, Reichenbach, when faced with the notorious problem of how to confirm or disconfirm statements regarding limits of relative frequency has to resort either to a problematic finitization, or to the utilization of a probability-logic which bears a vague though suggestive resemblance to a theory of degree of confirmation. Add to this that Carnap's degree of confirmation,

28

according to his own theory, is equivalent to an estimate of relative frequency; and that the two rival theories are, of course, isomorphic to the extent that they both yield the customary axioms and theorems of the calculus of probabilities—and one begins to wonder whether Carnap and Reichenbach are as far apart from one another as is generally believed.

Perhaps an even more convincing, and for our present purposes extremely important, common feature of the two theories is the justification of induction. According to Carnap there is a large class, in fact a continuum, of inductive rules (or what is tantamount: of definitions of degree of confirmation), of which Reichenbach's rule is an element, which all share the following significant feature: If the world has some degree of order at all, predictions made according to any one of the inductive rules will in the long run (strictly speaking, in the limit) not only converge with the others, but can also be shown (deductively!) to be the only type of predictions that utilize evidence methodically and are capable of anticipating that order of nature. In some of my early papers (16, 17) I had been groping for this sort of solution of the problem of induction and I think I came fairly close to a tenable formulation in the paper of 1934. But with genuine appreciation I credit the late Hans Reichenbach (see especially 37) with the independent discovery and the more elaborate presentation of this solution.

Let me now show in some detail that this solution implies that there are no ultimate factual presuppositions of science. The search for invariant first principles may be humanly understandable, but in the light of the history of science (as I briefly sketched it in the beginning of this paper) it must be considered as misguided. The inductive and hypothetico-deductive methods of science do not logically presuppose any premises concerning the uniformity of nature. The invariant character of the basic rules of scientific method hinges exclusively upon the aims of scientific inquiry. In order to take the air of dogmatism out of my formulation, I shall state it in the form of a doubly conditional proposition: If it is the goal of scientific investigation to discover lawful relationships and thereby to render the observed phenomena maximally predictable, then the methods of (normal) inductive generalization and of theory construction will attain this goal, provided it is attainable at all, i.e., if nature is at all uniform in some sense, some aspect, and to some degree.

Herbert Feigl

Hume has shown once and for all that no matter what type or degree of order our observations may have confirmed thus far, it is logically conceivable that this type or degree of order may not prevail in the as yet unexplored domains of nature. These domains may be the future, or distant regions of space, or untested ranges of the magnitudes that figure in the functionally formulated quantitative laws of nature. A survey of the conceivable types and degrees of order (uniformity, dependence, independence) is a matter for purely formal analysis in modern logic and mathematics. A study of the criteria of confirmation for the empirical actuality of any one of these types and degrees of order is a task for philosophical analysis and for the theory of probability. Despite the present controversies in the theory of probability, it seems safe to say that there is one basic rule of procedure for the extrapolation from the known to the inferred portions of the universe: "Generalize on the basis of as broad a background of experience as can be secured, and in accordance with the principles of factual simplicity." If there is an order of nature, not too complicated or too deeply hidden, to be discoverable by limited human beings, then this rule of procedure will yield successful predictions. This last statement is of course a tautology. But I think it is illuminating nevertheless. It shows that, while it is impossible to *validate* any *over-all* assumptions concerning the uniformity of nature, the *procedure* of induction which posits *specific* uniformities can be pragmatically justified or "vindicated" (18). If the degree of uniformity in our world were much lower than it actually is, the rule of induction would still be a helpful tool in the anticipation of the as-yet-unknown. Even in a universe so completely chaotic that all specific generalizations were invariably fruitless, there would yet be one very modest generalization which would hold: namely, the expectation that the chaos will continue. And is this not also an induction?

The principle of induction when interpreted as a rule of procedure, and not as a postulate regarding the order of nature, is of course not subject to confirmation or disconfirmation. Its adoption depends merely on our purpose: to discover and generalize, tentatively and self-correctively, whatever type or degree of uniformity the accumulating observational evidence suggests. Perhaps the dim recognition of the implicit functioning of this most basic rule of all empirical knowledge led so many philosophers to mistake it for a genuinely synthetic truth concerning the universe that could be known on the basis of pure reason.

Waiving important technical questions which are still highly controversial, I venture to state rather succinctly the following tentative conclusions:

A. No matter how strong or how weak the uniformities are in our world, the procedure of normal induction is the only methodical procedure of which we can prove *deductively* that it *can* disclose such uniformities.

B. Our world, as we have come to appraise it through the guidance of the principle of induction, seems to contain a vast amount of independencies (nonuniformity, disorder) in addition to a limited amount of dependencies (uniformity, order of various types, such as the causal and the statistical). This *inductively* established very general assumption serves indeed as a presupposition—or, if you will, as a postulate—for all types of more special causal and statistical research. But this postulate is "philosophical" only in the somewhat regrettable sense that it is terribly vague and abstract. It is certainly not metaphysical in the sense of being either untestable or a priori (i.e., it is not independent of the jurisdiction of experience).

C. While differing in technical points, as well as in the specific values of probabilities based on relatively small amounts of evidence, such inductive methods as R. A. Fisher's (of maximum likelihood), Reichenbach's (rule of induction), and Carnap's (definition of degree of confirmation c^*) yield in the long run equal results and are perhaps merely different versions of one and the same basic idea.

D. This basic idea (again waiving controversial issues) may be formulated as follows: If we wish for a method of generalization or of individual predictive inference that utilizes evidence and yields (at least in the limit) unique results, then the "normal" method (or methods) of induction are quite distinct from any "perverse" ones. The "perverse" methods are either insensitive to the testimony of accumulating evidence—and therefore *not* self-corrective—or else they lack the *uniqueness* that is characteristic of the methods of *simplest* generalization or of *maximum* likelihood.

E. Confronted with the specific problem of determining the most adequate value for the limiting frequency of some statistical phenomenon (as, for example, in radioactive disintegration, quantum-transitions of various sorts, or in Mendelian inheritance, etc.), we may choose either straightforward generalization of the statistical ratios obtaining for specifiable aspects under operationally identifiable conditions; or else construct a theory, an essential part of which must be assumptions regarding statistical distributions, in such a fashion that the observed data will have a maximum likelihood (according to a non-perverse definition of likelihood) in the light of the assumed theoretical model. This suggests that the "Star" method or something very close to it could be given an objectively justifiable preference.

F. In testing the correctness of a specific estimate of a limit of relative frequency, it would indeed be "perverse" to assume that the available samples are not representative. They may of course not be representative for all that. We may at any time, or even all the time, be the victims of what in the light of further evidence would appear as a "terribly improbable" run of bad luck. But to assume this to start with not only makes our estimates nonunique (it opens the floodgates to limitless possible hypotheses) but would amount to a complete defeatism. The method of science is that of a fallibilistic optimism. ("If at first you don't succeed, try, try again!") We must work with what we have and cautiously utilize every bit of uniformity that a broad domain of evidence suggests for generalization. This I accept as the most valuable core of the contribution to epistemology and the logic of science contained in the pragmatist philosophies of C. S. Peirce, John Dewey, and C. I. Lewis.

G. There is one very important issue which I wish to propose for further discussion (I have not yet attained a stable decision on it myself): Are scientific *laws*, and *theories with lawlike assumptions*, subject to appraisal in terms of any concept of inductive probability? It should be noted that unlimited generalizations from finite evidence receive invariably a degree of confirmation of zero, according to Carnap's theory of induction. Laws can therefore be appraised only on the basis of their instance-confirmation. This suggests that any assignment of inductive probabilities really presupposes a set of assumptions of lawfulness, certainly of the statistical type and, possibly, in addition, some of the deterministic type. These assumptions would then be *posits* in Reichenbach's sense, i.e., tentative assumptions to which we cannot assign any numerical or even comparative probabilities. This is in keeping with the prevalent view of theoretical physicists, according to which the basic premises of scientific theories may be accepted or rejected as they are more or less fruitful, convenient, simple, or expedient.

Probabilities can be determined only relative to a chosen frame of those basic theoretical assumptions. Far from being metaphysical (again in the sense of being exempt from the jurisdiction of experience) these basic posits are held, until further notice, that is to say as long as they provide the frame from which specific testable conclusions can be derived and successfully confirmed by the data of observation. It seems indeed questionable as to whether theories which introduce new magnitudes, as, for example, the electromagnetic field theory of Faraday and Maxwell, could be appraised as more or less probable in the light of experimental evidence. The introduction of new magnitudes semantically considered consists in an essential enrichment of the language of science; and it seems that probability estimates presuppose such a semantical frame but are not applicable to it, as it were, from the outside (19). Perhaps here is a point of genuine agreement between Burks and myself. Moreover, these lines of thought seem in accordance with the conception of natural law in terms of modal logic mentioned earlier and labeled "pragmatic a priori." At the risk of making a bad joke, this sort of view could be said to maintain the existence of synthetic a priori truths that are indistinguishable from analytic a posteriori truths (see 45, 46).

H. In short, the position I am inclined to favor is this: Instead of postulating any general principle of uniformity, I think it is philosophically more defensible to retain the sound core of that principle, either by absorbing it (à la Carnap) in a definition of *inductive probability* or even more explicitly by formulating it (à la Reichenbach) in terms of a rule of procedure, or as William Kneale very aptly put it, as a feature of the *policy* of induction. The tentative assumption of specific causal and statistical laws then *is* subject to confirmation in the sense of acceptance or rejection in the light of evidence. But these laws are not capable of probabilification—precisely because they function as the premises of all specific predictions and hypotheses whose probabilities can be ascertained only on the basis of those more fundamental posits.

By way of a brief summary I should like to say that there are postulates of science, but they are neither philosophical nor metaphysical in any fruitful sense of these words. The postulates of science are the basic assumptions which make up the scientific theories themselves.

The explication of the methods by which we confirm physical laws, hypotheses, or theories has been attempted in three ways: presupposi-

Herbert Feigl

tionally, definitionally, and procedurally. Burks, in agreement with Kant, Mill, Keynes, and others finds the presuppositional approach illuminating. He feels that without reference to untestable presuppositions the other two approaches remain incomplete, arbitrary, or unjustified. Carnap's definitional and Reichenbach's procedural reconstruction of inductive probability, despite other important divergencies, do agree in the only essential point for our concern: the pragmatic justification of the inductive method. This justification can be derived from the most central purpose of the scientific enterprise: the achievement, through the utilization of empirical evidence, of a maximum of predictability among the observed phenomena. The rules of induction and of the hypothetico-deductive method of theoretical physics can be explicated as well as justified without reference to metaphysical assumptions.

Space unfortunately does not permit any discussion of the new developments in the work of Reichenbach and others on the philosophic foundations of quantum mechanics, on the problem of time, etc., or on recent developments in the moral philosophy of logical empiricism.*

I have tried to convey my impression that the philosophy of science of logical empiricism, after twenty-five years of development, compares favorably with the earlier logical positivism, in that it is, firstly, more *logical*. It recognizes some of the erstwhile suppressed but nevertheless valid claims of "rationalism." Secondly, it is more *positive*, i.e., less negativistic. This is clearly evident in the abandonment of reductive phenomenalism and of ultra-operationism in favor of a more constructive "realism." Thirdly, logical empiricism today is more *empirical*, in that it refrains from ruling out by decree ontologies or cosmologies which do not harmonize with the preconceptions of classical positivism. Alternative and mutually supplementary logical reconstructions of the meaning of cognitive terms, statements, and theories have come increasingly to replace the dogmatic attempts at unique reconstructions. Logical empiricism has grown beyond its adolescent phase. It is rapidly maturing, it is coming of age. An enormous amount of important and difficult work is yet to be done in the logic and methodology of the sciences. The present outlook of logical empiricism holds high promise that these

* A succinct survey of the work of Carnap and Reichenbach on probability, with a fairly complete list of the relevant literature, is contained in (24). See also (38). A book on "The Direction of Time" by Reichenbach will be published posthumously by the University of California Press in 1956. Moral philosophy is briefly discussed in (41) and in (23).

endeavors will be carried out successfully. Even if we cannot (and should not) claim to have arrived at a philosophy to end all philosophies, it may perhaps be acknowledged that the new enlightenment has made considerable advances.

REFERENCES

NOTE: It is gratifying to note a certain convergence of recent philosophical opinion in regard to the problem of the justification of inductive inference. From the point of view of the new common-sense (or common-language) approach, Paul Edwards, Max Black, P. F. Strawson, Frederick Will, and others have in various ways exposed the confusions that underlie some attempts to furnish a justification of induction. If the standard of rationality is identified with the logical cogency, which is characteristic exclusively of deductive inference, then indeed one is hopelessly entangled in a pseudo problem. But it is not enough to point to the (undeniable) fact that "rationality" as commonly understood includes, besides deductive consistency and conclusiveness, the patterns of normal induction. It has to be shown that the normal inductive procedure is reasonable, not merely by definition in the light of common usage, but that this definition itself is not merely a result of linguistic habituation or of an arbitrary fiat. This can be achieved, as I have tried to show (16), if the adoption of the rule of induction is made a matter of practical justification (vindication) rather than a matter of theoretical justification (validation). But it is important to note that vindication in this case does not require factual premises. We are dealing here with an extreme case of practical justification by means of purely tautological reasoning. This view, long ago formulated by Reichenbach and myself, seems essentially shared by Carnap (7), Kneale (29), C. I. Lewis (31, p. 325), P. F. Strawson (48), and J. O. Wisdom (52).

1. Black, Max. Language and Philosophy. Ithaca, New York: Cornell Univ. Pr., 1949.
2. Braithwaite, R. B. Scientific Explanation. Cambridge: Cambridge Univ. Pr., 1953.
3. Burks, A. W. "Reichenbach's Theory of Probability and Induction," Review of Metaphysics, 4:377–93 (1951).
4. Burks, A. W. "The Presupposition Theory of Induction," Philosophy of Science, 20:177–97 (1953).
5. Campbell, Norman R. "The Structure of Theories," in H. Feigl and M. Brodbeck (eds.), Readings in the Philosophy of Science, pp. 288–308. New York: Appleton-Century-Crofts, 1953.
6. Carnap, Rudolf. "Testability and Meaning," Philosophy of Science, 3:420–68 (1936); 4:1–40 (1937).
7. Carnap, Rudolf. "On Inductive Logic," Philosophy of Science, 12:72–92 (1945).
8. Carnap, Rudolf. Meaning and Necessity. Chicago: Univ. of Chicago Pr., 1947.
9. Carnap, Rudolf. "Empiricism, Semantics and Ontology," Revue Internationale de Philosophie, 11:20–40 (1950). Reprinted in P. P. Wiener (ed.), Readings in Philosophy of Science, pp. 509–21. New York: Scribner's, 1953. Also reprinted in J. L. Jarrett and S. M. McMurrin (eds.), Contemporary Philosophy. New York: Holt, 1954.
10. Carnap, Rudolf. Logical Foundations of Probability. Chicago: Univ. of Chicago Pr., 1950.
11. Carnap, Rudolf. The Continuum of Inductive Methods. Chicago: Univ. of Chicago Pr., 1951.
12. Carnap, Rudolf. The Nature and Application of Inductive Logic (consisting of six sections from Logical Foundations of Probability). Chicago: Univ. of Chicago Pr., 1951.

Herbert Feigl

13. Carnap, Rudolf. "The Interpretation of Physics," in H. Feigl and M. Brodbeck (eds.), *Readings in the Philosophy of Science*, pp. 309–18. New York: Appleton-Century-Crofts, 1953.
14. Edwards, Paul. "Russell's Doubts About Induction," *Mind*, 58:141–63 (1949). Reprinted in A. Flew (ed.), *Logic and Language*. New York: Philosophical Lib., 1951.
15. Einstein, A. "Remarks on Bertrand Russell's Theory of Knowledge," in *Bertrand Russell's Philosophy*, pp. 277–292. "The Library of Living Philosophers" (P. A. Schilpp, ed.), 1st ed., 1944.
16. Feigl, Herbert. "Wahrscheinlichkeit und Erfahrung," *Erkenntnis*, 1:249–59 (1930–31).
17. Feigl Herbert. "The Logical Character of the Principle of Induction," *Philosophy of Science*, 1:20–29 (1935). Also reprinted in H. Feigl and W. Sellars (eds.), *Readings in Philosophical Analysis*, pp. 297–304. New York: Appleton-Century-Crofts, 1949.
18. Feigl, Herbert. "De Principiis Non Disputandum . . . ? On the Meaning and the Limits of Justification," in M. Black (ed.), *Philosophical Analysis*, pp. 119–56. Ithaca, New York: Cornell Univ. Pr., 1950.
19. Feigl, Herbert. "Existential Hypotheses," *Philosophy of Science*, 17:35–62 (1950).
20. Feigl, Herbert. "Logical Reconstruction, Realism and Pure Semiotic," *Philosophy of Science*, 17:186–95 (1950).
21. Feigl, Herbert. "The Mind-Body Problem in the Development of Logical Empiricism," *Revue Internationale de Philosophie*, 4:64–83 (1950). Reprinted in H. Feigl and M. Brodbeck (eds.), *Readings in the Philosophy of Science*, pp. 612–26. New York: Appleton-Century-Crofts, 1953.
22. Feigl, Herbert. "Principles and Problems of Theory Construction in Psychology," in W. Dennis (ed.), *Current Trends of Psychological Theory*, pp. 174–213. Pittsburgh: Univ. of Pittsburgh Pr., 1951.
23. Feigl, Herbert. "Validation and Vindication: The Nature and the Limits of Ethical Argument," in W. Sellars and J. Hospers (eds.), *Readings in Ethical Theory*, pp. 667–80. New York: Appleton-Century-Crofts, 1952.
24. Feigl, Herbert. "Scientific Method Without Metaphysical Presuppositions," *Philosophical Studies*, 5:17–29 (1954).
25. Feigl, Herbert. "Physicalism, Unity of Science and the Foundations of Psychology," in P. A. Schilpp (ed.), *The Philosophy of Rudolf Carnap*. New York: Tudor (forthcoming).
26. Hempel, C. G. "Problems and Changes in the Empiricist Criterion of Meaning," *Revue Internationale de Philosophie*, 4:41–63 (1950). Reprinted in L. Linsky (ed.), *Semantics and the Philosophy of Language*, pp. 163–85. Urbana: Univ. of Illinois Pr., 1952.
27. Hempel, C. G. *Fundamentals of Concept Formation in the Empirical Sciences*, Vol. II, No. 7 of the *International Encyclopedia of Unified Science*. Chicago: Univ. of Chicago Pr., 1952.
28. Jörgensen, J. *The Development of Logical Empiricism*, Vol. II, No. 9 of the *International Encyclopedia of Unified Science*. Chicago: Univ. of Chicago Pr., 1953.
29. Kneale, William. *Probability and Induction*. New York: Oxford Univ. Pr., 1949.
30. Kraft, Victor. *The Vienna Circle*. (Translated by A. Pap.) New York: Philosophical Lib., 1953.
31. Lewis, C. I. *An Analysis of Knowledge and Valuation*. LaSalle, Ill.: Open Court Pub. Co., 1946.
32. Marhenke, Paul. "The Criterion of Significance," in the *Proceedings and Addresses of the American Philosophical Association*, 23 (1950). Reprinted in

L. Linsky (ed.), *Semantics and the Philosophy of Language*, pp. 139–59. Urbana: Univ. of Illinois Pr., 1952.

33. Mates, Benson. "Analytic Sentences," *Philosophical Review*, 60: 525–34 (1951).
34. Pap, Arthur. *Elements of Analytic Philosophy*. New York: Macmillan, 1949. (Especially Chap. 16, "Does Science Have Metaphysical Presuppositions?" reprinted in part in H. Feigl and M. Brodbeck (eds.), *Readings in the Philosophy of Science*, pp. 21–33. New York: Appleton-Century-Crofts, 1953.
35. Quine, W. V. "Two Dogmas of Empiricism," *Philosophical Review* 60: 20–43 (1951).
36. Reichenbach, H. *Experience and Prediction*. Chicago: Univ. of Chicago Pr., 1938.
37. Reichenbach, H. "On the Justification of Induction," *Journal of Philosophy*, 37:97–103 (1940). Reprinted in H. Feigl and W. Sellars (eds.), *Readings in Philosophical Analysis*, pp. 324–29. New York: Appleton-Century-Crofts, 1949.
38. Reichenbach, H. *Philosophical Foundations of Quantum Mechanics*. Berkeley, Calif.: Univ. of Calif. Pr., 1944.
39. Reichenbach, H. "The Logical Foundations of the Concept of Probability," in H. Feigl and W. Sellars (eds.), *Readings in Philosophical Analysis*, pp. 305–23. New York: Appleton-Century-Crofts, 1949. Also reprinted in H. Feigl and M. Brodbeck (eds.), *Readings in the Philosophy of Science*, pp. 456–74. New York: Appleton-Century-Crofts, 1953.
40. Reichenbach, H. *Theory of Probability*. Berkeley: Univ. of Calif. Pr., 1949.
41. Reichenbach, H. *The Rise of Scientific Philosophy*. Berkeley, Calif.: Univ. of Calif. Pr., 1951.
42. Russell, Bertrand. *Human Knowledge*. New York: Simon & Schuster, 1948.
43. Sellars, Wilfrid. "Concepts as Involving Laws and Inconceivable Without Them," *Philosophy of Science*, 15: 287–315 (1948).
44. Sellars, Wilfrid. "Realism and the New Way of Words," in H. Feigl and W. Sellars (eds.), *Readings in Philosophical Analysis*, pp. 424–56. New York: Appleton-Century-Crofts, 1949.
45. Sellars, Wilfrid. "Inference and Meaning," *Mind*, 62: 313–38 (1953).
46. Sellars, Wilfrid. "Is There a Synthetic A Priori?" *Philosophy of Science*, 20: 121–38 (1953).
47. Sellars, Wilfrid. "Some Reflections on Language Games," *Philosophy of Science*, 21: 204–28 (1954).
48. Strawson, P. F. *Introduction to Logical Theory*. London: Methuen; New York: Wiley, 1952.
49. Waismann, F. "Analytic-Synthetic," *Analysis*, 10: 25–40 (1949); 11: 25–38 (1950), 11: 49–61 (1951); 11: 116–24 (1951); 13: 1–14 (1952); 13: 74–89 (1953).
50. Will, Frederick. "Generalization and Evidence," in M. Black (ed.), *Philosophical Analysis*, pp. 384–413. Ithaca, New York: Cornell Univ. Pr., 1950.
51. Williams, D. C. *The Ground of Induction*. Cambridge, Mass.: Harvard Univ. Pr., 1947.
52. Wisdom, John O. *Foundations of Inference in Natural Science*. London: Methuen, 1952.

The Methodological Character of Theoretical Concepts

I. Our Problems

IN DISCUSSIONS on the methodology of science, it is customary and useful to divide the language of science into two parts, the observation language and the theoretical language. The observation language uses terms designating observable properties and relations for the description of observable things or events. The theoretical language, on the other hand, contains terms which may refer to unobservable events, unobservable aspects or features of events, e.g., to micro-particles like electrons or atoms, to the electromagnetic field or the gravitational field in physics, to drives and potentials of various kinds in psychology, etc. In this article I shall try to clarify the nature of the theoretical language and its relation to the observation language. The observation language will be briefly described in Section 2 of this paper. Then a more detailed account of the theoretical language and the connections between the two languages will be given in Sections III–V.

One of the main topics will be the problem of a criterion of significance for the theoretical language, i.e., exact conditions which terms and sentences of the theoretical language must fulfill in order to have a positive function for the explanation and prediction of observable events and thus to be acceptable as empirically meaningful. I shall leave aside the problem of a criterion of significance for the observation language, because there seem to be hardly any points of serious disagreement among philosophers today with respect to this problem, at least if the observation language is understood in the narrow sense indicated above. On the other hand, the problem for the theoretical language is a very serious one. There are not only disagreements with respect to the exact location of the boundary line between the meaningful and the meaningless, but some philosophers are doubtful about the very possibility of drawing any boundary line. It is true that empiricists today generally agree that certain criteria previously proposed were too narrow; for example, the requirement that all theoretical terms should be definable on the basis of those of the observation language and that all theoretical sentences should be translatable into the observation language. We are at present aware that these requirements are too strong because the rules connecting the two languages (which we shall call "rules of correspondence") can give only a partial interpretation for the theoretical language. From this fact, some philosophers draw the conclusion that, once the earlier criteria are liberalized, we shall find a continuous line from terms which are closely connected with observations, e.g., 'mass' and 'temperature,' through more remote terms like 'electromagnetic field' and 'psi-function' in physics, to those terms which have no specifiable connection with observable events, e.g., terms in speculative metaphysics; therefore, meaningfulness seems to them merely a matter of degree. This skeptical position is maintained also by some empiricists; Hempel, for instance, has given clear and forceful arguments for this view (see his articles, (14) and (15)). Although he still regards the basic idea of the empiricist meaning criterion as sound, he believes that deep-going modifications are necessary. First, the question of meaningfulness cannot, in his opinion, be raised for any single term or sentence but only for the whole system consisting of the theory, expressed in the theoretical language, and the correspondence rules. And secondly, even for this system as a whole, he thinks that no sharp distinction between meaningful and meaningless can be drawn; we may, at best, say something about its degree of confirmation on the basis of the available observational evidence, or about the degree of its explanatory or predictive power for observable events.

The skeptics do not, of course, deny that we can draw an exact boundary line if we want to. But they doubt whether any boundary line is an adequate explication of the distinction which empiricists had originally in mind. They believe that, if any boundary line is drawn, it will be more or less arbitrary; and, moreover, that it will turn out to be either too narrow or too wide. That it is too narrow means that some terms or sentences are excluded which are accepted by scientists as meaningful; that it is too wide means that some terms or sentences are included which scientifically thinking men would not accept as meaningful.

My attitude is more optimistic than that of the skeptics. I believe that, also in the theoretical language, it is possible to draw an adequate boundary line which separates the scientifically meaningful from the meaningless. I shall propose criteria of significance; the criterion for theoretical terms will be formulated in Section VI, and the question of its adequacy will be examined in Section VII; the criterion for theoretical sentences will be given in Section VIII.

Two alternative forms for the introduction of scientific concepts into our two-language system will be explained and their comparative usefulness examined (Sections IX and X). One kind is that of theoretical concepts introduced into the theoretical language by postulates. The other kind I call "disposition concepts." They may be introduced into an extended observation language. Concepts defined by so-called operational definitions and the so-called intervening variables belong to this kind. I shall try to show that the introduction in the form of theoretical concepts is a more useful method because it allows greater freedom in the choice of conceptual forms; moreover, it seems more in accord with the way the scientists actually use their concepts.

In the last section, I discuss briefly the possibilities and advantages of the use of theoretical concepts in psychology.

II. The Observation Language L_o

The total language of science, L, is considered as consisting of two parts, the observation language L_o and the theoretical language L_T. I shall here briefly indicate the nature of L_o; the later discussion will chiefly concern L_T and its relations to L_o. Without actually specifying it, we assume that the logical structure of L_o is given. This would include a specification of the primitive constants, divided into logical and descriptive (i.e., nonlogical) constants. Let the observational vocabulary V_o be the class of the descriptive constants of L_o. Further, for each language part the admitted types of variables are specified. In L_o, it may suffice to use only individual variables, with observable events (including thing-moments) taken as individuals. Then rules of formation, which specify the admitted forms of sentences, and rules of logical deduction are given.

Let us imagine that L_o is used by a certain language community as a means of communication, and that all sentences of L_o are understood by all members of the group in the same sense. Thus a complete interpretation of L_o is given.

40

The terms of V_O are predicates designating observable properties of events or things (e.g., "blue," "hot," "large," etc.) or observable relations between them (e.g., "x is warmer than y," "x is contiguous to y," etc.).

Some philosophers have proposed certain principles which restrict either the forms of expression or the procedures of deduction in "the language," in order to make sure that everything said in the language is completely meaningful. It seems to me that the justification of such requirements depends upon the purpose for which the language in question is used. Since L_O is intended for the description of observable events and therefore is meant to be completely interpreted, the requirements, or at least some of them, seem to have merit. Let us consider the most important requirements that have been proposed for some or any language L.

1. Requirement of *observability* for the primitive descriptive terms.
2. Requirements of various degrees of strictness for the nonprimitive descriptive terms.
   (a) Explicit *definability*.
   (b) *Reducibility* by conditional definitions (e.g., by reduction sentences as proposed in (5)).
3. Requirement of *nominalism*: the values of the variables must be concrete, observable entities (e.g., observable events, things, or thing-moments).
4. Requirement of *finitism*, in one of three forms of increasing strictness:
   (a) The rules of the language L do not state or imply that the basic domain (the range of values of the individual variables) is infinite. In technical terms, L has at least one finite model.
   (b) L has only finite models.
   (c) There is a finite number n such that no model contains more than n individuals.
5. Requirement of *constructivism*: every value of any variable of L is designated by an expression in L.
6. Requirement of *extensionality*. The language contains only truth-functional connectives, no terms for logical or causal modalities (necessity, possibility, etc.).

Any language fulfilling these requirements is more directly and more completely understandable than languages transgressing these limitations. However, for the language as a whole, the requirements are not justified; we shall reject them later for the theoretical language L_T.

Since then we have in the part L_T all the freedom of expression desired, we may well accept some or all of these requirements for L_0.

We have already accepted requirements 1 and 3. The decision about requirement 2 depends upon our intention concerning disposition terms (e.g., "soluble," "fragile," "flexible"). We shall not include them in L_0 itself; thus L_0 is here taken as a *restricted observation language* fulfilling the stronger requirement 2(a). Later (in Section IX) the possibility of an extended observation language L'_0, which allows the introduction of disposition terms, will be explained. Another method consists in representing the disposition concepts by theoretical terms in L_T (Section X).

The weakest requirement 4(a) of finitism is fulfilled in L_0. Therefore it is easily possible to satisfy requirement 5. Further, we take L_0 as an extensional language; thus requirement 6 is fulfilled.

III. The Theoretical Language L_T

The primitive constants of L_T are, like those of L_0, divided into logical and descriptive constants. Let the theoretical vocabulary V_T be the class of the descriptive primitive constants of L_T. We shall often call these constants simply "theoretical terms." (They are often called "theoretical constructs" or "hypothetical constructs." However, since the term "construct" was originally used for explicitly defined terms or concepts, it might be preferable to avoid this term here and use instead the neutral phrase "theoretical term" (or "theoretical primitive"). This use seems to be in better accord with the fact that it is, in general, not possible to give explicit definitions for theoretical terms on the basis of L_0.)

We may take it for granted that L_T contains the usual truth-functional connectives (e.g., for negation and conjunction). Other connectives, e.g., signs for logical modalities (e.g., logical necessity and strict implication) and for causal modalities (e.g., causal necessity and causal implication) may be admitted if desired; but their inclusion would require a considerably more complicated set of rules of logical deduction (as syntactical or semantical rules). The most important remaining problem for the specification of the logical structure concerns the ranges of values for the variables to be admitted in universal and existential quantifiers, and thereby the kinds of entities dealt with in L_T. This problem will be discussed in Section IV.

A *theory* is given, consisting of a finite number of *postulates* formulated in L_T. Let T be the conjunction of these postulates. Finally, *correspondence rules* C are given, which connect the terms of V_T with those of V_O. These rules will be explained in Section V.

IV. The Problem of the Admissibility of Theoretical Entities

It seems that the acceptance of the following three conventions $C1$–$C3$ is sufficient to make sure that L_T includes all of mathematics that is needed in science and also all kinds of entities that customarily occur in any branch of empirical science.

Conventions about the domain D of entities admitted as values of variables in L_T.

C1. D includes a denumerable subdomain I of entities.

C2. Any ordered n-tuple of entities in D (for any finite n) belongs also to D.

C3. Any class of entities in D belongs also to D.

I shall now indicate briefly how these conventions yield all the customary kinds of entities referred to in scientific theories. To facilitate the understanding, I shall first use the customary way of speaking and the customary terms for certain kinds of entities, and only later add a warning against a possible misinterpretation of these formulations.

First about mathematical entities. Since the subdomain I stipulated in $C1$ is denumerable, we may regard its elements as the natural numbers 0, 1, 2, etc. If R is any relation whose members belong to D, then R may be construed as a class of ordered pairs of its members. Therefore, according to $C2$ and $C3$, R belongs also to D. Now the (positive and negative) integers can, in the usual way, be constructed as relations of natural numbers. Thus, they belong also to D. Analogously, we proceed to rational numbers as relations among integers, to real numbers as classes of rational numbers, and to complex numbers as ordered pairs of real numbers. Furthermore, we obtain classes of numbers of these kinds, relations among them, functions (as special kinds of relations) whose arguments and values are numbers, then classes of functions, functions of functions, etc. Thus D includes all those kinds of entities needed in the purely mathematical part of L_T.

Now we proceed to physics. We assume that L_T is based upon a particular space-time coordinate system; thus the space-time points are ordered quadruples of real numbers and hence, according to $C2$, belong

43

to D. A space-time region is a class of space-time points. Any particular physical system of which a physicist may speak, e.g., a material body or a process of radiation, occupies a certain space-time region. When a physicist describes a physical system or a process occurring in it or a momentary state of it, he ascribes values of physical magnitudes (e.g., mass, electric charge, temperature, electromagnetic field intensity, energy, and the like) either to the space-time region as a whole or to its points. The values of a physical magnitude are either real numbers or n-tuples of such. Thus a physical magnitude is a function whose arguments are either space-time points or regions and whose values are either real numbers or n-tuples of such. Thus, on the basis of our conventions, the domain D contains space-time points and regions, physical magnitudes and their values, physical systems and their states. A physical system itself is nothing else than a space-time region characterized in terms of magnitudes. In a similar way, all other entities occurring in physical theories can be shown to belong to D.

Psychological concepts are properties, relations, or quantitative magnitudes ascribed to certain space-time regions (usually human organisms or classes of such). Therefore they belong to the same logical types as concepts of physics, irrespective of the question of their difference in meaning and way of definition. Note that the logical type of a psychological concept is also independent of its methodological nature, e.g., whether based on observation of behavior or on introspection; philosophers seem sometimes not to realize this. Thus the domain D includes also all entities referred to in psychology. The same holds for all social sciences.

We have considered some of the kinds of entities referred to in mathematics, physics, psychology, and the social sciences and have indicated that they belong to the domain D. However, I wish to emphasize here that this talk about the admission of this or that kind of entity as values of variables in L_T is only a way of speaking intended to make the use of L_T, and especially the use of quantified variables in L_T, more easily understandable. Therefore the explanations just given must not be understood as implying that those who accept and use a language of the kind here described are thereby committed to certain "ontological" doctrines in the traditional metaphysical sense. The usual ontological questions about the "*reality*" (in an alleged metaphysical sense) of numbers, classes, space-time points, bodies, minds, etc., are pseudo questions without cognitive content. In contrast to this, there is a good sense of the word "real," viz., that used in everyday language and in science. It may be useful for our present discussion to distinguish two kinds of the meaningful use of "real," viz., the common sense use and the scientific use. Although in actual practice there is no sharp line between these two uses, we may, in view of our partition of the total language L into the two parts L_O and L_T, distinguish between the use of "real" in connection with L_O, and that in connection with L_T. We assume that L_O contains only one kind of variable, and that the values of these variables are possible observable events. In this context, the question of reality can be raised only with respect to possible events. The statement that a specified possible observable event, e.g., that of this valley having been a lake in earlier times, is real means the same as the statement that the sentence of L_O which describes this event is true, and therefore means just the same as this sentence itself: "This valley was a lake."

For a question of reality in connection with L_T, the situation is in certain respects more complicated. If the question concerns the reality of an event described in theoretical terms, the situation is not much different from the earlier one: to accept a statement of reality of this kind is the same as to accept the sentence of L_T describing the event. However, a question about the reality of something like electrons in general (in contradistinction to the question about the reality of a cloud of electrons moving here now in a specified way, which is a question of the former kind) or the electromagnetic field in general is of a different nature. A question of this kind is in itself rather ambiguous. But we can give it a good scientific meaning, e.g., if we agree to understand the acceptance of the reality, say, of the electromagnetic field in the classical sense as the acceptance of a language L_T and in it a term, say 'E,' and a set of postulates T which includes the classical laws of the electromagnetic field (say, the Maxwell equations) as postulates for 'E.' For an observer X to "accept" the postulates of T, means here not simply to take T as an uninterpreted calculus, but to use T together with specified rules of correspondence C for guiding his expectations by deriving predictions about future observable events from observed events with the help of T and C.

I said previously that the elements of the basic domain I may be regarded as natural numbers. But I warned that this remark and the others about real numbers, etc., should not be taken literally but merely as a didactic help by attaching familiar labels to certain kinds of entities or, to say it in a still more cautious way, to certain kinds of expressions in L_T. Let the expressions corresponding to the domain I be "O," "O'," "O''," etc. To say that "O" designates the number zero, "O'" the number one, etc., gives merely the psychological help of connecting these expressions for the reader with useful associations and images, but should not be regarded as specifying part of the interpretation of L_T. All the interpretation (in the strict sense of this term, i.e., observational interpretation) that can be given for L_T is given in the C-rules, and their function is essentially the interpretation of certain sentences containing descriptive terms, and thereby indirectly the interpretation of the descriptive terms of V_T. On the other hand, the essential service that the expressions "O" etc. give, consists in the fact that they represent a particular kind of structure (viz., a sequence with an initial member but no terminal member). Thus the structure can be uniquely specified but the elements of the structure cannot. Not because we are ignorant of their nature; rather, there is no question of their nature. But then, since the sequence of natural numbers is the most elementary and familiar example of the sequential structure here in question, no harm is done in saying that those expressions designate entities and that these entities are the natural numbers, as long as we are not misled by these formulations into asking metaphysical pseudo questions.

In the earlier discussion of the observation language L_0 (Section II), we considered certain restrictive requirements, like those of nominalism, finitism, etc., and found them acceptable. However, the situation with respect to the theoretical language is entirely different. For L_T we do not claim to have a complete interpretation, but only the indirect and partial interpretation given by the correspondence rules. Therefore, we should feel free to choose the logical structure of this language as it best fits our needs for the purpose for which the language is constructed.

Thus here in L_T there is no reason against the three conventions, although their acceptance violates the first five requirements mentioned in Section II. First, before the C-rules are given, L_T, with the postulates T and the rules of deduction, is an uninterpreted calculus. Therefore the earlier requirements cannot be applied to it. We are free in the construction of the calculus; there is no lack of clarity, provided the rules of the calculus are clearly given. Then the C-rules are added. All they do is, in effect, to permit the derivation of certain sentences of L_0 from certain sentences of L_T or vice versa. They serve indirectly for derivations of conclusions in L_0, e.g., predictions of observable events, from given premises in L_0, e.g., reports of results found by observation, or for the determination of the probability of a conclusion in L_0 on the basis of given premises in L_0. Since both the premises and the conclusion belong to L_0, which fulfills the restricting requirements, there can be no objection against the use of the C-rules and of L_T, as far as the meaningfulness of the results of the derivation procedure is concerned.

V. The Correspondence Rules C

There is no independent interpretation for L_T. The system T is in itself an uninterpreted postulate system. The terms of V_T obtain only an indirect and incomplete interpretation by the fact that some of them are connected by the rules C with observational terms, and the remaining terms of V_T are connected with the first ones by the postulates of T. Thus it is clear that the rules C are essential; without them the terms of V_T would not have any observational significance. These rules must be such that they connect sentences of L_0 with certain sentences of L_T, for instance, by making a derivation in the one or the other direction possible. The particular form chosen for the rules C is not essential. They might be formulated as rules of inference or as postulates. Since we assume that the logical structure of the language is sufficiently rich to contain all necessary connectives, we may assume that the rules C are formulated as postulates. Let C be the conjunction of these *correspondence postulates*. As an example, we may think of L_T as a language of theoretical physics, based on a space-time coordinate system. Among the rules C there will be some basic ones, concerning space-time designations. They may specify a method for finding the coordinates of any observationally specified location, e.g., the method used by navigators for determining the position (the spatial coordinates: longitude, latitude, and altitude) and time. In other words, these C-rules specify the relation R which holds between any observable location u and the coordinates x, y, z, t, where x, y, z are the spatial coordinates and t is the time coordinate of u. More exactly speaking, the relation R relates to an observable space-time region u, e.g., an observable event or thing, a class u' of coordinate quadruples which may be specified by intervals around the coordinate values x, y, z, t.

On the basis of these C-rules for space-time designations, other C-rules are given for terms of V_T, e.g., for some simple physical magnitudes like mass, temperature, and the like. These rules are spatiotemporally general, i.e., they hold for any space-time location. They will usually connect only very special kinds of value-distributions of the theoretical magnitude in question with an observable event. For example, a rule might refer to two material bodies u and v (i.e., observable at locations u and v); they must be neither too small nor too large for an observer to see them and to take them in his hands. The rule may connect the theoretical term "mass" with the observable predicate "heavier than" as follows: "If u is heavier than v, the mass of u' (i.e., the mass of the coordinate region u' corresponding to u) is greater than the mass of v'." Another rule may connect the theoretical term "temperature" with the observable predicate "warmer than" in this way: "If u is warmer than v, then the temperature of u' is higher than that of v'."

As these examples show, the C-rules effect a connection only between certain sentences of a very special kind in L_T and sentences in L_O. The earlier view, that for some terms of V_T there could be definitions in terms of V_O, called either 'correlative definitions' (Reichenbach) or 'operational definitions' (Bridgman), has been abandoned by most empiricists as an oversimplification (see Section X). The essential incompleteness of the interpretation of theoretical terms was pointed out in my *Foundations of Logic and Mathematics* (6) and is discussed in detail by Hempel in (15, §3) and (16, §7). Moreover, it cannot be required that there is a C-rule for every term of V_T. If we have C-rules for certain terms, and these terms are connected with other terms by the postulates of T, then these other terms thereby also acquire observational significance. This fact shows that the specification, not only of the rules C, but also of the postulates T, is essential for the problem of meaningfulness. The definition of meaningfulness must be relative to a theory T, because the same term may be meaningful with respect to one theory but meaningless with respect to another.

In order to have a more concrete picture, we may think of the terms of V_T as quantitative physical magnitudes, e.g., functions from space-time-points (or finite space-time-regions) to real numbers (or n-tuples of real numbers). The postulates T may be conceived of as representing the fundamental laws of physics, not other physical statements, however well established. Let us think of the postulates T and the rules C as being completely general with respect to space and time—that is as not containing references to any particular position in space or in time.

In the above examples, the C-rules have the form of universal postulates. A more general form would be that of statistical laws involving the concept of statistical probability (which means roughly, relative frequency in the long run). A postulate of this kind might say, for example, that, if a region has a certain state specified in theoretical terms, then there is a probability of 0.8 that a certain observable event occurs (which means that, on the average, in 80 per cent of those cases this event occurs). Or it might, conversely, state the probability for the theoretical property, with respect to the observable event. Statistical correspondence rules have so far been studied very little. (The probability conception of the psi-functions in quantum mechanics might perhaps be regarded as an example of probabilistic C-rules, as some customary formulations by physicists would suggest. I think, however, that this conception constitutes a probability connection *within* L_T rather than between L_T and L_O. What physicists often call "observable magnitudes," e.g., mass, position, velocity, energy, frequency of waves, and the like, are not "observable" in the sense customary in philosophical discussions of methodology, and therefore belong to the theoretical concepts in our terminology.) For the sake of simplicity, in most of my discussions here I shall think of the C-rules as postulates of universal form.

VI. A Criterion of Significance for Theoretical Terms

My task is to explicate the concept of the empirical meaningfulness of theoretical terms. I shall use "empirical significance" or, for short, "*significance*" as a technical expression for the desired explication. In preparation for the task of explication, let me try to clarify the explicandum somewhat more, i.e., the concept of empirical meaningfulness in its presystematic sense. Let 'M' be a theoretical term of V_T; it may designate a physical magnitude M. What does it mean for 'M' to be empirically meaningful? Roughly speaking, it means that a certain assumption involving the magnitude M makes a difference for the prediction of an observable event. More specifically, there must be a certain sentence S_M about M such that we can infer with its help a sentence S_O in L_O. (The inference may be either deductive, as I shall take it to be in the following discussion, or, more generally, probabilistic.) It is, of course, not required that S_O is derivable from S_M alone.

49

It is clear that we may use in the deduction the postulates T and the rules C. If now S_M contains not only 'M' but also other terms of V_T, then the fact that S_O is deducible does not prove that 'M' is meaningful, because this fact may just be due to the occurrence of the other terms. Therefore I shall require that S_M contain 'M' as the only term of V_T. Now it may be that any assumption involving only the magnitude M is in itself too weak to lead to an observational consequence, and that we have to add a second assumption S_K containing other terms of V_T but not 'M'. Let K be the class of these other terms. For example, S_M may say that, at a certain space-time point, M has the value 5, and S_K may say that, at the same space-time point or in its surroundings, certain other magnitudes have specified values. If S_O can be deduced from the four premises S_M, S_K, T, and C, while it cannot be deduced from S_K, T, and C alone, then the sentence S_M makes a difference for the prediction of an observable event, and therefore has observational significance. Since 'M' is the only descriptive term in S_M, 'M' itself has observational significance. However, this result must be qualified by a proviso. Since we have used the second assumption S_K involving the terms of K, we have shown only that 'M' is meaningful provided that the terms of K are meaningful. For this reason the definition of the significance of 'M' must be made relative not only to T and C, but also to the class K. 'M' is shown by the indicated procedure to be significant provided the terms of K have been found by a previous examination to be significant. Therefore the terms of V_T must be examined in a serial order. The first terms of V_T must be such that they can be shown to be significant without presupposing the significance of other descriptive terms. This will be the case for certain terms of V_T which are directly connected by C-rules with L_O. Other terms of V_T can then be shown to be significant by using the proved significance of the first terms, and so on. The total V_T can be regarded as significant only if we can show for a certain sequence of its terms that each term is significant relative to the class of the terms preceding it in the sequence.

It is clear that the definition must be relative to T, because the question whether a certain term in L_T is significant cannot possibly be decided without taking into consideration the postulates by which it is introduced. Perhaps the objection might be raised that, if significance is dependent upon T, then any observation of a new fact may compel us to take as nonsignificant a term so far regarded as significant or vice versa. However, it should be noted first that the theory T which is here presupposed in the examination of the significance of a term, contains only the postulates, that is, the fundamental laws of science, and not other scientifically asserted sentences, e.g., those describing single facts. Therefore the class of the terms of L_T admitted as significant is not changed whenever new facts are discovered. This class will generally be changed only when a radical revolution in the system of science is made, especially by the introduction of a new primitive theoretical term and the addition of postulates for that term. And note further that the criterion here proposed is such that, although the whole of the theory T is presupposed in the criterion, the question of significance is still raised for each term separately, not only for the vocabulary V_T as a whole.

On the basis of the preceding considerations, I shall now give definitions for the concept of significance of descriptive terms in the theoretical language. The definition $D1$ will define the auxiliary concept of *relative significance*, i.e., the significance of 'M' relative to a class K of other terms. Then the concept of significance itself will be defined in $D2$. According to our previous considerations, the concept of significance must furthermore be relative to the theoretical language L_T, the observation language L_0, the set of postulates T, and the correspondence rules C. We presuppose that the specifications of the languages L_T and L_0 contain also a specification of the classes of descriptive terms, that is, V_T and V_0, respectively.

$D1$. A term 'M' is significant relative to the class K of terms, with respect to L_T, L_0, T, and $C =_{Df}$ the terms of K belong to V_T, 'M' belongs to V_T but not to K, and there are three sentences, S_M and S_K in L_T and S_0 in L_0, such that the following conditions are fulfilled:

(a) S_M contains 'M' as the only descriptive term.
(b) The descriptive terms in S_K belong to K.
(c) The conjunction $S_M.S_K.T.C$ is consistent (i.e., not logically false).
(d) S_0 is logically implied by the conjunction $S_M.S_K.T.C$.
(e) S_0 is not logically implied by $S_K.T.C$.

The condition (c) is only added to assure that the situation described in S_M and S_K is possible, i.e., not excluded by the postulates T and the C-rules; otherwise the condition (d) would be trivially fulfilled.

$D2$. A term 'M_n' is significant with respect to L_T, L_0, T and $C =_{Df}$ there is a sequence of terms 'M_1', . . ., 'M_n' of V_T, such that every term 'M_i' $(i = 1, . . ., n)$ is significant relative to the class of those terms which precede it in the sequence, with respect to L_T, L_0, T, and C.

The sequence of terms referred to in $D2$ must obviously be such that the first term 'M_1' can be shown to be significant without the help of other terms of V_T. In this case 'M_1' satisfies $D1$; the class K is the null class; the sentence S_K contains no descriptive terms; it is logically true and can therefore be omitted. In the simplest case of this kind, 'M_1' occurs in a C-rule, like "mass" and "temperature" in our previous examples. Suppose that the first three terms of our sequence are of the kind described. Then for the fourth term, the sentence S_K may contain any one or all three of these terms. In this way we may proceed, step by step, to other terms, which may be more and more remote from direct observation.

(A slightly stronger criterion might be taken into consideration, obtained by the following modification of $D1$. In addition to the sentence S_M, another sentence S'_M is used, which contains likewise 'M' as the only descriptive term. Then the analogue to condition (c) for S'_M is added, and furthermore the analogue to condition (d) with S'_M taking the place of S_M and the negation of S_O taking the place of S_O. Thus here the assumption S_M leads to an observable consequence, as in $D1$, but another assumption S'_M about M, incompatible with S_M, leads to another observable consequence. However, the simpler criterion stated in $D1$ seems sufficient as a minimum requirement for significance.)

In the informal discussion at the beginning of this section, I have referred to the *deduction* of S_O from certain premises. Correspondingly, $D1$(d) requires that S_O is logically implied by the premises. However, this simple situation holds only if the C-postulates have universal form, as we mostly assume in our discussions. In the more general case that also statistical laws are admitted as C-postulates (see the remark at the end of Section V) and perhaps also as postulates of T, then the result is a probability connection between $S_M.S_K$ on the one hand, and S_O on the other. In this case, the conditions (d) and (e) in $D1$ are to be replaced by the condition that the probability of S_O relative to $S_M.S_K$, presupposing T and C, is different from the probability of S_O relative to S_K alone.

VII. The Adequacy of the Criterion of Significance

The criterion here proposed is admittedly very weak. But this is a result of the development of empiricism in these last decades. The original formulations of the criterion were found to be too strong and too narrow. Therefore, step by step, more liberal formulations were introduced. Hempel has given in his article (15) a clear survey of this development. One change was the replacement of the principle of verifiability by the weaker requirement of confirmability or testability, as formulated in my paper (5). At the time of that paper, I still believed that all scientific terms could be introduced as disposition terms on the basis of observation terms either by explicit definitions or by so-called reduction sentences, which constitute a kind of conditional definition (see Section X). Today I think, in agreement with most empiricists, that the connection between the observation terms and the terms of theoretical science is much more indirect and weak than it was conceived either in my earlier formulations or in those of operationism. Therefore a criterion of significance for L_T must likewise be very weak.

In discussions of the requirement of confirmability (or, in earlier times, verifiability) the question was sometimes raised whether the possibility of the event which constitutes the confirming evidence was to be understood as logical possibility or as causal possibility (i.e., compatibility with the laws of nature or the laws of a given theory). According to Schlick's conception (22, p. 153) the possibility should be understood in the widest sense, as logical possibility. His main argument was the uncertainty about possibility in an empirical sense. He pointed out that the observer does not know whether certain operations are empirically possible for him or not. For example, he does not know whether he is able to lift this table; he is quite certain that he cannot lift an automobile; but both events are still conceivable and should therefore be regarded as possible evidence. Schlick's point was that a question of significance should never be dependent upon contingent facts.

On the other hand, Reichenbach and I (5, p. 423) maintained the view that logical possibility is not sufficient, but that physical (or, more generally, causal) possibility is required. The question whether a given sentence of L_T is confirmable must be taken as relative to a theory T. In examining such a question, a proposed evidence or a proposed test procedure could certainly not be accepted if they were incompatible with T. For example, on the basis of modern physics, which takes the velocity of light as the maximum signal velocity, any proposed test or evidence involving a signal with a higher velocity could not be accepted as proof of significance. The definition $D1$ is based on this conception. The conjunction $S_M.S_K.T.C$ is required to be consistent by condition (c). Since S_0 is logically implied by this conjunction, $S_M.S_K.S_0$ is

Rudolf Carnap

compatible with T and C and thus causally possible. However, it is to be noted that causal possibility as here understood is much weaker than the kind of empirical possibility which Schlick had seemed to have in mind. In Schlick's example, neither the lifting of the table nor that of the automobile is excluded by our criterion, because these events are not incompatible with the T (and C); T contains only the fundamental laws of science, while those events are merely excluded by our empirical knowledge of the observer's ability to lift things.

I shall now examine the question of the adequacy of our criterion in more specific terms. Let us consider the case that the vocabulary V_T consists of two parts, V_1 and V_2, such that the terms of V_1 are empirically meaningful, while those of V_2 are entirely devoid of any empirical meaning. To make this presupposition about V_1 and V_2 more specific, we assume the following:

(1) If S_1 and S_2 are any sentences of L such that all descriptive terms of S_1 belong to V_1 or to the observational vocabulary V_0 and those of S_2 to V_2, then neither of the two sentences logically implies the other, unless the implying sentence is logically false or the implied sentence is logically true.

Now a proposed criterion for the significance of terms of V_T should be regarded as too narrow if it excluded a term of V_1, and as too broad if it admitted a term of V_2. It would be adequate only if it were neither too narrow nor too broad.

For example, we might think of V_1 as containing terms of physics, and of V_2 as containing meaningless terms of speculative metaphysics such that the supposition (1) holds.

First let us consider a postulate system T' consisting of two parts, T'_1 and T'_2, T'_1 containing only terms of V_1, and T'_2 only terms of V_2. T'_1 may, for example, consist of fundamental laws of physics, and T'_2 of metaphysical principles. A criterion of significance which is adequate in this special case can easily be given. We call a postulate of a system T an *isolated postulate* if its omission from T does not diminish the class of sentences in L_0 which are deducible from T with the help of the C-rules. Then we take a term of V_T as significant if it occurs in a C-rule or in a non-isolated postulate of T. In the case of the above system T', according to (1), all postulates of T'_2 and no others are isolated; therefore all terms of V_1 and no others fulfill the criterion of significance just mentioned.

This criterion is, however, not generally adequate. It would, for example, not work for a theory T''' logically equivalent to T' but such that no postulate of T''' is isolated. Those who are sceptical about the possibility of a criterion of significance for L_T have probably a situation of this kind in mind. (Hempel discusses a similar example.) They believe that it is not possible to give a criterion for postulate systems like T'''. However, I think that the criterion for terms proposed in Section VI is adequate for cases of this kind. Consider for the postulate system T''' the sequence of terms which is required in D2. This sequence must necessarily begin with physical terms of V_1, because, according to our assumption (1), there are no C-rules for any of the metaphysical terms of V_2. Then the sequence may go on to further physical terms, which are connected with L_0 not directly by C-rules, but indirectly by other physical terms. Now we shall see that the sequence cannot reach any term of V_2; thus our criterion is not too broad for systems like T'''. We will show this by an indirect proof. We assume that the sequence reaches terms of V_2; let 'M' be the first term of V_2 in the sequence; hence the preceding terms belong to V_1, and thus are meaningful. 'M' is significant relative to the class K of the preceding terms, with respect to L_T, L_0, T''', and C, in the sense of D1. Intuitively speaking, 'M' must then be meaningful, in contradiction to our presupposition about V_2. Our task is, to derive formally a contradiction with the presupposition (1).

According to D1(d):

(2) $S_M.S_K.T'''.C \supset S_0$ is logically true.

Now T''' is logically equivalent to T' and thus to $T'_1.T'_2$. Hence we obtain from (2) with a simple transformation:

(3) $S_M.T'_2 \supset U$ is logically true, where U is $S_K.T'_1.C \supset S_0$.

Hence:

(4) $S_M.T'_2$ logically implies U.

Now all descriptive terms in $S_M.T'_2$ belong to V_2, and those in U belong to V_1 or V_0. Thus (4) is in contradiction to (1), because

(5) $S_M.T'_2$ is not logically false (by D1(c)), and

(6) U is not logically true (by D1(e)).

This shows that the sequence cannot reach the terms of V_2.

Rudolf Carnap

We have shown that our criterion is not too broad if the given set of postulates T''' is logically equivalent to a set T' which consists of two parts, one containing only meaningful terms of V_1, the other only meaningless terms of V_2. The situation would be different for a theory T that did not fulfill this condition. In this case, T must include a postulate A such that A contains terms from both V_1 and V_2, but A is not logically equivalent to a conjunction $A_1 . A_2$ in which A_1 contains only terms of V_1, and A_2 only terms of V_2. But such a postulate A would express a genuine connection between the occurring terms of V_2 and those of V_1. Therefore these terms of V_2 would not be entirely devoid of empirical meaning, against our assumption.

The result that our criterion of significance is not too broad depends essentially on the following feature of our definitions. We refer in $D2$ to a *sequence* of terms, and we require in effect for the significance of a term 'M' of the sequence that 'M' is significant (in the sense of $D1$) relative to the class K of the terms which precede 'M' in the sequence and which therefore have already been found to be significant. We can easily see that the criterion would become too broad if we were to change $D2$ so as to give up the requirement just mentioned. More specifically, we can show the following. A meaningless term 'M_2' of V_2 can, according to $D1$, be significant relative to a class K which contains, in addition to terms of V_1, also a meaningless term of V_2 different from 'M_2', say 'M'_2.' We shall show this first informally. The decisive point is that now, in distinction to our actual definition $D2$, we can have as the additional assumption S_K a sentence connecting the meaningless term 'M'_2' with a meaningful (physical) term of V_1, say 'M_1.' Now there may be a (metaphysical) postulate A_2 of T which connects M_2 with M'_2. With the help of this postulate, we can derive from the assumption S_M about M_2 alone a sentence about M'_2; from this with the sentence S_K mentioned above a physical sentence about M_1, and from this with a suitable C-rule an observation sentence.

The formal derivation is as follows. We take as a postulate of T:

(A_2) For every space-time point, the value of M'_2 is higher than that of M_2 by one.

We take as an instance of a C-rule:

$$(C_1)\ M_1(a') = 5 \supset S_0,$$

where a' is the set of coordinates corresponding to the location a referred to in S_0. Finally we take S_K and S_M as follows:

$$(S_K) \quad M_1(a') = M'_2(a'),$$
$$(S_M) \quad M_2(a') = 4.$$

Now we can derive from S_M with A_2:

(i) $$M'_2(a') = 5,$$

hence with S_K:

(ii) $$M_1 a' = 5,$$

and hence with C_1:

(iii) $$S_0.$$

Thus the condition (d) in $D1$ is fulfilled. Therefore, 'M_2' is significant relative to the class K of the terms 'M_1' and 'M'_2'.

We have just seen that, in the definition of the significance of 'M' relative to K, we must not admit a meaningless term in K and thereby in the additional assumption S_K, because otherwise an observation sentence could be derived, leading to a deceptive appearance of significance. This is indeed excluded by $D2$. However, $D1$ allows other premises for the derivation which contain meaningless terms, viz., postulates of T. Not only the postulates which contain the meaningful terms of V_1 and the term 'M' in question are allowed but also postulates containing any terms of V_2. Could this not lead to the same false appearance of significance for an actually meaningless term 'M' as the use of meaningless terms in S_K would do? In the above example, S_K connected a meaningless term 'M'_2' with a meaningful term 'M_1', and this fact led to the undesired result. Now the use of T would lead to the same result if a postulate of T were to make a connection between those terms. For example, a postulate might yield as an instance the sentence "$M_1(a') = M'_2(a')$" which was used as S_K in the earlier example. Thus the same observation sentence S_0 could be derived from S_M even without the use of any second assumption S_K. As an alternative, a postulate might state a connection between 'M'_2' and 'M_1' in a conditional form, which, though weaker, would likewise make possible a derivation of an observation sentence. Does then the fact that $D1$ permits the use of all postulates T make this definition inadequate? It does not, because the occurrence of a postulate making a genuine connection between a term of V_1 and one of V_2 is excluded by our presupposition that the terms of V_1 are meaningful and those of V_2 meaningless. By virtue of such a postulate, the term of V_s (in the example, 'M'_s') would obtain some measure of empirical meaning, as we observed earlier in this section with reference to the postulate A. The essential difference between the two cases is the following. If a sentence connecting a meaningful term with another term in an inseparable way (e.g., by an equation, a conditional, a disjunction or the like, in distinction to a conjunction, which can be separated into its components) is a postulate or provable on the basis of postulates, then it is stated as holding with physical necessity; therefore it conveys some empirical meaning on the second term. On the other hand, if the same sentence is not provable but is merely used as the additional assumption S_K in D1, then it has no such effect; it need not even be true.

The preceding considerations have shown that our criterion of significance, formulated in D1 and D2, is not too liberal. It does not admit a term entirely devoid of empirical meaning. Now we shall consider the question whether the criterion might be too narrow. Suppose that the term 'M' has some empirical meaning. Then it will be possible to derive an observation sentence from a suitable assumption S involving 'M' and other terms. Could it then still happen that our criterion would exclude 'M'? The definitions D1 and D2, while permitting the inclusion of all postulates T and C among the premises for the derivation of the observation sentence, allow in addition only the two sentences S_K and S_M, for which specific restrictions are stated, especially the following:

(1) S_K may contain only terms of V_T which are different from 'M' and have to be significant; hence the following terms are not allowed in S_K:

    (a) terms of V_s,
    (b) terms of V_O,
    (c) The term 'M'.

(2) S_M contains 'M' as the only descriptive term.

We will now examine whether these restrictions are narrower than is necessary and thus might lead to the exclusion of a meaningful term 'M.'

1a. We found earlier that it is necessary to exclude the terms of V_s from S_K, because otherwise the criterion would become too broad.

1b. Is it necessary to exclude the observational terms V_O from the premises? Could it not be that, for the derivation of an observational conclusion S_0 from S_M, we need, in addition to T and C and the assumption S_K in theoretical terms, some assumption in observation terms, say S'_0? This might well happen. But then the conditional sentence $S'_0 \supset S_0$ is derivable from the premises specified in $D1$, and this is a sentence in L_0. Thus 'M' would fulfill $D1$, with the conditional sentence taking the place of S_0.

$1c$ and 2. The condition (a) in $D1$ requires that S_M contain 'M' as the only descriptive term. The question might be raised whether this requirement is not too strong. Could not the following situation occur? 'M' and the terms of K are meaningful, and S_0 can indeed be derived with the help of T and C from an assumption S containing no other descriptive terms than 'M' and the terms of K, but S cannot be split up into two sentences S_M and S_K such that S_M contains only 'M' and S_K does not contain 'M.' Let us assume that the sentence S refers to space-time points of a certain spatiotemporal region a'. Then we can form sentences S_M and S_K which fulfill the requirements of $D1$ in the following way. Since S is supposed to be compatible with T and C, there must be a possible distribution of values of M for the space-time points of the region a', which is compatible with T, C, and S. Let 'F' be a logical constant, designating a mathematical function which represents such a value distribution. Then we take the following sentence as S_M: "For every space-time point in a', the value of M is equal to that of F." This sentence S_M is compatible with $T.C.S.$ Then we take as S_K the sentence formed from S by replacing the descriptive term 'M' by the logical constant 'F'. Then S_M contains 'M' as the only descriptive term and S_K contains only terms of K. Furthermore, S is logically implied by S_M, and S_K. S_0 is logically implied by $S.T.C.$, according to our assumption, and hence also by $S_M.S_K.T.C.$ Therefore 'M' fulfills the definition $D1$.

Thus we have not found a point in which our criterion is too narrow.

VIII. A Criterion of Significance for Theoretical Sentences

The following two problems are closely connected with each other: first, the problem of a criterion of significance for descriptive constants, and second, the problem of the logical forms to be admitted for sentences. For the theoretical language, the connection between these problems is still closer than for the observation language. In the latter, we may decide to have primitive predicates like "blue," "cold," "warmer than," and the like, while we are still undecided as to the forms of sentences, especially of general sentences, and the structure of the logic to be built into the language. On the other hand, if we wish to have terms like "temperature," "electromagnetic field," etc. as primitives in L_T, then we need also the accepted postulates for them, and thus we have to admit real number expressions, general sentences with real number variables, etc.

It seems to me that the best approach to the problem of a criterion of significance for sentences is the following. We look first for solutions to the two problems mentioned above; and then we take the most liberal criterion of significance for sentences which is compatible with those solutions. That is to say, we then accept as a significant sentence any expression that has any of the admitted logical forms and contains only descriptive constants which are significant. (I have used a similar approach for L_0 in (5).) I propose to apply this procedure now to L_T.

A criterion of significance for descriptive terms was given in Section VI. Some of the questions concerning the logical forms of sentences were discussed in Section IV, especially the question of the kinds of variables to be admitted in universal and existential quantifiers. We decided to admit at least those kinds of variables and forms of sentences which are essential for classical mathematics. Without actually specifying here the details of the rules, we shall now assume that the logical forms of sentences have been chosen on the basis of the considerations in Section IV, and that the rules of formation for L_T have been laid down in accordance with this choice. Then, applying the procedure proposed above, we define as follows:

D3. An expression A of L_T is a significant sentence of $L_T =_{Df}$
   (a) A satisfies the rules of formation of L_T,
   (b) every descriptive constant in A is a significant term (in the sense of D2).

The procedure used in this definition might perhaps appear as obvious. However, a closer examination shows that this is not the case. In fact, this form of the definition (aside from the question of its content, i.e., the choice of the particular rules of formation and of the particular significance criterion for terms) is not in agreement with certain very narrow criteria of significance which were sometimes proposed. For example, verifiability as a condition for the significance of a sentence was sometimes understood in the strict sense of the actual possibility of carrying out a procedure which would lead either to a verification or a falsification of the sentence. According to this criterion, in contrast to *D3*, the significance of a sentence is not only dependent upon its logical form and the nature of the descriptive constants occurring in it, but also upon the location in space and time referred to and the development of technology. For example, an empiricist applying this narrow criterion would regard as significant a sentence ascribing an observable property *P* to a body in his laboratory, while he would reject as nonsignificant another sentence which ascribes the same property to a body not accessible to him or not accessible to any human being, e.g., because of technical difficulties or remoteness in space or time.

However, even at the time of the Vienna Circle, we did not interpret the principle of verifiability in this narrow sense. We emphasized that the principle required, not the actual possibility of determination as true or false, but only the possibility *in principle*. By this qualification we intended to admit cases in which the determination was prevented only by technical limitations or by remoteness in space or time. We accepted, for example, a sentence about a mountain on the other side of the moon as meaningful. We stated the general rule that, if a description of an event in our neighborhood is regarded as meaningful, then an analogous description of an event in prehistoric times, or an event on the earth before there were human beings, or before there were any organisms, or at a future time when human beings will not exist any more, should likewise be accepted as meaningful. On the basis of this conception, the space-time location referred to in a sentence was regarded as irrelevant for the question of meaningfulness; this is in accord with *D3*.

If *D3* is accepted and, in line with our earlier considerations in Section IV, all constants, variables and forms of sentences of classical mathematics are admitted in L_T, then the class of significant sentences of L_T is very comprehensive. We must realize that it includes certain sentences for which no observational evidence can ever be relevant, e.g., the sentence: "The value of the magnitude *M* at a certain space-time point is a rational number," where '*M*' is significant. But every physicist would reject a language of physics so restricted that sentences of this and similar kinds were excluded. He would regard their inclusion as a negligible price to be paid for the great convenience of using the whole of classical mathematics. It seems to me that no serious objections can be raised against these sentences, since it is in any case not possible to give an observational interpretation for more than a small part of the sentences of L_T. We should require no more than that for such a magnitude there are certain sentences which have an influence on the prediction of observable events and thus the magnitude itself has some amount of observational meaning.

I wish to emphasize that the proposed criterion for the significance of sentences is not meant to guarantee the fruitfulness of T. If all terms of V_T fulfill D2 and the postulates T are in accord with the rules of formation, then these postulates are indeed regarded as significant. But this should by no means be understood as implying that T must then be a scientifically satisfactory theory. T may still contain postulates which are of very little use from a scientific point of view. But the question of scientific fruitfulness of sentences and of a theory should be clearly distinguished from the question of empirical significance. There is no sharp boundary line between fruitful and useless hypotheses or theories: this is rather a matter of degree. It seems even doubtful whether it is possible to formulate in a completely general way a definition of a quantitative degree of fruitfulness of a scientific theory.

It should be noted that the significance criterion for L_T cannot be simply absorbed into the rules of formation. These rules determine only the forms of sentences, not the choice of primitive descriptive terms. The significance of these terms depends on other rules of L_T, viz., the list of postulates T and of C-postulates and the rules of logical deduction, as a glance at the essential condition (d) in D1 shows. (The rules of deduction may be given either in a syntactical form, as rules of derivation in a calculus, or in a semantical form, in terms of logical implication. I have used in D1 the latter form because it is more comprehensive; it presupposes rules specifying models and ranges, not given in this article.)

IX. Disposition Concepts

Among the descriptive terms which do not belong to the observation language L_O there are two different kinds, which today, in distinction to my previous conception, I should like to regard as essentially different. One kind is that of the theoretical terms, which we have discussed in detail in this article. The other kind I will call (pure) disposition terms. In my view, they occupy an intermediate position between the observational terms of L_o and the theoretical terms; they are more closely related to the former than to the latter. The name 'observation language' may be understood in a narrower or in a wider sense; the observation language in the wider sense includes the disposition terms. In this article I take the observation language L_o in the narrower sense. All primitive predicates in this language designate directly observable properties or relations of observable things or events; and a nonprimitive term is admitted in L_o only if it can be defined on the basis of the primitive terms by an explicit definition in an extensional form, that is, not involving either logical or causal modalities. The *extended observation language* L'_o is constructed from the original observation language L_o by the addition of new terms in a way now to be described. Suppose that there is a general regularity in the behavior of a given thing of such a kind that, whenever the condition S holds for the thing or its environment, the event R occurs at the thing. In this case we shall say that the thing has the disposition to react to S by R, or for short, that it has the property D_{SR}. For example, elasticity is a disposition of this kind; a thing is called elastic if it shows the following regularity: whenever it is slightly deformed and then released (S), it resumes its original form (R). Or, an animal may have the disposition to react to a light in an otherwise dark environment (S), by approaching the light (R). Thus, S is sometimes a stimulus, and R is the response characteristic for the disposition in question (if we allow ourselves to use the terms 'stimulus' and 'response' not only in their literal sense applied to certain processes in organisms, as in the last example, but in a wider sense also to processes with inorganic bodies). When both S and R are specified, then the disposition concept D_{SR} is thereby completely characterized in its meaning. If both S and R can be described in L'_o, then we admit the introduction of the disposition term 'D_{SR}' as a new predicate in L'_o. The introduction of the first disposition terms in L'_o must be of such a kind that in each case both S and R are expressible in L_o. But once some disposition terms have been introduced in this way, then further disposition terms may be introduced in such a way that S and R are described by using not only the terms of L_o, but also the previously introduced disposition terms of L'_o.

(We will not discuss here the possible forms for the rule by which a

Rudolf Carnap

disposition term is introduced on the basis of given S and R. This involves some technicalities which are not necessary for our present discussions. I will only mention two different forms for such rules that have been proposed. The first consists of so-called reduction sentences, which I proposed in (5). They represent a kind of conditional definition which uses only truth-functional connectives, but no modalities. The other method uses an explicit definition of a special form, involving logical and causal modalities; the exact form of definitions of this kind is at present not yet sufficiently clarified, but still under discussion.)

Sometimes multiple dispositions are used: $D_{S_1R_1, S_2R_2}, \ldots, _{S_nR_n}$ is the disposition to react to S_1 by R_1, to S_2 by R_2, . . ., and finally to S_n by R_n. (In (5) I proposed to introduce a concept of this kind by several pairs of reduction sentences.) However, it seems preferable to admit only simple dispositions. Something similar to a multiple disposition can still be expressed by a conjunction of simple dispositions. Bridgman has emphasized that, strictly speaking, for one concept not more than one test procedure must be given. If we specify, say for "electric charge," three test procedures, then thereby we have given operational definitions for three different concepts; they should be designated by three different terms, which are not logically equivalent. As far as disposition concepts are concerned, in distinction to theoretical terms, I would agree with Bridgman in this point.

Let us now consider an important special kind of disposition. Let L''_o be that sublanguage of L'_o, in which the introduction of a disposition term 'D_{SR}' is permitted only if S and R are such that the observer is able to produce the condition S at will (at least in suitable cases), and that he is able to find out by suitable experiments whether the event R does or does not occur. In this case, by specifying S and R, a test procedure for the disposition D_{SR} is given. This procedure consists in producing the test condition S and then finding out whether or not the positive test result R occurs. If the observer finds for a given thing a sufficient number of positive instances, in which S is followed by R, and no negative instances, i.e., S followed by non-R, he may inductively infer that the general regularity holds and thus that the thing possesses the disposition D_{SR}. Let us call a disposition of this kind a "testable disposition." The class of testable properties includes observable properties and testable dispositions. All predicates in L''_o designate testable properties. The manipulations by which the experimenter produces the test condition S are sometimes called *test operations*. The introduction of D_{SR} by a specification of the test operations and the characteristic result R is therefore sometimes called an *operational definition*. There is actually no sharp line between observable properties and testable dispositions. An observable property may be regarded as a simple special case of a testable disposition; for example, the operation for finding out whether a thing is blue or hissing or cold, consists simply in looking or listening or touching the thing, respectively. Nevertheless, in the reconstruction of the language it seems convenient to take some properties, for which the test procedure is extremely simple (as in the three examples just mentioned), as directly observable and use them as primitives in L_O.

The view has often been maintained, especially by empiricists, that only terms of the kind just described, may be regarded as empirically meaningful. Thus testability was taken as a criterion of significance. The *principle of operationism* says that a term is empirically meaningful only if an operational definition can be given for it. The requirements of testability and of operationism as represented by various authors are closely related to each other, differing only in minor details and in emphasis. (In my simplifying account above they even appear as identical.) The principle of operationism, which was first proposed in physics by Bridgman and then applied also in other fields of science, including psychology, had on the whole a healthy effect on the procedures of concept formation used by scientists. The principle has contributed to the clarification of many concepts and has helped to eliminate unclear or even unscientific concepts. On the other hand, we must realize today that the principle is too narrow.

That the requirements of testability and of operationism exclude some empirically meaningful terms, can easily be seen. Suppose that 'S' and 'R' are both testable and hence accepted as meaningful by a scientist who takes testability as a criterion of significance. Since now the meaning of the term 'D_{SR}' is given by the specification of S and R, there cannot be any good reason for him to reject this term as meaningless, even if the condition S cannot be produced at will. In the latter case, D_{SR} is not testable; but S may still occur spontaneously and then, by finding R or non-R, the observer may determine whether or not D_{SR} holds. Thus it seems preferable not to impose the restriction as in L''_O, but to allow the general procedure as in L'_O: we start with observable

Rudolf Carnap

properties and allow the introduction of any disposition D_{SR}, provided that S and R are already expressible in our language L'_0.

(In (5), I gave an example of a meaningful but not testable term (p. 462) of the kind just described. I expressed there (§27) my preference for the more general procedure (as in L'_0) in comparison with that restricted by the requirement of testability (as in L''_0). Later it became clear by the consideration of theoretical concepts (see the next section of this paper) that a far more extensive liberalization of operationism is needed; this was emphasized by Feigl in (7) and (10) and by Hempel in (16) and (17).)

X. The Difference between Theoretical Terms and Pure Disposition Terms

I think today that, for most of the terms in the theoretical part of science and especially in physics, it is more adequate and also more in line with the actual usage of scientists, to reconstruct them as theoretical terms in L_T rather than as disposition terms in L'_0. The choice of the form of reconstruction depends to some extent upon the interpretation which we wish to give to the term, and this interpretation is not uniquely determined by the accepted formulations in science. The same term, say "temperature," may be interpreted, as I do interpret it, in such a way that it cannot be represented in L'_0 but only in L_T; and, on the other hand, it may also be interpreted, e.g., by an operationist, in such a way that it fulfills the requirement of operationism. I shall now explain the reasons for my present view, which differs from that stated in (5).

A disposition term like 'D_{SR}' introduced by the general method described in the last section (for L'_0) may be called a "pure disposition term" in order to emphasize that it has the following characteristic features which distinguish it from terms in L_T:

1. The term can be reached from predicates for observable properties by one or more steps of the procedure described.

2. The specified relation between S and R constitutes the whole meaning of the term.

3. The regularity involving S and R, on which the term is based, is meant as universal, i.e., holding without exception.

The first characteristic distinguishes a pure disposition term like 'D_{SR}' from other disposition terms which are analogous to 'D_{SR}' but such that the condition S and the characteristic result R are formulated in L_T rather than in L_O or L'_O. (They might be called "theoretical disposition terms"; we shall not discuss them further.) The second characteristic distinguishes 'D_{SR}' from any theoretical term because the latter is never completely interpreted. In (5) I recognized this "open" character of scientific terms, that is, the incompleteness of their interpretation. At that time I tried to do justice to this openness by admitting the addition of further dispositional rules (in the form of reduction sentences; see my remarks in Section IX above on multiple dispositions). I think now that the openness is more adequately represented in L_T; whenever additional C-rules or additional postulates are given, the interpretation of the term may be strengthened without ever being completed.

The third characteristic leads to the following important consequence: (i) If the thing b has the disposition D_{SR} and the condition S is fulfilled for b, then it follows logically that the result R holds for b.

Therefore:

(ii) If S holds for b, but R does not, then b cannot have the disposition D_{SR}. Thus, from a premise in L'_O not involving D_{SR}, at least a negative sentence about D_{SR} is derivable. For a theoretical term, say 'M,' the situation is different. Let S_M be a sentence containing 'M' as the only descriptive term. In the situation described in $D1$ in Section VI, S_O is derivable from S_M and S_K (with the help of T and C, which may be regarded as belonging to the rules of L_T), and therefore non-S_M is derivable from non-S_O and S_K. Since S_K is not translatable into L_O or L'_O, the situation is here different from that in (ii). It is true that, for a term 'M' occurring in a C-rule, there are sentences S_M and S_O such that S_O is derivable from S_M alone without the need of a second premise S_K; and hence non-S_M is derivable from non-S_O, so that the situation is similar to that in (ii). However, this holds only for sentences of a very special kind. Most of the sentences about M alone, even if 'M' is a term occurring in a C-rule, are such that no C-rule is directly applicable, and therefore the derivation of an observation sentence is more indirect and needs additional premises in L_T, like S_K. Consider, for example, the term "mass," which is one of the physical terms most closely related to observational terms. There may be C-rules for "mass" (see the example in Section V). But no C-rule is directly applicable to a sentence S_M ascribing a certain value of mass to a given body, if the value is either so small that the body is not directly observable or so large that the observer cannot manipulate the body. (I mentioned in Section V the possibility of probabilistic C-rules. If all C-rules have this form, then no theoretical sentence is deducible from sentences in L_O or L'_O. Thus in a language of this kind, the difference between pure disposition terms and theoretical terms becomes still more striking.)

We have seen that pure disposition terms and theoretical terms are quite different in their logical and methodological characteristics. To which of these two kinds do scientific terms belong? For the terms of theoretical physics, both conceptions are represented among leading physicists. Bridgman interprets them in such a manner that they fulfill the requirement of operationism and thus are essentially pure dispositions. On the other hand, Henry Margenau emphasizes the importance of the method of introducing these terms by postulates and connecting only certain statements involving them with statements about observables; in this conception they are theoretical terms.

It seems to me that the interpretation of scientific terms as pure dispositions cannot easily be reconciled with certain customary ways of using them. According to (ii), the negative result of a test for a disposition must be taken as conclusive proof that the disposition is not present. But a scientist, when confronted with the negative result of a test for a certain concept, will often still maintain that it holds, provided he has sufficient positive evidence to outbalance the one negative result. For example, let I_o be the property of a wire carrying at the time t_o no electric current of more than 0.1 ampere. There are many test procedures for this property, among them one in which the test condition S consists in bringing a magnetic needle near to the wire, and the characteristic result R is the fact that the needle is not deflected from its normal direction by more than a certain amount. Suppose that the observer assumes from the arrangement of the experiment that I_o holds, e.g., because he does not see any of the ordinary sources of a current and he has obtained, in addition, positive results by some other tests for I_o (or for a physically equivalent property). Then it may be that he does not give up the assumption of I_o even if the above mentioned test with S and R leads to a negative result, that is, a strong deflection of the needle. He may maintain I_o because it is possible that the negative result is due to an unnoticed disturbing factor; e.g., the deflection of the needle may be caused by a hidden magnet rather than by a current in the wire. The fact that the scientist still assumes I_o in spite of the negative result, viz., S and non-R, shows that he does not take I_o as the pure disposition D_{SR} characterized by S and R, because, according to (ii), this disposition is logically incompatible with the negative result. The scientist will point out that the test procedure for I_o based on S and R should not be taken as absolutely reliable, but only with the tacit understanding "unless there are disturbing factors" or "provided the environment is in a normal state." Generally, the explicit or implicit inclusion of such an escape clause in the description of a test procedure for a concept M in terms of a condition S and a result R shows that M is not the pure disposition D_{SR}. Also, the name "operational definition" for the description of the test procedure is in this case misleading; a rule for the application of a term that permits possible exceptions should not be called a "definition" because it is obviously not a complete specification of the meaning of the term.

On the other hand, if the term in question, e.g., 'I_o', is a theoretical term, then the description of the test procedure involving S and R may well admit of exceptions in case of unusual disturbing factors. For example, it may be possible to derive from the postulates T, the C-rules, and factual premises about usual circumstances in a laboratory the conclusion that, if there is no strong current, there will not be a strong deflection of the needle, except in the case of unusual circumstances like a magnetic field from another source, a strong current of air, or the like.

Thus, if a scientist has decided to use a certain term 'M' in such a way, that for certain sentences about M, any possible observational results can never be absolutely conclusive evidence but at best evidence yielding a high probability, then the appropriate place for 'M' in a dual-language system like our system L_o-L_T is in L_T rather than in L_o or L'_o.

XI. Psychological Concepts

The method of reconstructing the language of science by the dual schema consisting of the observation language L_o and the theoretical language L_T and the distinction between pure dispositions and theoretical concepts were so far in this article illustrated mostly by examples taken from physics. In the historical development of science, physics was indeed the field in which the method of introducing terms by postulates without a complete interpretation was first used systematically. The beginning phase of this development may perhaps be seen in the classical mechanics of the eighteenth century; its character became more clearly recognizable in the nineteenth century, especially in the Faraday-Maxwell theory of the electromagnetic field and the kinetic theory of gases. The greatest and most fruitful application is found in the theory of relativity and in quantum theory.

We see at present the beginnings of similar developments in other fields of science, and there can be no doubt that here too the more comprehensive use of this method will lead in time to theories much more powerful for explanation and prediction than those theories which keep close to observables. Also in psychology, in these last decades, more and more concepts were used which show the essential features of theoretical concepts. The germs of this development can sometimes be found in much earlier periods and even, it seems to me, in some prescientific concepts of everyday language, both in the physical and psychological field.

In psychology still more than in physics, the warnings by empiricists and operationists against certain concepts, for which no sufficiently clear rules of use were given, were necessary and useful. On the other hand, perhaps due to the too narrow limitations of the earlier principles of empiricism and operationism, some psychologists became overcautious in the formation of new concepts. Others, whose methodological superego was fortunately not strong enough to restrain them, dared to transgress the accepted limits but felt uneasy about it. Some of my psychologist friends think that we empiricists are responsible for the too narrow restrictions applied by psychologists. Perhaps they overestimate the influence that philosophers have on scientists in general; but maybe we should plead guilty to some extent. All the more should we now emphasize the changed conception which gives much more freedom to the working scientist in the choice of his conceptual tools.

In a way similar to the philosophical tendencies of empiricism and operationism, the psychological movement of Behaviorism had, on the one hand, a very healthful influence because of its emphasis on the observation of behavior as an intersubjective and reliable basis for psychological investigations, while, on the other hand, it imposed too narrow restrictions. First, its total rejection of introspection was unwarranted. Although many of the alleged results of introspection were indeed questionable, a person's awareness of his own state of imagining, feeling, etc., must be recognized as a kind of observation, in principle not different from external observation, and therefore as a legitimate source of knowledge, though limited by its subjective character. Secondly, Behaviorism in combination with the philosophical tendencies mentioned led often to the requirement that all psychological concepts must be defined in terms of behavior or behavior dispositions. A psychological concept ascribed to a person X by the investigator Y either as a momentary state or process or as a continuing trait or ability, was thus interpreted as a pure disposition D_{SR} of such a kind that S was a process affecting a sensory organ of X but observable also by Y, and R was a specified kind of behavior, likewise observable by Y. In contrast to this, the interpretation of a psychological concept as a theoretical concept, although it may accept the same behavioristic test procedure based on S and R, does not identify the concept (the state or trait) with the pure disposition D_{SR}. The decisive difference is this: on the basis of the theoretical interpretation, the result of this or of any other test or, generally, of any observations, external or internal, is not regarded as absolutely conclusive evidence for the state in question; it is accepted only as probabilistic evidence, hence at best as a reliable indicator, i.e., one yielding a high probability for the state.

In analogy to what I said in the previous section about physical terms, I wish to emphasize here for psychological terms that their interpretation as pure disposition terms is not in itself objectionable. The question is only whether this interpretation is in accord with the way the psychologist intends to use the term, and whether it is the most useful for the purpose of the whole of psychological theory, which is presumably the explanation and prediction of human behavior. Suppose that the psychologist Y declares that he understands the term "an IQ higher than 130" in the sense of the pure disposition D_{SR} to react to a specified kind of test S by a response of a specified kind R, where S and R are specified in terms of overt behavior. He is free to choose this interpretation provided he is consistent in it and willing to accept its implications. Suppose that he assumes on the basis of ample previous evidence that (at present) the person X has an IQ higher than 130. Then, due to his interpretation, he is compelled to give up the assumption if today the test result is negative, i.e., X's response to the test S is not of the specified kind R. (This follows from (ii) in Section X.) He cannot even re-accept the assumption later when he learns that

71

during the test X was in a very depressed mood, which, however, he neither admitted on question nor showed in his behavior at the time of the test. Can the psychologist not escape from this embarrassing consequence by saying that X's later admission of his depressed state showed that the condition S was actually not fulfilled? Not easily. There would have to be a rule as part of the specification of S that would enable him to make the exception. Let us consider three possibilities for a rule.

1. Let the rule merely say that, at the time t_o of the test, there must be first a complete lack of any observable sign of a disturbed emotional state at time t_o and second a negative answer to a question about such a state. Here the condition S was actually fulfilled and thus the psychologist has no way out.

2. Let the rule add, moreover, that also at no later time must there be a sign indicating a disturbance at time t_o. In this case, S was indeed not fulfilled. But a test procedure containing a rule of this kind would be practically useless, because it could never be completed before the death of the person.

3. Finally, let the rule refer not to behavioral signs but to the emotional state itself. Here the test procedure is not a strictly behavioristic procedure; I_o is not defined as a behavior disposition.

If, on the other hand, "an IQ higher than 130" is taken as a theoretical term, the situation is entirely different. The same test procedure with S and R may still be accepted. But its specification is no longer regarded as an operational definition of the term. There cannot be a definition of the term on the basis of overt behavior. There may be various test procedures for the same concept. But no result of a single test nor of any number of tests is ever absolutely conclusive, although they may, under favorable circumstances, yield a high probability. Any statement ascribing the term in question to a person on the basis of a given test result may later be corrected in view of new evidence, even if there is no doubt that the test rules S were fulfilled and that the response R was made. If a psychologist accepts this non-conclusive, probabilistic character of a test, as, I suppose, practically all would do, then the concept tested cannot be a pure disposition and is best reconstructed as a theoretical term.

I think that, even on a prescientific level, many people would regard their psychological judgments about other people as in principle always open to correction in view of later observations of their behavior. To the extent that someone is willing to change his judgments in this way, his use of psychological terms might be regarded as a beginning of the development which leads finally to theoretical terms. By the way, it would be interesting to make an empirical investigation of the degree of rigidity and flexibility shown by non-psychologists (including philosophers) in making and changing psychological statements about other people and about themselves. This would give a clearer indication of the nature of their concepts than any answers to direct questions about the concepts.

The distinction between intervening variables and theoretical constructs, often discussed since the article by MacCorquodale and Meehl, seems essentially the same or closely related to our distinction between pure dispositions and theoretical terms. "Theoretical construct" means certainly the same as here "theoretical term", viz., a term which cannot be explicitly defined even in an extended observation language, but is introduced by postulates and not completely interpreted. The intervening variables are said to serve merely for a more convenient formulation of empirical laws and to be such that they can always be eliminated. Therefore it seems that they would be definable in a language similar to our extended observation language L'_0 but containing also quantitative terms; thus they seem essentially similar to pure dispositions.

Among empiricists, it was especially Feigl who early recognized and continually emphasized the importance of theoretical laws (which he called "existential hypotheses"; see his (8)). And he showed in particular that in the present phase of psychology the use of theoretical concepts and laws constitutes one of the most important methodological problems and tasks. He made important contributions to the clarification of this problem, especially in his article (10); there he points out the close analogy with the earlier development of physics.

Psychological theories with theoretical terms will no doubt be further developed, probably to a much larger extent than so far. There are good reasons for expecting that a development of this kind will prove to be very fruitful, while without it the possible forms of theory construction are too limited to give a good chance for essential progress. This does not imply that the so-called "molar" approach in terms of observable behavior is to be rejected; on the contrary, this approach will always be an essential part of psychological investigation. What is wrong is only the principle which demands a restriction of the psychological method to this approach. The molar approach in psychology has a function similar to that of macrophysics both in the historical development and in present research. In all fields, the study of macro-events is the natural approach in the beginning; it leads to the first explanations of facts by the discovery of general regularities among observable properties ("empirical laws"); and it remains always indispensable as the source of confirming evidence for theories.

In physics great progress was made only by the construction of theories referring to unobservable events and micro-entities (atoms, electrons, etc.). Then it became possible to formulate a relatively small number of fundamental laws as postulates from which many empirical laws, both those already known and new ones, could be derived with the help of suitably constructed correspondence rules. In psychology analogous developments have begun from two different starting points. The one development began with the introspective approach. It proceeded from introspectively observed events (feelings, perceptions, images, beliefs, remembrances, etc.) to unconscious, i.e., introspectively not observable, events. These were first conceived as analogous to the observable events, e.g., unconscious feelings, beliefs, etc. Later also, new kinds of entities were introduced, e.g., drives, complexes, the id, the ego, and the like; however, the laws involving these entities are so far only stated in a qualitative form, which limits their explanatory and still more their predictive power. The other development began with the molar behavioristic approach. It started with a study of observable events of behavior, and then proceeded to dispositions, tendencies, abilities, potentialities for such events, and further to more abstract entities. Here the stage of the first quantitative laws has been reached.

Both these approaches in psychology will probably later converge toward theories of the central nervous system formulated in physiological terms. In this physiological phase of psychology, which has already begun, a more and more prominent role will be given to quantitative concepts and laws referring to micro-states described in terms of cells, molecules, atoms, fields, etc. And finally, micro-physiology may be based on micro-physics. This possibility of constructing finally all of science, including psychology, on the basis of physics, so that all theoretical terms are definable by those of physics and all laws derivable from those of physics, is asserted by the thesis of *physicalism* (in its strong sense). (My recent views on the question of physicalism are not yet represented in my publications. Feigl (11) explains them, describes the historical development of physicalism in our movement, and gives an illuminating discussion of the theses of physicalism and the arguments for them.) By far the greater part of the development of psychology just outlined is, of course, today no more than a program for the future. Views vary a great deal as to the probability and even the possibility of such a development; and many will especially oppose, with either scientific or metaphysical arguments, the possibility of the last step, the assertion of physicalism. My personal impression, in view of the progress made within the last decades in psychology, physiology, the chemistry of complex organic molecules, and certain parts of physics, especially the theory of electronic computers, is that the whole development of psychology from the molar phase through the theoretical, the physiological, and the micro-physiological phases to the final foundation in micro-physics seems today much more probable and much less remote in time than it appeared even thirty years ago.

REFERENCES

1. Bridgman, P. W. *The Logic of Modern Physics.* New York: Macmillan, 1927.
2. Bridgman, P. W. *The Nature of Physical Theory.* Princeton: Princeton Univ. Pr., 1936.
3. Bridgman, P. W. "Operational Analysis," *Philosophy of Science,* 5:114–31 (1938).
4. Bridgman, P. W. "The Nature of Some of Our Physical Concepts," *British Journal for the Philosophy of Science,* 1:257–72 (February 1951); 2:25–44 (May 1951); 2:142–60 (August 1951). Reprinted as a separate monograph by Philosophical Lib., New York, 1952.
5. Carnap, Rudolf. "Testability and Meaning," *Philosophy of Science,* 3:420–68 (1936); 4:1–40 (1937). Reprinted as monograph by Whitlock's, Inc., New Haven, Connecticut, 1950. Parts reprinted in H. Feigl and M. Brodbeck (eds.), *Readings in the Philosophy of Science.* New York: Appleton-Century-Crofts, 1953.
6. Carnap, Rudolf. *Foundations of Logic and Mathematics,* Vol. I, No. 3 of the *International Encyclopedia of Unified Science.* Chicago: Univ. of Chicago Pr., 1939. A part ("The Interpretation of Physics") is reprinted in H. Feigl and M. Brodbeck (eds.), *Readings in the Philosophy of Science,* pp. 309–18. New York: Appleton-Century-Crofts, 1953.
7. Feigl, Herbert. "Operationism and Scientific Method," *Psychological Review,* 52:250–59 (1945). Reprinted, with some alterations, in H. Feigl and W. Sellars (eds.), *Readings in Philosophical Analysis,* pp. 498–509. New York: Appleton-Century-Crofts, 1949.
8. Feigl, Herbert. "Existential Hypotheses: Realistic Vs. Phenomenalistic Interpretations." *Philosophy of Science,* 17:35–62 (1950).

9. Feigl, Herbert. "Confirmability and Confirmation," *Revue Internationale de Philosophie*, 5:268–79 (1951). Reprinted in P. P. Wiener (ed.), *Readings in Philosophy of Science*, pp. 522–30. New York: Scribner's, 1953.

10. Feigl, Herbert. "Principles and Problems of Theory Construction in Psychology," in W. Dennis (ed.), *Current Trends in Psychological Theory*, pp. 179–213. Pittsburgh: Univ. of Pittsburgh Pr., 1951.

11. Feigl, Herbert. "Physicalism, Unity of Science, and the Foundations of Psychology," in P. A. Schilpp (ed.), *The Philosophy of Rudolf Carnap*. New York: Tudor (forthcoming).

12. Feigl, H., and M. Brodbeck (eds.). *Readings in the Philosophy of Science*. New York: Appleton-Century-Crofts, 1953.

13. Feigl, H., and W. Sellars (eds.). *Readings in Philosophical Analysis*. New York: Appleton-Century-Crofts, 1949.

14. Hempel, C. G. "Problems and Changes in the Empiricist Criterion of Meaning," *Revue Internationale de Philosophie*, 4:41–63 (1950). Reprinted in L. Linsky (ed.), *Semantics and the Philosophy of Language*, pp. 163–85. Urbana: Univ. of Illinois Pr., 1952.

15. Hempel, C. G. "The Concept of Cognitive Significance: A Reconsideration," *Proceedings of the American Academy of Arts and Sciences*, 80:61–77 (1951).

16. Hempel, C. G. *Fundamentals of Concept Formation in the Empirical Sciences*, Vol. II, No. 7 of the *International Encyclopedia of Unified Science*. Chicago: Univ. of Chicago Pr., 1952.

17. Hempel, C. G. "A Logical Appraisal of Operationism," *Scientific Monthly*, 79:215–20 (1954).

18. Hempel, C. G. "Implications of Carnap's Work for the Philosophy of Science," in P. A. Schilpp (ed.), *The Philosophy of Rudolf Carnap*. New York: Tudor (forthcoming).

19. MacCorquodale, Kenneth, and P. E. Meehl. "On a Distinction Between Hypothetical Constructs and Intervening Variables," *Psychological Review*, 55:95–107 (1948). Reprinted in H. Feigl and M. Brodbeck (eds.), *Readings in the Philosophy of Science*, pp. 596–611. New York: Appleton-Century-Crofts, 1953.

20. Margenau, Henry. *The Nature of Physical Reality*. New York: McGraw-Hill, 1950.

21. Schilpp, P. A. (ed.). *The Philosophy of Rudolf Carnap*. New York: Tudor (forthcoming).

22. Schlick, Moritz. "Meaning and Verification," *Philosophical Review*, 45:339–69 (1936). Reprinted in H. Feigl and W. Sellars (eds.), *Readings in Philosophical Analysis*, pp. 146–74. New York: Appleton-Century-Crofts, 1949.

Critique of Psychoanalytic Concepts and Theories

FREUD's great contribution to Western thought has been described as the application of the principle of cause and effect to human behavior. Freud demonstrated that many features of behavior hitherto unexplained—and often dismissed as hopelessly complex or obscure—could be shown to be the product of circumstances in the history of the individual. Many of the causal relationships he so convincingly demonstrated had been wholly unsuspected—unsuspected, in particular, by the very individuals whose behavior they controlled. Freud greatly reduced the sphere of accident and caprice in our considerations of human conduct. His achievement in this respect appears all the more impressive when we recall that he was never able to appeal to the quantitative proofs characteristic of other sciences. He carried the day with sheer persuasion—with the massing of instances and the delineation of surprising parallels and analogies among seemingly diverse materials.

This was not, however, Freud's own view of the matter. At the age of seventy he summed up his achievement in this way: "My life has been aimed at one goal only: to infer or guess how the mental apparatus is constructed and what forces interplay and counteract in it." (2) It is difficult to describe the mental apparatus he refers to in noncontroversial terms, partly because Freud's conception changed from time to time and partly because its very nature encouraged misinterpretation and misunderstanding. But it is perhaps not too wide of the mark to indicate its principal features as follows: Freud conceived of some realm of the mind, not necessarily having physical extent, but nevertheless capable of topographic description and of subdivision into regions of the conscious, co-conscious, and unconscious. Within this space, various mental events—ideas, wishes, memories, emotions, instinctive tenden-

NOTE: This paper appeared, in somewhat different form, in *The Scientific Monthly*, November 1954, and is reprinted by permission of the editor and the author.

77

cies, and so on—interacted and combined in many complex ways. Systems of these mental events came to be conceived of almost as subsidiary personalities and were given proper names: the id, the ego, and the superego. These systems divided among themselves a limited store of psychic energy. There were, of course, many other details.

No matter what logicians may eventually make of this mental apparatus, there is little doubt that Freud accepted it as real rather than as a scientific construct or theory. One does not at the age of seventy define the goal of one's life as the exploration of an explanatory fiction. Freud did not use his "mental apparatus" as a postulate system from which he deduced theorems to be submitted to empirical check. If there was any interaction between the mental apparatus and empirical observations, such interaction took the form of modifying the apparatus to account for newly discovered facts. To many followers of Freud the mental apparatus appears to be equally as real as the newly discovered facts, and the exploration of such an apparatus is similarly accepted as the goal of a science of behavior. There is an alternative view, however, which holds that Freud did not discover the mental apparatus but rather invented it, borrowing part of its structure from a traditional philosophy of human conduct but adding many novel features of his own devising.

There are those who will concede that Freud's mental apparatus was a scientific construct rather than an observable empirical system but who, nevertheless, attempt to justify it in the light of scientific method. One may take the line that metaphorical devices are inevitable in the early stages of any science and that although we may look with amusement today upon the "essences," "forces," "phlogistons," and "ethers," of the science of yesterday, these nevertheless were essential to the historical process. It would be difficult to prove or disprove this. However, if we have learned anything about the nature of scientific thinking, if mathematical and logical researches have improved our capacity to represent and analyze empirical data, it is possible that we can avoid some of the mistakes of adolescence. Whether Freud could have done so is past demonstrating, but whether we need similar constructs in the future prosecution of a science of behavior is a question worth considering.

Constructs are convenient and perhaps even necessary in dealing with certain complicated subject matters. As Frenkel-Brunswik shows (1),

Freud was aware of the problems of scientific methodology and even of the metaphorical nature of some of his own constructs. When this was the case, he justified the constructs as necessary or at least highly convenient. But awareness of the nature of the metaphor is no defense of it, and if modern science is still occasionally metaphorical, we must remember that, theorywise, it is also still in trouble. The point is not that metaphor or construct is objectionable but that particular metaphors and constructs have caused trouble and are continuing to do so. Freud recognized the damage worked by his own metaphorical thinking, but he felt that it could not be avoided and that the damage must be put up with. There is reason to disagree with him on this point.

Freud's explanatory scheme followed a traditional pattern of looking for a cause of human behavior inside the organism. His medical training supplied him with powerful supporting analogies. The parallel between the excision of a tumor, for example, and the release of a repressed wish from the unconscious is quite compelling and must have affected Freud's thinking. Now, the pattern of an inner explanation of behavior is best exemplified by doctrines of animism, which are primarily concerned with explaining the spontaneity and evident capriciousness of behavior. The living organism is an extremely complicated system behaving in an extremely complicated way. Much of its behavior appears at first blush to be absolutely unpredictable. The traditional procedure has been to invent an inner determiner, a "demon," "spirit," "homunculus," or "personality" capable of spontaneous change of course or of origination of action. Such an inner determiner offers only a momentary explanation of the behavior of the outer organism, because it must, of course, be accounted for also, but it is commonly used to put the matter beyond further inquiry and to bring the study of a causal series of events to a dead end.

Freud, himself, however, did not appeal to the inner apparatus to account for spontaneity or caprice because he was a thoroughgoing determinist. He accepted the responsibility of explaining, in turn, the behavior of the inner determiner. He did this by pointing to hitherto unnoticed external causes in the environmental and genetic history of the individual. He did not, therefore, need the traditional explanatory system for traditional purposes; but he was unable to eliminate the pattern from his thinking. It led him to represent each of the causal relationships he had discovered as a series of three events. Some environmental condition, very often in the early life of the individual, leaves an effect upon the inner mental apparatus, and this in turn produces the behavioral manifestation or symptom. Environmental event, mental state or process, behavioral symptom—these are the three links in Freud's causal chain. He made no appeal to the middle link to explain spontaneity or caprice. Instead he used it to bridge the gap in space and time between the events he had proved to be causally related.

A possible alternative, which would have had no quarrel with established science, would have been to argue that the environmental variables leave *physiological* effects that may be inferred from the behavior of the individual, perhaps at a much later date. In one sense, too little is known at the moment of these physiological processes to make them useful in a legitimate way for this purpose. On the other hand, too much is known of them, at least in a negative way. Enough is known of the nervous system to place certain dimensional limits upon speculation and to clip the wings of explanatory fiction. Freud accepted, therefore, the traditional fiction of a mental life, avoiding an out-and-out dualism by arguing that eventually physiological counterparts would be discovered. Quite apart from the question of the existence of mental events, let us observe the damage that resulted from this maneuver.

We may touch only briefly upon two classical problems that arise once the conception of a mental life has been adopted. The first of these is to explain how such a life is to be observed. The introspective psychologists had already tried to solve this problem by arguing that introspection is only a special case of the observation upon which all science rests and that man's experience necessarily stands between him and the physical world with which science purports to deal. But it was Freud himself who pointed out that not all of one's mental life was accessible to direct observation—that many events in the mental apparatus were necessarily inferred. Great as this discovery was, it would have been still greater if Freud had taken the next step, advocated a little later by the American movement called Behaviorism, and insisted that conscious, as well as unconscious, events were inferences from the facts. By arguing that the individual organism simply reacts to its environment, rather than to some inner experience of that environment, the bifurcation of nature into physical and psychic can be avoided.*

---

* Although it was Freud himself who taught us to doubt the face value of introspection, he appears to have been responsible for the view that another sort of direct

A second classical problem is how the mental life can be manipulated. In the process of therapy, the analyst necessarily acts upon the patient only through physical means. He manipulates variables occupying a position in the first link of Freud's causal chain. Nevertheless, it is commonly assumed that the mental apparatus is being directly manipulated. Sometimes it is argued that processes are initiated within the individual himself, such as those of free association and transference, and that these in turn act directly upon the mental apparatus. But how are these mental processes initiated by physical means? The clarification of such a causal connection places a heavy and often unwelcome burden of proof upon the shoulders of the dualist.

The important disadvantages of Freud's conception of mental life can be described somewhat more specifically. The first of these concerns the environmental variables to which Freud so convincingly pointed. The cogency of these variables was frequently missed because the variables were transformed and obscured in the course of being represented in mental life. The physical world of the organism was converted into conscious and unconscious experience, and these experiences were further transmuted as they combined and changed in mental processes. For example, early punishment of sexual behavior is an observable fact that undoubtedly leaves behind a changed organism. But when this change is represented as a state of conscious or unconscious anxiety or guilt, specific details of the punishment are lost. When, in turn, some unusual characteristic of the sexual behavior of the adult individual is related to the supposed guilt, many specific features of the relationship may be missed that would have been obvious if the same features of behavior had been related to the punishing episode. Insofar as the mental life of the individual is used as Freud used it to represent and to carry an environmental history, it is inadequate and misleading.

Freud's theory of the mental apparatus had an equally damaging effect upon his study of behavior as a dependent variable. Inevitably, it stole the show. Little attention was left to behavior per se. Behavior was relegated to the position of a mere mode of expression of the

experience is required if certain activities in the mental apparatus are to be comprehended. Such a requirement is implied in the modern assertion that only those who have been psychoanalyzed can fully understand the meaning of transference or the release of a repressed fear.

activities of the mental apparatus or the symptoms of an underlying disturbance. Among the problems not specifically treated in the manner that was their due, we may note five.

1. The nature of the act as a unit of behavior was never clarified. The simple occurrence of behavior was never well represented. "Thoughts" could "occur" to an individual; he could "have" ideas according to the traditional model; but he could "have" behavior only in giving expression to these inner events. We are much more likely to say that "the thought occurred to me to ask him his name" than that "the act of asking him his name occurred to me." It is in the nature of thoughts and ideas that they occur to people, but we have never come to be at home in describing the emission of behavior in a comparable way. This is especially true of verbal behavior. In spite of Freud's valuable analysis of verbal slips and of the techniques of wit and verbal art, he rejected the possibility of an analysis of verbal behavior in its own right rather than as the expression of ideas, feelings, or other inner events, and therefore missed the importance of this field for the analysis of units of behavior and the conditions of their occurrence.

The behavioral nature of perception was also slighted. To see an object as an object is not mere passing sensing; it is an act, and something very much like it occurs when we see an object although no object is present. Fantasy and dreams were for Freud not the perceptual *behavior* of the individual but pictures painted by an inner artist in some atelier of the mind which the individual then contemplated and perhaps then reported. This division of labor is not essential when the behavioral component of the act of seeing is emphasized.

2. The dimensions of behavior, particularly its dynamic properties, were never adequately represented. We are all familiar with the fact that some of our acts are more likely to occur upon a given occasion than others. But this likelihood is hard to represent and harder to evaluate. The dynamic changes in behavior that are the first concern of the psychoanalyst are primarily changes in probability of action. But Freud chose to deal with this aspect of behavior in other terms—as a question of "libido," "cathexis," "volume of excitation," "instinctive or emotional tendencies," "available quantities of psychic energy," and so on. The delicate question of how probability of action is to be quantified was never answered, because these constructs suggested dimensions

to which the quantitative practices of science in general could not be applied.

3. In his emphasis upon the genesis of behavior, Freud made extensive use of processes of learning. These were never treated operationally in terms of changes in behavior but rather as the acquisition of ideas, feelings, and emotions later to be expressed by, or manifested in, behavior. Consider, for example, Freud's own suggestion that sibling rivalry in his own early history played an important part in his theoretical considerations as well as in his personal relationships as an adult.

An infant brother died when Freud himself was only one and a half years old, and as a young child Freud played with a boy somewhat older than himself and presumably more powerful, yet who was, strangely enough, in the nominally subordinate position of being his nephew. To classify such a set of circumstances as sibling rivalry obscures, as we have seen, the many specific properties of the circumstances themselves regarded as independent variables in a science of behavior. To argue that *what was learned* was the effect of these circumstances upon unconscious or conscious aggressive tendencies or feelings of guilt works a similar misrepresentation of the dependent variable. An emphasis upon behavior would lead us to inquire into the specific acts plausibly assumed to be engendered by these childhood episodes. In very specific terms, how was the behavior of the young Freud *shaped* by the special reinforcing contingencies arising from the presence of a younger child in the family, by the death of that child, and by later association with an older playmate who nevertheless occupied a subordinate family position? What did the young Freud *learn to do* to achieve parental attention under these difficult circumstances? How did he avoid aversive consequences? Did he exaggerate any illness? Did he feign illness? Did he make a conspicuous display of behavior that brought commendation? Was such behavior to be found in the field of physical prowess or intellectual endeavor? Did he learn to engage in behavior that would in turn increase the repertoires available to him to achieve commendation? Did he strike or otherwise injure young children? Did he learn to injure them verbally by teasing? Was he punished for this, and if so, did he discover other forms of behavior that had the same damaging effect but were immune to punishment?

We cannot, of course, adequately answer questions of this sort at so late a date, but they suggest the kind of inquiry that would be prompted

B. F. Skinner

by a concern for the explicit shaping of behavioral repertoires under childhood circumstances. What has survived through the years is not aggression and guilt, later to be manifested in behavior, but rather patterns of behavior themselves. It is not enough to say that this is "all that is meant" by sibling rivalry or by its effects upon the mental apparatus. Such an expression obscures, rather than illuminates, the nature of the behavioral changes taking place in the childhood learning process. A similar analysis could be made of processes in the fields of motivation and emotion.

4. An explicit treatment of behavior as a datum, of probability of response as the principal quantifiable property of behavior, and of learning and other processes in terms of changes of probability is usually enough to avoid another pitfall into which Freud, in common with his contemporaries, fell. There are many words in the layman's vocabulary that suggest the activity of an organism yet are not descriptive of behavior in the narrower sense. Freud used many of these freely; for example, the individual is said to discriminate, remember, infer, repress, decide, and so on. Such terms do not refer to specific acts. We say that a man discriminates between two objects when he behaves differently with respect to them; but discriminating is not itself behavior. We say that he represses behavior which has been punished when he engages in other behavior just because it displaces the punished behavior; but repressing is not action. We say that he decides upon a course of conduct either when he enters upon one course to the exclusion of another, or when he alters some of the variables affecting his own behavior in order to bring this about; but there is no other "act of deciding." The difficulty is that when one uses terms which suggest an activity, one feels it necessary to invent an actor, and the subordinate personalities in the Freudian mental apparatus do, indeed, participate in just these activities rather than in the more specific behavior of the observable organism.

Among these activities are conspicuous instances involving the process of self-control—the so-called "Freudian mechanisms." These need not be regarded as activities of the individual or any subdivision thereof—they are not, for example, what happens when a skillful wish evades a censor—but simply as ways of representing relationships among responses and controlling variables. I have elsewhere tried to demonstrate this by restating the Freudian mechanisms without reference to Freudian theory (3).

5. Since Freud never developed a clear conception of the behavior of the organism and never approached many of the scientific problems peculiar to that subject matter, it is not surprising that he misinterpreted the nature of the observation of one's own behavior. This is admittedly a delicate subject, which presents problems that no one, perhaps, has adequately solved. But the act of self-observation can be represented within the framework of physical science. This involves questioning the reality of sensations, ideas, feelings, and other states of consciousness which many people regard as among the most immediate experiences of their life. Freud himself prepared us for this change. There is, perhaps, no experience more powerful than that which the mystic reports of his awareness of the presence of God. The psychoanalyst explains this in other ways. He himself, however, may insist upon the reality of certain experiences that others wish to question. There are other ways of describing what is actually seen or felt under such circumstances.

Each of us is in particularly close contact with a small part of the universe enclosed within his own skin. Under certain limited circumstances, we may come to react to that part of the universe in unusual ways. But it does not follow that that particular part has any special physical or nonphysical properties or that our observations of it differ in any fundamental respect from our observations of the rest of the world. I have tried to show elsewhere (3) how self-knowledge of this sort arises and why it is likely to be subject to limitations that are troublesome from the point of view of physical science. Freud's representation of these events was a particular personal contribution influenced by his own cultural history. It is possible that science can now move on to a different description of them. If it is impossible to be wholly nonmetaphorical, at least we may improve upon our metaphors.

The crucial issue here is the Freudian distinction between the conscious and unconscious mind. Freud's contribution has been widely misunderstood. The important point was not that the individual was often unable to describe important aspects of his own behavior or identify important causal relationships, but that his ability to describe them was irrelevant to the occurrence of the behavior or to the effectiveness of the causes. We begin by attributing the behavior of the individual to events in his genetic and environmental history. We then note that because of certain cultural practices, the individual may come to describe some of that behavior and some of those causal relationships. We may say that he is conscious of the parts he can describe and unconscious of the rest. But the act of self-description, as of self-observation, plays no part in the determination of action. It is superimposed upon behavior. Freud's argument that we need not be aware of important causes of conduct leads naturally to the broader conclusion that awareness of cause has nothing to do with causal effectiveness.

In addition to these specific consequences of Freud's mental apparatus in obscuring important details among the variables of which human behavior is a function and in leading to the neglect of important problems in the analysis of behavior as a primary datum, we have to note the most unfortunate effect of all. Freud's methodological strategy has prevented the incorporation of psychoanalysis into the body of science proper. It was inherent in the nature of such an explanatory system that its key entities would be unquantifiable in the sense in which entities in science are generally quantifiable, but the spatial and temporal dimensions of these entities have caused other kinds of trouble.

One can sense a certain embarrassment among psychoanalytic writers with respect to the primary entities of the mental apparatus. There is a predilection for terms that avoid the embarrassing question of the spatial dimensions, physical or otherwise, of terms at the primary level. Although it is occasionally necessary to refer to mental events and their qualities and to states of consciousness, the analyst usually moves on in some haste to less committal terms such as *forces, processes, organizations, tensions, systems,* and *mechanisms.* But all these imply terms at a lower level. The notion of a conscious or unconscious "force" may be a useful metaphor, but if this is analogous to force in physics, what is the analogous mass that is analogously accelerated? Human behavior is in a state of flux and undergoing changes that we call "processes," but what is changing in what direction when we speak of, for example, an affective process? Psychological "organizations," "mental systems," "motivational interaction"—these all imply arrangements or relationships among *things,* but what are the things so related or arranged? Until this question has been answered the problem of the dimensions of the mental apparatus can scarcely be approached. It is not likely that the problem can be solved by working out independent units appropriate to the mental apparatus, although it has been proposed that such a step be undertaken in an attempt to place psychoanalysis on a scientific footing.

Before one attempts to work out units of transference, or scales of anxiety, or systems of mensuration appropriate to the regions of consciousness, it is worth asking whether there is not an alternative program for a *rapprochement* with physical science that would make such a task unnecessary. Freud could hope for an eventual union with physics or physiology only through the discovery of neurological mechanisms that would be the analogues of, or possibly only other aspects of, the features of his mental apparatus. Since this depended upon the prosecution of a science of neurology far beyond its current state of knowledge, it was not an attractive future. Freud appears never to have considered the possibility of bringing the concepts and theories of a psychological science into contact with the rest of physical and biological science by the simple expedient of an operational definition of terms. This would have placed the mental apparatus in jeopardy as a life goal, but it would have brought him back to the observable, manipulable, and pre-eminently physical variables with which, in the last analysis, he was dealing.

REFERENCES

1. Frenkel-Brunswik, Else. "Meaning of Psychoanalytic Concepts and Confirmation of Psychoanalytic Theories," *Scientific Monthly*, 79:293–300 (1954).
2. Jones, E. *Life and Work of Sigmund Freud*, Vol. 1. New York: Basic Bks., 1953
3. Skinner, B. F. *Science and Human Behavior*. New York: Macmillan, 1953.

A Study of Radical Behaviorism

THOSE who cry "No politics" often thereby support bad politics, and those in whose prefaces philosophy is abjured often proceed to expound bad philosophy. In this paper, I want to examine the views of a man who has recommended the abolition of theories: Professor B. F. Skinner.

But I shall not be trying to show that Skinner's theories are bad; I wish to show only that he does employ them, and that his general arguments against the adoption of theories (or at least certain kinds of theory) are not altogether satisfactory. It is, indeed, only because I regard his work so highly and his arguments as so persuasive that I hope to compensate a little for his influence in the methodological sphere. I shall be especially concerned with his 1954 article "Critique of Psychoanalytic Concepts and Theories" (CPCT) in the *Scientific Monthly* (10; reprinted in this volume), but also with his amplification of certain of these points in his 1953 book *Science and Human Behavior* (SHB; 9) and in the 1950 article "Are Theories of Learning Necessary?" (ATLN; 7).*

The general point I hope to make is this: Skinner's position on almost every issue admits of two interpretations—one of them exciting, controversial, and practically indefensible; the other moderately interesting, rather widely accepted, and very plausible—and Skinner's views quite often appear to be stated in the first form but defended in the second.

Specifically, I wish to suggest that

1. Skinner's idea of the relationship between the "pure" molar behavior approach and neurological, mentalistic, or conceptual theories

---

* The present paper developed out of an attempt to improve the comments which I made as a member of the symposium at which CPCT was first read—in Boston, December 1953—and which were published in the same issue as that paper. Three very good discussions of Skinner's earlier work should be noted: at a general level, by Dr. Feigl in his paper "Principles and Problems of Theory Construction in Psychology" (PPTCP; 1); with reference to ATLN, by Arthur Ginsberg in "Operational

is seriously oversimplified in a way that, if corrected, renders untenable most of his objections to the latter.

2. Skinner's analysis of causation, explanation, and classification is subject to correction in the same way.

Imagine that, as a trained psychologist, you are a member of the first survey team sent out to the Alpha Centauri system, and that an inhabited planet is discovered there. On landing, you find that the atmosphere is unbreathable and that you have to remain in a space suit. The first sight you get of the inhabitants raises the question whether they are actually indigenous, since they also appear to be wearing space suits. You might think of the alternative possibilities that severe changes in the atmosphere have required them to devise these garments in order to survive, or that they come from a more hospitable part of the planet, perhaps underground. These hypotheses are not theories or parts of theories in Skinner's sense. Suppose that, after a long period of study, you discover a large number of laws concerning their habits, needs, and social structuring, and you organize these into various categories so that you can predict and control and understand the behavior of the Centaurians, (who exhibit, in particular, a remarkable power of memory and a great fondness for aniseed); moreover, you can converse with them and exchange technological data with them. Thus fortified, you consider publishing some of this material in a paper called "A Theory of Social Behavior Among the Centaurians." Skinner would prefer that you refrain from using that title, because he would not wish you to imagine that he was opposing *that* sort of an activity. But suppose that one day it occurred to you that the extraordinary success exhibited by the Centaurians in recognizing people apparently on the basis of descriptions alone might be due to small television signal receivers in their suits feeding direct into their optic nerves: *then* you have a theory ("any explanation of an observed fact which appeals to events . . . at some other level of observation" [ATLN, p. 193]). As a matter of fact, even a complex mathematical formalization of your data would count as a theory, at least in a sense (ATLN, p. 216); and certainly, if you introduced such concepts as "excitatory potential of a habit" in organizing your thought about Centaurian dispositions, let alone "the significance of the Terran

Definitions and Theories" (ODT; 3); and, with special reference to the 1938 book *The Behavior of Organisms* (8), by W. S. Verplanck in his 1954 paper in *Modern Learning Theory* (11).

landing in the eyes of the Centaurian Council," you would indeed be guilty of theorizing (ATLN, p. 195; SHB, p. 89).

Now Skinner has two approaches to theories in his sense of "theories." At the very least, he wants to argue that bothering with them is pragmatically unjustifiable (ATLN, p. 194). This is, of course, not the same as saying that such theories do not produce practically useful results: it is to say that there is a *better* way to obtain these results. *In view of this better way,* theories are, pragmatically speaking, a luxury. Professor Ginsberg cannot, therefore, get very far by calling on Skinner "to account for [the] fabulous success [of micro-theories] in physics" (ODT, p. 241) since Skinner would not have to deny this success, although he would, at the very least, suggest that other methods might have been preferable. ("It would be foolhardy to deny the achievements of theories of this sort in the history of science. The question of whether they are necessary, however, has other implications . . ." [ATLN, p. 194].)

But Skinner will, on occasion, go considerably further than this. He regards it as distinctly possible that the attempt to theorize has resulted in a net absolute loss in the history of science—not a relative loss compared to the alternative he prefers, but an over-all loss. It would appear that this position could be seriously supported only if we can establish that there are more unsolved problems or pseudo solutions in science today than there have been successes. Now it is clear that in terms of Skinner's favorite criterion, the possibility of conttol, we have advanced enormously since, say, 1300. How can we evaluate the losses? Certainly, more scientists are working on more problems than ever before, and in that very positivistic sense the area of darkness is larger; but even under Skinner's direction the same situation would of course arise, so this will not support the relative point he makes, let alone the absolute one. If we are not going to appeal to the number of problems known to be unsolved for evidence of retrogression, then we must insist that many of the solutions in which we commonly believe are, in fact, unsound. Clearly, this alternative is more consistent with Skinner's general position. Throughout his work runs the trail of the debunker, the cry of a man who is by no means afraid to say that what we have always known to be true is, in fact, false—for example, our belief in what he calls "the traditional fiction of the mental life" (CPCT, p. 302). Could he really point out enough pseudo explanations to show that the progress of modern science has been apparent, not real? To do so, he would certainly have to pass very adverse judgment on many fields other than his own. I think we should conclude that, on the whole, when adopting this extreme position, he is trying to bring us up short, make us worry whether the approach we have taken for granted can really be justified rather than trying to convince us of a literal truth. One of the reasons why it would be so difficult to show that there has been a net absolute loss from the use of theories in the history of science is the curious disanalogy between net progress in science and net profit on a balance sheet. If at time t_2 we definitely have certain laws which predict with some reliability and which we did not have at t_1 ($t_1 < t_2$), and we have not lost any laws which we did have at t_1, then there is a straightforward sense in which it can be definitely said that our science has progressed—no matter whether we have also adopted large numbers of useless theories or misleading explanations. We cannot regard an inaccurate belief as cancelling out an accurate one in the way that a loss cancels out a profit. Of course, it is certainly possible that progress has been *slowed up* by such paraphernalia, but this is a comparative point, a more moderate point. *Relative to* other methods, we may have done poorly. We shall certainly consider this interpretation of Skinner's position.

But there is a more subtle point involved, one which does not fall naturally into the two categories we have established—reasons supporting the relative loss position and those supporting the absolute loss position. While Skinner would not be able to support a claim of actual error in other sciences, he would—as I understand him—be more inclined to argue that the theoretical approach has stultified or prevented research into certain important and actually open questions. These questions concern the correlation between the supposed theoretical event or state that is said by the theorist to explain the observed phenomena (in our case, the minute television receiver is said to explain the hyper-recognition phenomenon) and its own antecedent causes (in our case, the action of the Centaurians when they inserted the apparatus). According to Skinner, the basic fallacy of the theoretical approach is the idea that a proper explanation of the observed phenomena can be given in terms of the theoretical event alone. For Skinner, the essential question would still remain, What are the causes of the theoretical event? Referring to learning theory, he says, "When we assert that an animal acts in a given way because it expects to receive food, then what began as the task of accounting for learned behavior becomes the task of accounting for expectancy" (ATLN, p. 194). My justification for believing that Skinner at least suspects that this criticism applies to science in general stems not only from hearing him say it but also from the fact that he always avoids denying it in print, even when it would greatly simplify his argument, and that he regards it as closely analogous to metaphorical thinking, of which he says ". . . if modern science is still occasionally metaphorical, we must remember that theorywise it is also still in trouble" (CPCT, p. 101).

Yet, would he really deny that the discovery of a television receiver in the Centaurian cranial enclosure constitutes an adequate explanation of the observed phenomenon? In an attempt to answer this, we may ask what he says about the corresponding explanations in the field of human behavior. He is willing to concede (in CPCT) that a neurophysiological account of neurosis may one day provide a useful accessory to, or translation of, a science of behavior (p. 302). But the tone of ATLN is less compromising; although he does not wish to deny that neural events may "actually occur or be studied by appropriate sciences" (p. 194), he does not concede that they will ever be in the least useful for a science of behavior—and the same goes for conceptual and mentalistic theories. In SHB, he again makes clear that he thinks neurology, at best, a different subject (p. 28) and, at worst, a misleading fantasy when he suggests that shock treatment or medical treatment of psychiatric disorders is based on a conception "not far removed from the view—which large numbers of people still hold—that neurotic behavior arises because the Devil or some other intruding personality is in temporary 'possession' of the body" (p. 374). Here, again, we have an example of one of Skinner's extreme positions emerging for a moment— a position which, in the three years since SHB was written, has become much less tenable. As he himself has said, "Advance estimates of the limits of science have generally proved inaccurate" (SHB, p. 20). But Skinner's extreme position in this issue is not merely a matter of pessimism about certain lines of research. It springs from a methodological point. He is not merely arguing that reference to theoretical, e.g. neural, events will stultify our thinking, "create a false sense of security, an unwarranted satisfaction with the *status quo*" (ATLN, p. 194); he wants to suggest that it is, in some sense, a logical error to suppose that such an analysis can solve our problems in a science of behavior.

Eventually a science of the nervous system based upon direct observation rather than inference will describe the neural states and events which immediately precede, say, the response, "No, thank you." These events in turn will be found to be preceded by other neurological events, and these in turn by others. This series will lead us back to events outside the nervous system and, eventually, outside the organism. (SHB, p. 28)

Thus the basic question is only postponed: What are the relations between these original independent environmental variables and the eventual behavior? Neurology has not really advanced the inquiry.

It is worth pausing for a moment in our survey to note that we have already discovered an extreme and a moderate interpretation of Skinner's position on (1) the role of neural theories in a science of behavior (either methodological mistakes, or merely pragmatically worthless); (2) the extent of the role of theories in various fields (unnecessary in any science; unnecessary in a science of behavior); and (3) the success of theories (more harm than good; more harm than the functional approach). The combinations of these points alone provide him with eight alternatives, and I make no excuse for trying to simplify the issue by making some judgments as to the foundation-stones of his methodological analysis and concentrating on these points.

Let us begin by distilling out of ATLN Skinner's actual answer to the rhetorical question comprising the title, but using the term "theory" in its ordinary sense. I take Skinner to be saying, "Theories that are very abstract are premature; theories involving neural, mentalistic, or postulationally defined concepts are (a) misleading, (b) possibly based on a logical error, and (c) certainly unnecessary, since theories involving terms defined operationally by reference to observable behavior are perfectly adequate."

I am not interested in the merely verbal question whether we attach the label of "theory" to Skinner's position, but I am interested in the underlying analyses which have led him to reject it, and me to favor it. There must be, if there is any logic to his position, certain reasons why Skinner thinks that the gap between his methods of prediction and control and those of Hull is more significant than the gap between Hull and, say, Allport. I wish to examine those reasons a little further and see whether we cannot come to some conclusion about their validity and the validity of their extrapolations as criticisms of psychoanalytic theory in particular.

93

Michael Scriven

Certainly, we can agree that Skinner's position is *less* theoretical than even Tolman's; the question is whether it is non-theoretical. I shall argue that it is not, and that Skinner has elevated the relatively untheoretical nature of his approach into a sterile purity that his approach fortunately lacks, thereby illicitly obtaining the semantically somewhat shocking slogan, "The science of human behavior requires no theories."

"Theory" is ordinarily taken in a wider sense than Skinner's. Webster gives as the two most relevant senses, "A more or less plausible or scientifically acceptable general principle offered to explain phenomena" and "The general or abstract principles of any body of facts"; and defines "abstract" as "considered apart from any relation to a particular object." An abstract principle is, hence, one which involves concepts that refer to a class rather than to an individual. Ginsberg starts with a very similar definition (ODT, p. 233), but later goes on to tighten the notion up in a way that is clearly related to a particular philosophical analysis (originally that of N. Campbell), although it, too, would cover Skinner's account of behavior. Feigl has argued (especially in his article "Some Remarks on the Meaning of Scientific Explanation") that a distinguishing characteristic of the set of propositions comprising a theory T of domain D is that we can deduce ("explain") *all* the empirical laws L of D from any proper T of D; whereas from any L, he says, we can only deduce particular facts F of D or other L's of D. Thus $(T \rightarrow L \rightarrow F)D$, where " $\rightarrow$ " represents entailment. Skinner's position would then be expressed by saying that there is no need to go beyond the L level, except for purposes of guessing at further possible L's—and such guessing has no place in a scientific report, which should contain only the results of the tests performed on the putative L's. The appropriate reply is that this procedure does not answer the perfectly proper question, "Why do these particular L's hold in this particular D?" Skinner's response could take several forms:

a. The question is *not* proper because it is not within the province of science to ask why the world is the way it is, only to describe how it is. But Chapter 3 of SHB is entitled "Why Organisms Behave," so Skinner does not reject such questions; however, the answers he offers do not apply to the *basic* laws—e.g., the Law of Effect in his system. Clearly, it would be unsatisfactory to reject such a question in connection with any law (unless an illegitimate type of teleological answer is expected); we can give a perfectly respectable scientific answer to the question, Why do rarefied gases at normal temperatures obey Boyle's Law? in terms of the kinetic theory and gas molecules.

b. The question is not proper *within a science of behavior*. If a science of behavior is concerned to "clarify these uniformities [the ones noticed by everyone in the course of their ordinary social contacts] and make them explicit" (SHB, p. 16), then its task does *not* extend to explaining the basic laws themselves. Yet it is quite obviously appropriate for some part of the scientific enterprise to be devoted to such questions, and they do *concern* behavior. This answer is, therefore, in part, a persuasive definition of the term "science of behavior"; it is as though I were to say, "Chemistry is concerned to describe the composition and the interaction properties of all substances." Then a man who tried to find out *why* an acid combines with a base to produce a salt would not be doing chemistry. Well, we could call him a physicist or a physical chemist instead, but there's nothing illegitimate about his activity; and we may reasonably expect his discoveries to be very useful to chemists, e.g., in predicting ways in which substances with only some of the properties of an acid may be expected to react with bases. And here too, of course, it *might* be possible to answer this question without recourse to the micro-level.

c. Skinner could simply reply that *nobody* knows why these particular L's hold yet, so the only practical way to do a science of behavior is to find out more L's. For example, he says, "At the moment we have no way of directly altering neural processes . . ."; hence, reference to neurophysiology "is useless in the *control* of behavior" (SHB, p. 34). (Although this section begins by dealing with *explanation* rather than control, he does not make any comments about the possibility that neural processes might have explanatory power even if we could not manipulate them; compare the possibility of explaining death as due to an inoperable cancer.) Again, he says, "The objection to inner states is not that they do not exist, but that they are not relevant in a functional analysis. We cannot account for the behavior of a system while staying wholly inside it . . ." (SHB, p. 35). This is a somewhat stronger position than saying we can't do it yet, though not as strong as saying that inner states are completely irrelevant (position b.), since, at the end of the same paragraph he says, "Valid information about [inner states] . . . may throw light upon this relationship [between antecedent environmental conditions and eventual behavior] but can in no way alter it." Superfluous certainly—"we may avoid many tiresome and exhausting digressions" by examining the relationship directly, without reference to inner states—but not quite irrelevant.

The only difficulty inherent in Skinner's position with respect to this point, then, is that he cannot offer an explanation of his *basic* laws within what he regards as the limits of a science of behavior, and he can offer only one rather restricted type of explanation of the other laws, although he suggests that the functional approach can provide a complete account of behavior. It is most important to realize that he does provide an explanation of many observed laws of behavior—by deducing them from more basic laws together with some particular information—and it is partly for this reason that I think it appropriate to say that Skinner has a theory of behavior. For, although theories of domain D often do refer to events that are micro-with-respect-to D, and I would go so far as to say that it is almost always the case that there is, or should be, one or more such T for any D, there are some T, in the ordinary sense, which are exceptions. The theory of evolution, for example, seeks to explain the origin of species, amongst other phenomena, in terms of *observable* small differences between individuals of the same species and the differential survival value of these variations in a complex environment. The theory of gravitation, with the basic law formulated in terms of acceleration rather than force, is another possible candidate.

Looking at the Webster definition again, we can see that Feigl might be inclined to feel it included too much, even mere laws, since there is a sense in which they could fall under the heading of "general or abstract principles of any body of facts" and could each be regarded individually as a "general principle offered to explain phenomena." But the law by itself would not, I think, be regarded as providing the *whole* set of "abstract *principles*" of D nor, usually, as providing a *complete* "explanation" of D. A matter of emphasis, perhaps, and the theory of gravitation is little more than a law. It is chiefly the existence of a *selected ordered set of basic laws*, carefully chosen so that the entire range of empirically observed laws can be derived, that turns Skinner's system into a theory; though, as I shall argue below, other important aspects of it would suffice, especially the terminology. Yet I have used the qualification "usually" above, because there are certain borderline cases in which we talk of a theory without undertaking to *go further than* (though we *do* more *than*) stating the law, e.g., the "theory of gravitation." I think there are certain special reasons why we do not regard it as necessary in these cases to go beyond the law (cf. Skinner's inability to derive the Law of Effect itself), and I would regard them as showing that Feigl's criterion is too narrowly drawn. For reasons that will be expounded in the next volume of this series, I think the basis for Feigl's criterion can be shown to be a comparatively unimportant formal truth; and its general, but not inevitable, applicability is due to an empirical fact, namely, that we very rarely get to the point of isolating a particular D from other D's without having discovered some L's of D. That we sometimes do is illustrated by the cases above.

But the fact remains, and we shall need to remember it below, that Skinner's system offers no explanation of its basic laws. Describing a demonstration of the Law of Effect, Skinner says, "Anyone who has seen such a demonstration knows that the Law of Effect is no theory" (ATLN, p. 200). Anyone who has seen an Eötvös balance give a direct reading of the gravitational pull of a block of lead might be tempted to say something similar. But, just as the law of gravitation forms the foundation of the *theory* of gravitation, the Law of Effect forms the foundation of the *theory* of behavior. It is even more obvious that a system based explicitly on probability of response ("The business of a science of behavior is to evaluate this probability and explore the conditions that determine it" [ATLN, p. 198]) cannot explain every response individually with more than a probability determinable only by prior manifest behavior. There is a limit to the resolving power of the molar approach, and Skinner takes it to be a certain level of probability in explaining the individual response. It is a perfectly respectable scientific enterprise to examine the proximate (neural) causes of a response in order to increase this probability, whether or not we can do it now or prefer never to call it part of a science of behavior.

In understanding the role of theory in psychology, the most important single point is that in this subject, unlike every other scientific subject as it now stands, a considerable proportion of the highly inferential knowledge (or supposed knowledge) is embodied in our everyday talk; and there is a great deal there. It took many thousands of years after man devised a language for him to produce a satisfactory science of dynamics; but common sense had long since incorporated a "theory" of motion according to which certain norms were defined

Michael Scriven

such that only deviations from these norms required explanation, and a very comprehensive pattern of explanations was available. Perhaps we could call it an early application of "pre-Aristotelian dynamics" when Egyptian bird-hunters blamed the wind for their inability to cast a throwing stick the usual distance, but we might as well call it common sense—a common-sense theory. Today, the theory of dynamics is very far removed from the everyday language. In the same sense, the language of "possession" in the history of psychopathology and that of "humours" in psychology were as much part of the theoretical activity as appeal to "reinforcement" or "reserve strength" have been recently. The difference is that both are far less abstract than terms from current dynamics. The mistake is to imagine that they are not past the logical threshold for the application of the term "theory."

To much of this, Skinner would agree. ("We all know thousands of facts about behavior. . . . We may make plausible generalizations about the conduct of people in general. But very few of these will survive careful analysis. . . . The next step is the discovery of some sort of uniformity. . . . Any plausible guess about what a friend will do or say in a given circumstance is a prediction based upon some such uniformity" [SHB, pp. 14–16].) I am more struck than Skinner is, apparently, by the extent to which we successfully predict the behavior of our friends. Now, the language which reflects these uniformities is the sophisticated language of character traits, of attitudes, needs, beliefs, of degrees of intelligence and carelessness. It is not the naive observation language of acts, colors, sounds, shapes, and sensations. Whether one calls this vast conceptual apparatus a theory or merely the common-sense language of behavior analysis is unimportant. It *is* important that this language is an enormously long way from the naive observation language: it tells us a great deal about the probabilities of certain responses, though not with the accuracy we would like; if it did not, indeed "we could scarcely be effective in dealing with human affairs" (SHB, p. 16). What militates against calling it a theory in a scientific sense is its lack of organization and of explicit formulation, the absence of a sufficient number of basic experiments whose results can be predicted with extreme accuracy and of knowledge about the results of cross-validation checks, inter-judge reliability, and so on. It is precisely these objections that Hull and Allport were seeking to overcome and which make us all, including Skinner, willing to call their systems

98

"theories." But it is also these remaining (scientific) imperfections in
the common-sense language about behavior which Skinner himself has
sought to overcome by the careful choice of carefully defined categories,
by the careful organization of the laws which he has discovered, and
by the standards of explanation that he attempts to meet. Let us now
examine the nature of the terms, as opposed to the laws, of theories.

There are two dimensions to the dichotomy "theoretical term-ob-
servational term." The one Skinner is conscious of is that along which
the appropriate dimensions of measurement change, means of or possibility of observation alters, and technique of definition varies (from
postulational "implicit definition" to "ostensive definition," presumably
via operational definition as he sees it). But the other dimension is
just as important. This we might call the teleological as opposed to
the ontological dimension, although, of course, both are methodological
in the general sense. Whereas one can invent or select one's terms (i.e.,
entities) according to either of the two positions Skinner would
distinguish as the theoretical and the functional points of view—i.e.,
according to one's ontological assumptions, *presupposing the purpose* of
explanation-prediction—so along the other axis one introduces or adopts
one's terms according to different purposes, ranging from the sense-
datum or visual-field neutral-description vocabulary to the explanation-
prediction, i.e., the *theoretical* language, presupposing some ontological
position. And, on this axis, Skinner is fairly and squarely a theorist. He
selects the segments of behavior to label as a result of theoretical considerations, i.e., considerations of predictive power, experimental verifiability, etc. Naturally, the psychology of learning being in the state
of development described above, where even the most highly theoretical
terms of any "plausible or scientifically acceptable" account are comparatively close to common-sense language, we can often just as well
talk of these considerations as being those of common sense rather
than of theory. But common sense is what makes us obey speed limits,
at least when a patrol car is behind us, and what leads us to fill our
gas tanks at the second or third "Last Stop" before crossing the Nevada
desert. These are not very theoretical activities—i.e., they involve very
rudimentary induction and merely hedonistic evaluation. The particular
type of common sense we need in picking out the categories for a science
of behavior incorporates, according to Skinner, the belief that we should
so choose them as to obtain data "showing orderly changes characteristic

of the learning process" (ATLN, p. 215). But, *ex hypothesi*, we have no reliable account of the learning process at this point. What makes Skinner think that the changes "characteristic of the learning process" are really "orderly"? This is an excellent example of a theoretical conclusion already embedded in the common-sense language. We can call it a theorem of the *background theory*, to use Professor Wilfrid Sellar's term, which guides our continuing attempts to provide a more powerful and further-reaching theory. Skinner fully recognizes the existence of this background theory—except that he does not apply the wicked term itself—both in the above quotation and later, when he instructs the psychologist to discover his independent variables "through a *common sense* exploration of the field" (ATLN, p. 215; italics mine). For the reasons given, it seems sensible to recognize that this is a very special part of common sense—that part concerned with the explanation-prediction-control *approach* to *the field of* learning—and we can better call it a *background-theoretical* "exploration of the field." After all, Skinner would hardly wish to insist that common sense could not be radically mistaken.

Let us look more carefully at Skinner's practice and see if we can detect other cases where the background theory is affecting his choice of, or definition of, terms, remembering that "Beyond the collection of uniform relationships lies the need for a formal representation of the data reduced to a minimum number of terms"—as long as it does not "refer to another dimensional system" (ATLN, pp. 215–16).

Skinner has always had one rather imprecise notion in his vocabulary—one which occupies a key position: the idea of *topographically differentiable* responses. The way in which this term is treated is characteristic of the interplay between background theory and the current working vocabulary of the developing theory. We begin with the observation that certain instrumental or motor activities are associated with certain objects in the world: we pick up and chew bananas; we throw stones; we embrace our parents; etc. We wish to produce a general account of the development of all these associations, since we have observed certain similarities in the developmental process. We want our generalization to extend, not only over two successive movements of the jaw (that would be the subject for another study, e.g., on extinction), but also over all these activities. Now the most promising looking lever in our background theory derives from our longitudinal S-R studies in everyday life, and we wish to retain a link with them; so the word "response" is appropriate. The sense in which the various responses mentioned above are different from each other appears pretty straightforward, so we talk of "topographically different responses." Then the troubles begin: Is the response of raising the hand "topographically different" from that of raising the arm? Background knowledge makes it obvious that these two could not be conditioned wholly independently; indeed, it leads us to believe that there will be certain types of relationship between the times required to successfully condition first the hand and then the arm. How are we to cut the pie of past and future experiments? Vast reservoirs of evidence to aid our choice are already in the history of scientific theory-building. We select as the basic term "topographically wholly independent responses" and include "induction," "reinforcement," and "latency" as three other useful-looking bricks with which to construct our account. Notice the powerful background-theoretical content that has been built into each of those extra bricks by their previous existences in other theory-structures, including the background theory, i.e., the common-sense explanation systems. This makes them far more useful, though, of course, when we have begun to see exactly how this building will have to be shaped, they may have their dangers for the new bricklayer who has not yet caught up on their latest connotations; he may tend to treat them in a previously but no longer appropriate way. Thus the word "response," which began in Pavlov's day as a fairly simple-to-use brick, in Skinner's system has to cover not just "striking-a-key" but "changing-to-the-other-key-and-striking" as opposed to "striking-the-same-key-a-second-time" (ATLN, p. 211); and it begins to become less readily distinguishable from what previously would have been identified as a *series of responses*. But if we regarded it in that way, we would find it quite impossible to uncover those very desirable "orderly changes characteristic of the learning process" which the background theory very much prefers to have at the expense of a little redefinition of the term "response." The operant versus respondent distinction can be woven into the system here to tighten up the incipient fraying.

Meehl and MacCorquodale provide (5, pp. 218–31) an extremely thorough analysis of the maze through which any psychological theorist must guide his definition of the term "response." It is clear, as they point out, that defining the response in terms of achievement is a very easy way to build one's theory into one's definitions with deplorable consequences for the interpretation of the experiments said to be confirmatory of the theory. They recommend the elimination, in the definition of "response," of "language which refers even implicitly to the properties of other intervals or to stimulation *not present to the organism at the time the response is being admitted*" (p. 231). This is an excellent prophylactic with respect to the disease of defining responses in terms of goals. But I am not sure that, in the process, it does not make life awkward for Skinner and others who refer to the *past* in defining some of their responses, e.g., changing keys. In such a simple case, perhaps we can suppose stimulation to be still present from the past behavior without trouble. But more complex cases referring to organisms responding and reinforced at a very low rate—e.g., to visual stimuli by differential blinking—would render progressively more theoretical the assertion that the response of "changing response" refers only to stimulation present at the time the response is completed * ("emitted" will hardly do: an organism can't "emit" a change—it emits a response which is in fact a change). The possibility of entering into a jungle like the one in which the fractional anticipatory goal response was last reported begins to appear. One can read the latent learning controversy directly as a battle over the workability of various definitions of "response," including implicitly Skinner's. Kendler's paper (4, pp. 269–77) illustrates the connection well.

This process of redefining in order to save the regularities is a very important, legitimate, and useful part of the procedure of theory-building. The history of the concepts of "temperature," "intelligence," and, more recently, "anxiety" affords some striking examples of this point. Why did we abandon the definition of temperature in terms of the ideal gas scale? Principally because we came to see that the behavior of no physical gas could possibly give us that smooth monotonic curve, which the background theory insisted on for a base line, in the regions to which thermodynamics had turned. It is significant of an inadequate realization of this redefinition maneuver that, in his attack on mentalistic and psychoanalytic explanation, Skinner twice produces what he takes to be terms dating from early animistic explanations, both of which have been transformed as the general theory incorporating

---

* See Skinner's comments on the great difference between sixty-second and fifteen-second intervals in producing "superstitious" behavior in pigeons (SHB, p. 85).

them has been transformed. Both "force" and "visviva" have been respectively redefined as the product of mass and acceleration and twice the kinetic energy, and the view that their original use involved explicit animism is as speculative as the view that Skinner's use of the term *strength* (of a response) involves the same commitment.* It is not even true that Skinner's terms are, in any sense, operationally definable, as we shall see later.

Skinner starves his pigeons to 80 per cent of their *ad lib* weight; he is fortunate that such a simple procedure yields workable results. We may expect, with some confidence, that with higher organisms this regimen will not yield quite such high intra-species predictability. The pigeons show greatly different response rates but the same type of learning behavior under these conditions; apes may display basically different learning behavior in the same circumstances. Skinner would be ready to introduce new qualifications to the laws (perhaps by widening his "emotional behavior" escape valve) or so to extend the meaning of his terms as to provide the greatest generality. It is instructive to consider the differences between SHB and *The Behavior of Organisms* published fifteen years earlier, in 1938. For an author who, in the earlier book, considered himself to be almost above producing explanations or hypotheses (p. 44), there have been substantial changes in the description of behavior. They are not due solely to early error, but rather to a present preference for a different formulation—for theoretical reasons, ones which were by no means wholly absent in the 1938 discussion (see W. S. Verplanck's chapter on Skinner, (11)). This is the theoretical approach. Hull was supposedly operating in the same way, Hebb and Tolman too, and, as we shall see, Freud. It is comparatively unimportant methodologically that some of them start by trying, or talking about, a more ambitious goal than Skinner's—i.e., a tie-in with neurology; it is a matter of practical interest if, by so doing, they fail to achieve the primary goal. What is important is that Skinner's terms are defined and redefined for purposes of optimizing their value in a systematic account of behavior, that his observations are referred back to a hierarchy of laws for explanation in an orderly way with the Law of Effect forming the keystone, and that his intentions are of a certain kind, namely, the discovery of causal (functional) laws. These

* For a further discussion of this point, see the discussion of "metaphorical devices" below.

are the marks of the theorist. I repeat that I am not here saying anything about the more moderate Skinnerian claim that the neural, mentalistic, and conceptual theorizers have not done as well in discussing learning theory as Skinner has. I am stressing the fact that this is a dispute between proponents of various theories, albeit theories of different levels of abstraction, strictly comparable to that between the proponents of classical and statistical thermodynamics, between macrochemistry and the valence theorists, and to a dozen other disputes in the history of science. I wish to argue that there is no logical or methodological error involved in the approach to behavior through the C.N.S. (whether the "C" stands for "Conceptual" or "Central") or the drive-reduction model, unless we wish to argue that trying to run before we can walk is (a) a relevant criticism and (b) a methodological error. Even there, especially in view of the latent learning experiments, it is difficult to establish conclusively that the time for running is so far away that expectancy theory never got moving.*

Before I conclude this discussion of learning theory, it is perhaps worth commenting on the very casual way that the term "learning" itself is defined by the theorists. Skinner, an environmentalist to the end, says, "We may define learning as a change in probability of response . . ." (ATLN, p. 199). No account of learning which is part of a Skinnerian science of human behavior will ever accomplish this, since the changes in the probability of a response following a disease infection such as chicken pox (increased strength of the scratching response, etc.), an injury, involutional changes, and genetic changes are all forever beyond the reach of a molar theory of *psychology*, although it is by no means easy to exclude them by a watertight definition. Indeed, from this difficulty springs another justification for a subcutaneous rounding out of the theory of learning—via the attempt to explain variations (intra- or inter-individual) in the capacity to learn or in the basic laws—just as the difficulty of excluding genetics from evolutionary theory makes the attempt arbitrary and costly. As Skinner

* Perhaps I should add the comment, quite irrelevant to the methodological discussion in which this paper consists, that, in my view, the practical achievements of the Skinner-box (and the teaching machine) and the theoretical analyses of their inventor will rank as more lasting contributions to learning theory than his methodological arguments. But if Skinner's methodology is unsound, it is in part a needed reaction against the colossal failure of Hull's theory-building attempts. In his review of "Principles of Behavior" (7) Skinner presents some insuperable criticisms, that only in their later overgeneralization become invalid (ATLN, SHB, CPCT).

admits, in a revealing passage with which I shall conclude my discussion of his approach to learning,

A biological explanation of reinforcing power is perhaps as far as we can go in saying why an event is reinforcing. Such an explanation is probably of little help in a functional analysis for it does not provide us with any way of identifying a reinforcing stimulus as such before we have tested its reinforcing power upon a given organism (SHB, p. 84).

This implies that appropriate developments in biochemistry and physiology could even make them *useful* for a functional approach; i.e., Skinner is here conceding that there are no methodological errors involved in micro-theorizing.

Skinner's critique of psychoanalytic theories and concepts, to which I now wish to direct my arguments, is based on certain extensions of the basic position considered above.

One can understand his approach better if one bears in mind two points which are already pretty clear in his discussion of learning theories. First, he is almost exclusively concerned with the *applications* of a study of behavior, the control aspect, and he is consequently somewhat intolerant of considerations which *do not at the moment* display signs of giving us more control over behavior. Second, the self-application of the first point makes it very important to him to state his arguments as forcefully as possible—to convince people to change the way they spend their research hours, the way they think. I shall argue that the first of these points makes Skinner too impatient with psychoanalytic theory, and that the second makes him overstate his case, leads him to put it in terms that suggest logical error rather than lack of practical consequences. And, surely, it takes a man strongly affected by both these considerations to say, "When the individual is wholly out of control, it is difficult to find effective therapeutic techniques. Such an individual is called psychotic" (SBH, p. 380). Psychoanalytic terminology has its defects indeed, but it is surely not quite so outcome-oriented.

My specific contentions will be that Skinner, in general, underestimates (a) the empirical content and (b) the practical utility of propositions about 'mental states,' including unconscious ones, and that he overestimates the commitments of psychoanalytic theory and hence the deleterious effects of Freud's influence.

Let us consider some of Skinner's proffered analyses of 'mental-state' ascriptions. At a very general level, he considers descriptions of purpose to be open to the same objections, and I shall begin by taking one such example.

. . . we ask him what he is doing and he says, "I am looking for my glasses." This is not a further description of his behavior but of the variables of which his behavior is a function; it is equivalent to "I have lost my glasses," "I shall stop what I am doing when I find my glasses," or "When I have done this in the past, I have found my glasses." These translations may seem unnecessarily roundabout, but only because expressions involving goals and purposes are abbreviations (SHB, p. 90).

Without agreeing or disagreeing with the thesis that "expressions involving goals and purposes are abbreviations," we may show that such expressions involve (i.e., are equivalent to, or imply) a great deal more than any one of Skinner's suggested "translations." If a man correctly describes himself or another as "looking for his glasses," then we can infer *all* of the following:

(1) He owns glasses or believes he does.

(2) He does not now know where they are.

(3) He is engaging in operant behavior of a type that has previously led him or others of whom he knows to find objects of this kind (Skinner's restriction to the man's *own* experience with *lost* glasses is clearly too narrow).

(4) The aspect of his behavior described under (3) will cease when he discovers his glasses.

There are certain 'mental-state' references in (1), (2), and (3). These, in turn, may be reduced to Skinnerian terminology (with or without loss—I am not now passing judgment on that aspect of the issue). To say that the man believes he owns glasses is necessary, since one could not correctly describe someone as "looking for *his* glasses" unless he believed that he possessed glasses. It is too strong a condition to require that he *actually* own glasses since they may, in fact, have fallen into the wastebasket and been long since consumed. But we do not have to imagine that beliefs are mysterious states of the man's forever unobservable mind; we can, in turn, reduce "X believes Y" to a series of statements, at least some of which are conditional and all of which involve probability of specified observable responses. We can, in fact, avoid the conditional element (again, perhaps, at some cost) by restricting the type of prediction we make. Without going to this extreme (the arguments for so doing are entirely philosophical, since the conditional has an extremely respectable place in the logical vocabulary of science and mathematics), we can expect the analysis of "X believes Y" to involve a series of statements such as the following.

(a) If X is asked "Do you believe Y?" under standard conditions, he will reply "Yes" or "Indeed" or "Of course" with 80 per cent probability.

(b) If X is hypnotized or injected with specified amounts of sodium ethyl thiobarbiturate, he will respond as in (a) with 75 per cent probability.

In the same way, we can analyze statements (2) and (3), in which the word "know" occurs.

Two comments on these subsidiary analyses should be made. In the first place, each of the samples given contains arbitrary probability figures, presumably not based on research. How could one give a more precise analysis? Secondly, giving a *complete* list of the stimulus-response patterns that would be relevant is clearly a problem of equal difficulty. It is in the face of the peculiar intransigence of these problems that Skinner, amongst others, is led to abandon the entire vocabulary of 'mental-state' descriptions. Why not, he says, stick to the unambiguous observation language in view of the remarkable achievements possible within its boundaries (the moderate position) and the eventual necessity of returning to it, assuming that one could successfully complete the analysis of "believe," "know," etc. (the extreme position). The reply is that, if we are seeking to analyze any purpose, goal, desire, intention, or mentalistic language, we can succeed only by doing the analysis, not by considering another problem; it should be clear from the discussion above that Skinner's suggested "translations" are thoroughly inadequate.

This is not to deny that Skinner can do a great deal, much of it related to this problem, without actually solving the problem. One might ask whether the original problem is really worth troubling with, when we come to see the extreme vagueness of ordinary language. But the original problem and its relatives make up the problem of analyzing purposive behavior, i.e., *what we ordinarily call* purposive behavior (or mentalistic language of the other varieties mentioned); and we can't palm off an analysis of something that our intuition suggests is the "essential behavioral component" instead, because intuition isn't objective argument and people have widely varying intuitions on this matter. In fact, the subtleties involved in ordinary language are considerable and, as I shall later argue, highly functional. The arguments so far given are intended to support the thesis that Skinner's analysis is much too simple, and that a complete reduction to Skinnerian language ('operationally' definable terms in response probability statements) is extremely *difficult*. Now, before we conclude that some simplified reduction will have to be made if any scientific investigation is ever to be possible, let us examine some of Skinner's own "operationally definable" language and see whether it is really free of what we can call (after Waismann) the "open texture" of the ordinary language of intending, knowing, and believing, and a fortiori of unconscious attitudes. If it is not, we shall have to decide whether the gain involved in the "simplification" is actually sufficient to compensate for the confusion involved in changing the meaning of many familiar terms. After all, we could not get very far by defining "intelligence" as "the average rating on a 1–10 scale scored by three friends"; the proposed operational definition corresponds very poorly to our background notion of intelligence since it will not be at all constant for each individual—and it doesn't analyze the notion itself, merely referring it to others for analysis. Furthermore, it is spuriously operational since there is no one such rating, and it is a spurious improvement for all these reasons. Are Skinner's "reductions" substantially better than the original terms? He makes a poor start with "intelligent," of which he says it "appears to describe properties of behavior but in reality refers to its controlling relations" (SHB, p. 36). The reality is that its describes a property of behavior, which does not at all prevent its analysis from involving reference to its controlling relations. Skinner's belief in the incompatibility of these alternatives presages an unsound analysis of the permissible and useful modes of definition.

Consider another example: in CPCT Skinner refers to

. . . another pitfall into which Freud, in common with his contemporaries, fell. There are many words in the layman's vocabulary that suggest the activity of an organism yet are not descriptive of behavior in the narrower sense. Freud used many of these freely—for example, the individual is said to discriminate, remember, infer, repress, decide, and so on. Such terms do not refer to specific acts. We say that a man discriminates between two objects when he behaves differently with respect to them; but discriminating is not itself behavior. We say that he represses behavior which has been punished when he engages in other behavior *just because* it displaces the punished behavior; but repressing is not action. We say that he decides upon a course of conduct either when he enters upon one course to the exclusion of another, or when he alters some of the variables affecting his own behavior in order to bring this about; but there is no other "act of deciding" (p. 304).

Looking at this example of Skinnerian analysis, we can again ask (a) whether or how nearly the products of the analysis are equivalent to the original, and (b) whether they are really acceptable for Skinner's purpose, i.e., operationally pure. In this instance, I wish to concentrate attention on the second question. Skinner's analytic base here includes the following crucial terms: "behaves"; "behaves differently with respect to X and Y"; "behavior segment X displaces behavior segment Y"; "enters upon X to the exclusion of Y"; "alters variables affecting own behavior." Elsewhere in this paper, we find him using (not quoting from Freud) such terms as "reinforces," "verbally injures," "pattern of behavior," etc. Now, we all know pretty well what these terms mean. But it must be noted that to say an organism "behaves" is *not* to describe its behavior in Skinner's "narrower sense"; and to say that some of its behavior "displaces" other behavior is no more to describe behavior in Skinner's sense than to say that one course of action was decided on rather than another (unless one makes the erroneous assumption that the latter necessarily refers to some inaccessible inner activity, which Skinner would scarcely wish to do). It appears that one could reply to this complaint by giving a list of actions or activities of an organism such that the disjunction of them all is equivalent to "behaves." But, clearly, one could never complete such a list. Alternatively, then, could one not equate "behaves" to some concatenation of anatomically-physio-logically defined movements? But this is a very awkward alternative, since there are clearly certain movements, like the patellar reflex, PGR, epilep-tic frenzies, paretic and aphasic behavior, which cannot be explained at all within molar psychology; and there are many 'motionless' states, rang-ing from the catatonic to the reflective, which Skinner thinks are susceptible to his type of explanation. It is significant that Skinner never attempts to define "behavior" in his book *Science and Human Behavior*. After all, the anatomical-physiological definition would be likely to create great difficulties in excluding physiological explanatory theories; and the alternative of a long list definition would, equally clearly, be interminable, especially since the progress of a science of behavior will itself bring about the extension of the list. Even more serious difficulties arise over the term "displaces"; deeply embedded as it is in a spatial analogy, it has in addition all the problems involved in defining its range of application, viz. segments of behavior.

Skinner constantly reiterates his complaints about certain metaphors and their awful effects ("When one uses terms which describe an activity, one feels it necessary to invent an actor . . ." [CPCT, p. 304]; qualified by "The point is not that metaphor or construct is objectionable but that particular metaphors and constructs have caused trouble and are continuing to do so" [CPCT, p. 301—the rest of the paper makes it fairly clear that he doubts the utility of any metaphors or constructs in a science of behavior]). It is as well to remember that the whole language of reinforcement, displacement, satiation, etc. used by Skinner is loaded with metaphorical meaning, and meaning to which serious objections can be raised (especially if one takes the very tough line that Skinner does about metaphors—for example, he objects to "motivational interaction" on the grounds that it implies "arrangements or relationships among things, but what are the things so related or arranged?" [CPCT, p. 305]). I have discussed earlier in this paper the utility and legitimacy of using such concepts on a trial basis; their success and that of their subsequent partial redefinition is a matter for scientific appraisal. I want to stress the fact that, although Skinner raises the ghost of his extreme position in CPCT ("It would be difficult to prove or disprove . . . that metaphorical devices are inevitable in the early stages of any science" [p. 301] certainly suggests their superfluity in later stages), he could not possibly avoid these charges against his own system. For amongst "metaphorical devices" he includes the use of terms such as "force" and "essence," on which he says we "look with amusement [as part of the] science of yesterday" (CPCT, p. 301; he elsewhere, as previously mentioned, gives "vis viva" as an example [SHB, p. 27]). It is clear that these terms, which came into the scientific language with some metaphorical connotations, are now entirely respectable terms in mechanics, oleo-chemistry, and dynamics ("vis viva" = twice the kinetic energy) and retain the greater part of their original connotations. For example, Skinner says, "The motion of a rolling stone was once attributed to its vis viva" (SHB, p. 27); it still is. As far as I know, the ancients never imagined the stone was actually alive; they merely attached a name to the hypothesized property which would explain the motion—the property which turned out to be a multiple of the kinetic energy. They chose a word which would carry some connotation of "explanatory of motion" from the field which they best understood, where motion distinguished living things. They were saying, in effect, "Moving inanimate objects have some of the properties of living things; let us name the concept that explains this aspect of their behavior their type of 'life-force.'" It was exactly this line of thought which led to the introduction of the term "response"; there may have been, or still be, people so stupid as to feel it "necessary to invent an actor" who gives the response, but it seems unlikely.

Now, it may be the case that so many people have been misled by the use of terms such as "repress," "sublimate," "project," that the contribution of psychoanalytic theory has been neutralized; but at least the introduction of these terms was as legitimate as that of Skinner's terms. Certainly, at the level of criticism which Skinner introduces, he is no better off; for example, he says, "The notion of a conscious or unconscious 'force' may be a useful metaphor, but if this is analogous to force in physics, what is the analogous mass that is analogously accelerated?" (CPCT, p. 305). Analogies are defined as incomplete parallels: the "force" analogy comes not from mechanics, where the term has been partially redefined, but from the same place that mechanics got it, ordinary usage—and force is not defined as the product of mass and acceleration in ordinary usage but as "strength or energy; vigor" (Webster). Now, if no fundamental logical error is involved in using "metaphorical devices," as I have tried to show, then we should consider the possibility of redefining or reconstructing the theory rather than rejecting it. And, in fact, both Skinner in SHB and Ellis in this volume make serious attempts to do this.

Skinner's objections on this point—the use of "metaphorical devices"—are now, I think, boiled down to the claim that the ones he uses are less misleading than Freud's. And this ties in with his complaints about "Freud's explanatory scheme," to which I shall return in a moment. I hope to suggest that Skinner's explanatory scheme applied to psychoanalysis often provides an interpretation rather than an alternative.

Michael Scriven

The discussion of metaphor was introduced in the course of analyzing Skinner's own terminology for conformity to Skinner's standards. I hope that I have shown its success in meeting these standards is different at most only in degree from that of the terms to which Skinner takes exception; his own terms still retain the property of open texture; i.e., there is the same type of difficulty about categorically defining "behavior" or "displacement" as there is about "purpose" or "belief."

Yet, there hangs above us the pall of smoke from the battle over introspection.* "How can one deny that 'purpose' and 'belief' are words with an inner reference, and sometimes with no external manifestations?" say the introspectionists, while the radical behaviorists fidget at this metaphysics ("the traditional fiction of a mental life" [CPCT, p. 302]). Here I wish only to argue that Skinner's analysis is unsound, *even for a behaviorist,* and does not achieve what he thinks it will achieve. It is not a special feature of *mentalistic concepts* that they cannot be given an explicit unambiguous definition in basic observation language ("the left hand was raised three inches, the head turned to the right about 45°, eye fixation remained constant, etc."); but it is a feature of *all useful scientific concepts,* including Skinner's own. This point is fundamental; and it is difficult to accept because the whole trend of thought since scientists really became self-conscious about their definitions, say with Mach, has been in the opposite direction. Indeed, it sounds reasonable and admissible to insist on terms that can be explicitly and unambiguously defined in terms of basic observations. It is, in fact, a valuable exercise to attempt this at any stage in the development of a science; but, if successful, one is merely taking a still photograph of a changing scene, and the motion, not the snapshot, shows progress. Both the philosopher and the scientist can learn from the snapshots, but they will not understand the changes without a great many snapshots and a good deal of inference. So it is with the changing meaning of scientific concepts: at any stage it is possible to give their cash value in terms of observations, but to understand them properly

---

* Skinner's logical maneuvers in his skirmishes with introspection repay careful study. His case depends on a crucial misuse of perception language, e.g., a systematically ambiguous use of "see" (SHB, pp. 273–78). It is further weakened in CPCT by his argument that Freud's evidence for self-deception in introspection shows introspection not to be like observation. On the contrary, it shows how very much it is like observation (itself fallible), though it is not the observation of logically inaccessible inner states, but of states some of whose aspects are sometimes not externally displayed.

112

one must also know their role in the theory and have some idea of their future movements given certain contingencies. A term is fruitful only if it encourages changes in its own meaning; and, to some considerable extent, this is incompatible with operational definition. It is sometimes easier to learn how to use terms than to learn how to work out their cash value in a certain currency, and sometimes the reverse. We all know very well how to use terms such as "purpose" and "belief" and we can teach someone who doesn't speak the language how to use them (child or foreigner), but it's not easy to reduce them to Skinner's currency (and, some suspect, not possible). But Skinner won't pay in other currency, which he views with suspicion; and, if we want to collect the real value of our investment from him, we must compromise: collect a good deal from him on his terms and talk him around on the rest, perhaps by showing him some defects in his own coinage.

On Skinner's own terms, his analyses are not satisfactory; and, when we look at the currency itself, it seems to have the same weaknesses as the promissory notes that he won't negotiate.

There were two difficulties about our original analysis of "belief," which sprang from an attempt to improve Skinner's analysis of "looking for his glasses." The first, into which we have now gone at some length, stems from the impossibility of completely itemizing the units of behavior to which "belief" (in some way) refers, and is a difficulty which some of Skinner's basic terms share. The second was the difficulty of giving precise estimates of the response-probability in any of the component statements. He would, I think, be the first to agree that the corresponding statements in his own system—i.e., dispositional statements involving response induction or stimulus discrimination and generalization—could not contain exact values except by arbitrary redefinition. Corresponding to "S believes p" would be "S discriminates red keys from green keys in a Skinner-box." We had difficulty in giving a cutting frequency for affirmative responses (to the question "Do you believe p?" put to S as a stimulus) which would differentiate a state of belief in p from one of uncertainty about p. Similarly, Skinner could not guarantee in advance the response-frequency or, indeed, the existence of discrimination, if we set up conditions different from those under which the S was trained—for example, there is the possibility of what he terms "emotional behavior."

A great deal more could be said about the comparison here with reference to the Behaviorist's philosophical thesis, but I wish to avoid direct engagements with this and instead bring the above points to bear on Skinner's account of Freud's "explanatory scheme." I would conclude this examination of Skinner's attack on purposive and mentalistic terminology by saying that the substitute he offers is not obviously required, is not as good as it could be, and, even if it were improved to its natural limits, would be insufficiently distinguishable from the original to justify the effort. Skinner is practically allergic to even the most harmless references to the 'mental life'; and I think this prevents him from seeing that, if his translations were really satisfactory, then there would be a 'mind' in his system, too. Consider, for example, this quotation: "One who readily engages in a given activity is not showing an interest, he is showing the effect of reinforcement" (SHB, p. 72). But a *very special type* of effect, one which it is *extremely important to distinguish* from the readiness to engage in a given activity springing from severe punishment for failure to do so. One can no more deny that Skinner has shown an interest in psychology during much of his academic life—i.e., the propriety of the phrase "showing an interest" in this case—than one can deny that this book has pages (i.e., since standard conditions obtain, the propriety of the phrase "books have pages") even if it does suggest ownership. We shall see how this hypersensitivity to one interpretation (quite possibly an unfortunate or unproductive one) leads him to underestimate the utility of psychoanalytic theory. It is by no means necessary to interpret these phrases in this way; and, in fact, we can improve Skinner's suggested behavioral analysis to the point where it provides a good scientific substitute for the original phrase. This could be described as 'translating the mind into behavioral terms'; or, equally well, it could be said to show that the reference to mind was not objectionable in the first place. To say that such phrases as "making up one's mind," "having an idea," etc. are "obvious" cases in which the mind and ideas are "being invented on the spot to provide spurious explanations" (SHB, p. 30) is to miss the point that these are genuine explanations but do not involve reference to some scientifically inaccessible realm. No one, without stretching an etymological point, reads into such phrases what Skinner objects to in them; they are invariably used as shorthand for a set of descriptive plus dispositional propositions, just as "believe," "behave," and "beta-particle" are.

Taking the bull by the horns, I shall argue that Skinner, partly because of errors of translation of the kind just discussed, underestimates the practical value and logical validity of explanations of behavior in terms of 'mental events.' Basic to all his arguments is the belief that any reference to inner states is an unnecessary complication, since eventually one has to explain *them* in terms of environmental variables. The counterargument that the egg comes before the chicken and that we must, therefore, get back inside the skin to the organism's inherited genetic composition in order to achieve a complete explanation would presumably cut no ice because, Skinner would say, we can't control the genes (or neurons). But we mustn't be misled by the combination of Skinner's use of the word "control" and Skinner's analyses of familiar processes. For example, he argues that "awareness of cause [of one's actions] has nothing to do with causal effectiveness" (CPCT, p. 305). But this is a verbal trick. He is not really denying (as he appears to) that the patient who attains insight into his aggressive remarks to his brother will often abandon them subsequently. He is (essentially) arguing that, since both insight and behavior improvement are due to changes in other environmental variables, it is wrong to say one of them causes the other, i.e., wrong to say that it is the awareness of the hostile impulses that reduces their effectiveness. He is not denying that the first might always be followed by the second or that the second might never occur without the first, i.e., that the process of bringing about the insight produces the remission of the symptoms. Now, analysts, including Freud, have long stressed the fact that mere enunciation of the relation between unconscious hostility and aggressive remarks will not bring an end to the latter. Thus the analyst believes

(1) The hostile feelings (C_1) cause the aggressive behavior (E_1).

(2) Getting the patient to the stage where he volunteers the interpretation—i.e., getting-him-to-achieve-insight-in-this-respect (C_2)—causes the symptoms' disappearance (E_2).

Now, achieving insight is the standard psychoanalytic case of "awareness of cause," and it is followed by the termination of the causal relation (1); moreover, the process of achieving insight actually causes the improvement (as stated in (2)). It is, therefore, extremely misleading of Skinner to say "awareness of cause has nothing to do with causal effectiveness." It is trivially true that if A causes B under conditions C, and C does not contain a provision excluding an observer, then A will still cause B even if there is an observer. The analytic discovery

115

was that, in certain cases of caused behavior, C *does* include such a prohibition and A no longer produces B in a patient P when P has learned about the connection (this schema oversimplifies in certain respects). It might appear that Skinner is making a more substantial point, that he is suggesting something empirically distinguishable from Freud. I am not clear that he is. The following quotation suggests there is no such tangible difference, but only a difference of emphasis: "Therapy consists, not in getting the patient to discover the solution to his problem, but in changing him in such a way that he is able to discover it" (SHB, p. 382). But on other occasions this is not clear: "The parallel between the excision of a tumor, for example, and the release of a repressed wish from the unconscious is quite compelling and must have affected Freud's thinking" (CPCT, p. 301)—and Skinner has made clear to me in conversation that he regards this as perhaps Freud's most serious error. Now, what is the pattern of explanation here? We have

1. The tumor (C_1) causes illness (E_1)
2. Removal-of-the-tumor (C_2) causes recovery (E_2)

and the analogy, which Skinner disputes, would be

1'. The repressed wish (C'_1) causes, say, stuttering (E'_1)
2'. Release-of-the-wish (C'_2) causes cure (E'_2).

If Freud thought that the "releasing of a suppressed wish from the unconscious" meant the mere uttering of the words, perhaps even parrot-wise, after the analyst, and was in itself *curative*, then Skinner is disagreeing with Freud on empirical grounds. It seems clear enough that this was not Freud's view. But if Freud thought that the mere verbalization had little or no therapeutic value, whereas the 'spontaneous' *release* of a wish marked the penultimate stage of therapy for this symptom (culminated by the application of this insight), then I am not sure that Skinner would disagree, in view of the fact that he is presenting no new evidence. After all, discovering the wish makes it possible for P and the analyst to reorient P's behavior accordingly, and the fact that it has been voluntarily produced makes it likely the behavior will be successfully reoriented. If the reorientation is successful, could one not then say that producing the wish produced the cure *under these circumstances?* The hard work goes into achieving C'_2, but if we define cure as the actual vanishing of symptoms, then it *is* the release of the wish that produces it. Thus, we might agree with Skinner that *therapy* consists in changing the patient until he can achieve C'_2, but that the (proximate) cause of the *cure* is C'_2. And Freud would not, as far as I can see, disagree with this. I do not think this position justifies such strong statements as the following:

Freud's contribution . . . [was] . . . not that the individual was often unable to describe important aspects of his own behavior, or identify important causal relationships but that his ability to describe them *was irrelevant to* the occurrence of the behavior or the effectiveness of the causes (CPCT, p. 304; my italics).

I have gone into this point in detail because I think it well illustrates the difficulty of dealing with Skinner's criticisms of Freud. An attempt to wholly disentangle his ideas about the formal status of psychoanalytic theory would be unrewarding, but I think it important to show that it rests on an erroneous dichotomy, which explains a great deal about the rest of his approach. He says, "No matter what logicians may eventually make of this mental apparatus, there is little doubt that Freud accepted it as real *rather than* as a scientific construct or theory" (CPCT, p. 301; my italics).

Skinner is here reaping the whirlwind of early positivism, and this eddy affects his position more seriously than his other philosophical inheritances from the same source.* The idea that scientific constructs are not "real" but are mere "explanatory fictions," as he goes on to describe them, is untenable; but, if one believes it, one will not be encouraged to invent many. It is a little misleading to insist that scientific constructs are real, although it is certainly better than the alternative (I have never heard anyone arguing whether theories are real: what would an unreal theory be like?). The issue is a spurious one; such constructs should always be said to be real in such-and-such a respect, but unreal—i.e., unlike such earthily real things as platypuses—in such-and-such another respect, etc., etc. Few are observable like animals but many have observable consequences, like the neutrino, and their existence is said to be confirmed when these consequences eventuate. Philosophy has outgrown such questions as "Do groups exist over and above their members?" "Do electrons really exist?" though it learned much

---

* E.g., "Certain basic assumptions, essential to any scientific activity, are sometimes called theories. That nature is orderly rather than capricious is an example" (ATLN, p. 193).

from answering them. The answer must always be, "In a certain sense, yes, and in a certain sense, no." The important point is that a theory can and does proceed without having to distinguish each construct as "real" or "explanatory fiction"; there are other rules to be obeyed (those of factor-analysis in certain cases, for example) but not this rule. We may have grave reservations about the meaning, if any, of "libido," which we may awkwardly express by asking whether there really is a libido; but if a satisfactory answer can be given, it does not show that "libido" is not a scientific concept, that it is an observable: it would be a scientific construct, it would 'exist,' but it need not be actually observable as long as it has effects we can observe. The libido has to undergo the same examinations as Spearman's g, the concept of isostasy, and cultural lag. If they are satisfactory constructs, they may figure in explanations in a way we shall consider, although they are not observables and not all operationally definable in terms of observables. But that does not make them "*fictions*"; indeed, "explanatory fiction" is a contradiction in terms: abbreviatory devices are not normally explanatory, and explanatory devices are never fictitious.

There is no obligation on the libido to be located in the brain, or to have spatial location at all; the rules are flexible, they require only that we be able to make some objective distinction between cases in which the term can be properly applied and the rest. The same applies to Skinner's use of "reserve" (of responses—ATLN, p. 203) or the physicist's concept of entropy. But Skinner believes in the "observable-or-explanatory-fiction dichotomy," so he is at great pains in SHB to show that introspection is not a form of observation and, hence, that "conscious, as well as unconscious events [are] inferences from the facts" (CPCT, p. 302)—hence, are constructs and hence unreal. On one occasion, he puts it in this way: ". . . the act of self-observation [sic] can be represented within the framework of physical science. This involves questioning the reality of sensations, ideas, feelings, and other states of consciousness . . ." (CPCT, p. 304). The example which follows shows, as one might expect, that he is not going to question the *reality* of these things but the *reliability* of reports on them: the mystic's religious experience is not unreal but (according to Skinner's hypothesized psychoanalyst) incorrectly described as communion with a supernatural being. One can often show that someone's description of his sensations is inaccurate; it does not follow that he had none.

Having arrived at the conclusion that mental events are unreal, Skinner feeds it back into the argument and attacks explanations in terms of mental states as circular and/or superfluous. Only in this way, as he sees it, can one get past the Scylla of explaining how the mind and body interact and the Charybdis of explaining how we can know the contents of another's mind. Union rules prevent me from divulging the secret of the problems which provide a guaranteed annual wage for philosophers; but it is not too difficult to show some very important ways in which mental states can figure in extremely respectable explanations, in whose company, indeed, no behaviorist should feel ashamed to be seen.

Suppose that we accept the behaviorist analysis of mental states that Skinner is anxious to sell us, making some modifications to the actual model he is vending, along the lines suggested in our account of "He's looking for his glasses" and "He's showing an interest in this activity." Ignore, for the moment, the twin difficulties of inexhaustibility and inaccuracy in specifying the exact propositions in behavior-language to which we reduce the mental state. Then, taking a simple case,

"X is in mental-state M." = "If X is in circumstances Y, he will (with probability P) do Z."

Now, there will normally be many other circumstances $(Y', Y'', \ldots)$ under which X will also do Z. For example, he will drink a glass of water (Z) not only when thirsty (M)—i.e., when he has been deprived of water for some time, etc. (Y)—but also when there is a gun at his back even if he is satiated (Y'), when he has been deprived of food and no food is now present (Y''), etc. Suppose that X is in an observation room, taking part in an experiment of whose purposes you are ignorant. You do not know whether he is being paid, deprived, or intellectually stimulated. At 3:00 P.M. he looks at the clock, takes up a glass of water, and drinks it. You ask, having these other possibilities in mind: Why did he drink? A perfectly proper and informative explanation is "Because he is thirsty." It is informative because you now know (always assuming the behaviorist analysis to be correct) that this means circumstances Y must obtain, as opposed to $Y', Y'', \ldots$

This type of request for an explanation is perhaps the most common of all. Skinner would describe it as a request for information about "the external variables of which behavior is a function" because he thinks

119

that 'inner-state' language is really translatable into descriptions of external variables. But if it is, then explanations in terms of inner states are perfectly legitimate. And even if it is not, even if there is something more involved in reports on inner states, it is still true that they are connected with external variables, i.e., whatever "X is thirsty" may refer to, we know it is probabilistically connected with hours of deprivation, aversive preconditioning, etc., so that the worst charge that Skinner can lay is vagueness. Of course, he may not like the obscurity of the connection between a state of thirst and behavior; we can help him by accepting tentatively the identification of the two. Thus, one does not have to solve the mind-body problem in order to find out what independent variables are related to subjective reports of feelings of thirst, actual drinking without such reports, etc.; and even the decision that thirst is not *wholly* reducible to behavioral criteria does not imply that it is not a *good basis* for explanation, since it clearly has many behavioral consequences. It is not important to a public health officer in charge of mosquito control whether we *define* DDT in terms of its entomological effects or whether we define it chemically, as long as we don't *deny* its entomological effects; similarly, whether we say that thirst is or is not something more than a certain pattern of behavior is unimportant, as long as we agree that it is the psychologist who studies the *whole* behavioral aspect. The presence of vagueness not only affects his own more general concepts (notice the difficulties in distinguishing operant from response conditioning under certain circumstances) but also has certain virtues for a scientific concept in the field of behavior, a fact which will be further elaborated below.

The first point made, then, is that, on a radical behaviorist analysis of inner states, explanations in such terms are vital and legitimate. I did not say "on Skinner's analysis" because I have already made a number of improvements on that without abandoning radical behaviorism. To uncover some more of the very serious difficulties in Skinner's own analysis, I am going to examine one or two further instances of it, still on his own standards. Then I shall consider the results of our suggested changes in the radical behaviorist analysis of mental-state terminology, in an attempt to show that one can produce a fully scientific account that is much closer to being an analysis of the actual mental concepts we ordinarily employ, which Skinner views with such suspicion.

But what is Skinner's position?

To what extent is it helpful to be told "He drinks because he is thirsty"? If to be thirsty means nothing more than to have a tendency to drink, this is mere redundancy. If it means that he drinks because of a state of thirst, an inner causal event is invoked. If this state is purely inferential—if no dimensions are assigned to it which would make direct observation possible—it cannot serve as an explanation (SHB, p. 33).

All these conclusions are erroneous. Even if "to be thirsty means nothing more than to have a tendency to drink," it is by no means merely redundant to be told that *on this occasion* he drank because of that tendency *rather than* under compulsion or because of a tendency to eat or etc. To have a tendency is to have a certain disposition, and everyone has *some* disposition to drink, but it is not always that disposition which explains our drinking. When we are satiated, for example, we have a short-term disposition not to drink; and, in such a case, the statement that we drank because we were thirsty would not, even on Skinner's first analysis, be redundant; it would be false. It follows that Skinner does not see the importance of dispositions, nor does he see the nature of what I shall call "discrimination-explanations," i.e., explanations of event E as due to antecedents A *rather than* A' or A", all of which we realize are capable of producing E.

Of course, there are occasions on which pseudo explanations—looking rather similar to this one—are offered. If we explain someone's frequent sleepy appearance by saying he is a soporific type, we may well be deceiving ourselves. But to chastise the ordinary explanations of *individual events* by reference to dispositions, on the grounds that some explanations of *patterns of behavior* by reference to dispositions are redundant, is manifestly unfair. Skinner's failure to distinguish these is clearly shown in the following quotation:

When we say that a man eats *because* he is hungry, smokes a great deal *because* he has the tobacco habit, fights *because* of the instinct of pugnacity, behaves brilliantly *because* of his intelligence, or plays the piano well *because* of his musical ability, we seem to be referring to causes. But on analysis these phrases prove to be merely redundant descriptions. A single set of facts is described by the two statements: "He eats" and "He is hungry." A single set of facts is described by the two statements: "He smokes a great deal" and "He has the smoking habit." . . . (SHB, p. 31).

This is guilt by association! Every one of these examples except the

121

first is susceptible to Skinner's criticism; but the first is the vital one for his attack on mental states, partly because we don't introspect "having a smoking habit" whereas we do introspect "being hungry." It is a logical error, *even for a radical behaviorist*, to imagine that the same "set of facts" is described by "He eats" and "He is hungry" since, for a radical behaviorist, the second statement is equivalent to "He has a disposition to eat," i.e., "Under specifiable conditions it is P per cent probable that he will eat," which neither implies nor is implied by "He eats."

Skinner's third conclusion—that if thirst is a purely inferential state not susceptible to direct observation, it cannot serve as an explanation—is also in my view mistaken. I have argued above that it is only necessary for the hypotheses embodying scientific concepts to be susceptible to confirmation, not observation—or else temperature, inertial mass, and the spin of the electron would be illicit—and the argument applies here. Furthermore, it is possible to construct an example which will demonstrate this and, at the same time, answer any doubts that may have arisen in the reader's mind as to the propriety of explaining one observed drinking-event in terms of a disposition if the latter is interpreted as a construct out of drinking-events.

Suppose that we introduce the symbol Ω into psychological discourse in the following way: if an organism O is such that variable $v_1 > N_1$, while $v_2, v_3, \ldots v_n < N_2$, we shall say that O is in state $\Omega(\Omega(O))$. Further, if $v_1 \leqq N_1$ while $v_2 + v_3$ or $v_2 + v_4$ or $v_3 + v_4$ or $\ldots > 2N_1$ and $v_1, v_2, v_3, \ldots v_n < N_2$, we shall also say that $\Omega(O)$. And if some one of $v_2, v_3, \ldots v_n \geqq N_2$, we shall say that it is not the case that $\Omega(O)$. Notice that we have not said anything about the case $v_1, v_2, v_3, \ldots v_n \leqq N_1$, except under certain conditions on the ratio N_1/N_2 between the constants. This example is a rough model of a personality or pathology category, interpreted operationally. Now, we have not in any sense assigned dimensions to Ω, any more than we do to schizophrenia. According to Skinner, then, "it cannot serve as an explanation" since no direct observation is possible. But it may provide a most useful means of classifying organisms, such that laws can be stated in simpler forms—i.e., it can be a step toward a sort of theory which Skinner approves of ("a formal representation of the data reduced to a minimal number of terms" [ATLN, p. 216]), and it can certainly figure in discrimination-explanations. What can Skinner say to resolve this contradiction? The necessary compromise seems obvious: Ω is satisfactory because it at least is defined in terms of observables. So it appears. And yet the word "state" occurs. Can we really infer from any formal considerations that O is in a certain state? Indeed not: one could not introduce a state defined by reference to the number of people within a one-mile circle with center fifty miles south of O without changing the present meaning of "state." "State" is a word that needs a great deal of unpacking; it is appropriate only when we are sure that a causal account of the phenomena that differentiate "states" can be given in terms of actual physical changes in the organism corresponding to changes of "state" in the proposed sense.

This simple fact makes the language of states at once more complex and more useful than Skinner allows, and it partially explains how the tie-in of psychoanalysis or psychology with neurology is so strong. As it stands, Ω can give us discrimination-explanations of the fact that certain variables have certain values (e.g., that X drinks or stutters or produces neologisms) insofar as it contains a reference to other variables which are causally related to those observed, and *it can only do that by* referring to a current state. Even the thirst case, which appears as the simplest possible example, where v_1 is the only variable on which Ω depends as well as being that which is explained, is less simple than it appears since, for the explanation to be valid, it must be the case that the earlier history of v_1 variation has causally effected the present state of O. It is immaterial that we cannot demonstrate this physiologically. As long as we have no direct evidence against it and it works as an explanation, then we have evidence for it, indirect evidence. But it must be true. Moreover, it is not incumbent on us to say how the matter could be tested by direct observation at all. We may believe that this will be possible, e.g., by identification with some neural and intestinal configuration; but we may also believe it will never be possible, as long as we are prepared to give (a) the conditions which will count as *confirming* evidence for and against the use of the construct, and (b) reasons for believing that some causal connection is possible between the independent environmental variables and the behavioral output variables. Thus, one could not, in the world as it now is, argue that an Ω defined by reference to the past population density of an area geographically distant from O could explain either the present drinking behavior or indeed almost any other behavior of O, since one can give no reasons for thinking that it could produce any present effects on O at all.

Now, it is this basic process in science—the process of ascribing states to substances and organisms—which forms the first level of theory-building; and it is one that Skinner cannot avoid himself, for example, when he describes an organism as "satiated." This term would have to be abandoned even if Skinner's data was still accepted, if we did not believe that the gratification had produced an effect on the organism that, in fact, persisted. Our reason for thinking this is true is the change in response frequency after unrestricted eating (for example) is allowed, when the reinforcement is food. This striking result, we would argue, shows clearly that an effect has persisted on the organism. Let us call this effect "satiation"; it is a state of the organism. Now, Skinner overlooks the theoretical element in this analysis and imagines he can define the word without any reference to state: he views it as a summary of past history. I have already shown that he gives a bad summary; now I am arguing that he is committed to more than a summary. The reason is that one cannot believe the past history to affect the present behavior except via a present state—and science *as a whole* (not molar psychology) must explain how this implicit hypothesis (supported by every success of molar psychology) is justified. It is a rare explanation which does not produce new discoveries—and one need give no further justification for neurologically-oriented behavior research. Skinner is misled by the argument that neural states are dispensable and inaccessible (for molar psychology) into behaving as though they are scientifically dispensable, which they are not, even if inaccessible, and into imagining that he does not use them. So, states may be "purely inferential" and yet "serve as an explanation." It is psychologically unfortunate if other people are really misled by talking about states—conscious or unconscious—into imagining that science should not be concerned with discovering the antecedents, but the sin is no worse than that of imagining states to be dispensable.

Skinner is seriously in error on this whole issue, and understandably so—for if he too often acknowledges this implicit and necessary belief in the state-differences brought about by various schedules, he would have to face the question, What sort of state-differences do you have in mind? The reply that he means no more by the state than "that which is produced by the past reinforcement schedule and which produces the future responses" would, of course, be open to his own objection that it is an "explanatory fiction," unless he can give directly observable properties to it. Certainly it is obvious that if the organism reacts differently, it is in a different state; but insofar as its reactions are physically determined by its neurology, so far it is obvious that neurology must provide the foundations for this basic assumption of molar psychology. Now it becomes clear why Skinner prefers to talk of functional dependency rather than causal dependency: because causal dependency is necessarily mediated by a state of the organism about which Skinner can say nothing. We cannot object to what Skinner does positively; but in his criticisms he implies that the supplementary activities are unnecessary and invalid, and in this he is surely wrong. Of repression and the other defense mechanisms, he says in CPCT that they should not be regarded "as activities of the individual or any subdivision thereof . . . but simply as ways of representing relationships among responses and controlling variables." But they are activities (successions of states) of the individual, the very ones necessary to link the controlling variables to the responses; and we can *still* agree that they are to be distinguished by study of the functional relationships they mediate. Skinner does not hold the only alternative position—that the childhood trauma itself directly causes (across space and time) the neurotic behavior—but at times he sounds very like it. The state of anxiety, he says, "is of no functional significance, either in a theoretical analysis or in the practical control of behavior" (SHB, p. 181). Well, it is an absolute necessity in the total scientific study of behavior to have such states, and the anxiety-reducing drugs show that this one has considerable functional significance in the control of behavior, somewhat contrary to the implications of this passage or of the even more dogmatic statement preceding it—"Any therapeutic attempt to reduce the 'effects of anxiety' must operate upon these [controlling] circumstances, not upon any intervening state."

I want now to suggest that the psychoanalytic or group dynamic or historical or sociological approach is an alternative (to molar psychology) of a most respectable kind for dealing with certain areas of behavior. From a certain point of view, these approaches are simply examples of molar approaches: they are molar approaches to molar behavior in certain areas—they are branches of molar molar behavior science. The psychoanalyst is taking a particular *pattern* of behavior as his unit—say the deprivation-desire-deed pattern in analyzing defences—which to the molar psychologist is quite a complex structure. I think that Skinner is in the position of a man who is asked for his suggestions at a research conference in the chemistry department, where they are tackling the problem of yeast assessment for bread-making. He says, "Find out all the physical properties of enzyme molecules and you'll have the answer." True, but only if old age is conquered in the meantime. Physics will some day perhaps be able to account for all chemical reactions, but today we have to evolve a selective approach via the chemical properties. It may not work, it may be necessary to get down to bedrock before a solid foundation can be laid; but it's well worth trying—and in chemistry it has paid off for a long time. Similarly in the social sciences, we can build up from the bricks of individual psychology or try to make a useful building with the large blocks of stones lying around with just a little chipping and perhaps a little more quarrying. And in psychology, we can work up from physiology or neurology, or tackle the issues more directly. Skinner is defending an approach to psychology which he rejects as an approach to psychopathology.

It is useless to complain that this is only a part of psychology; such an assumption is (a) extremely speculative and (b) even if true, no more effective than the argument that chemistry is only part of physics, which has hardly prevented chemists from discovering useful concepts at their own level. Skinner's extreme aversion to anything that looks like animistic talk leads him to miss the great wealth that can be mined from a logically sophisticated behavioristic analysis (*not* reduction—this is unnecessary and begs the philosophical question) of mental-state talk.

In particular, we can return to the two oversimplifications we made when beginning the discussion of "psychic states." A behavioristic analysis of "know" or "believe" has these two dimensions of flexibility (a better word than "vagueness," whose negative connotations spring from a failure to appreciate the necessity and utility of open texture in scientific language). How can this be useful in a science of behavior? How can it be anything but a drawback? The questions are immensely vain: for they presuppose that psychology is appropriate for or capable of answering such questions as What is knowledge? And, on the other hand, they are overly modest; for they presuppose that we have no idea how to shape the lists or estimate the probabilities.

Psychology should, of course, not be mainly concerned with epistemological questions, even though (a) its results may sometimes be relevant to them, and (b) the inspiration and description of research should not be independent of epistemological thought. Thus, psychologists concerned with "knowledge" characteristically ask such questions as these: What do seventh-grade math pupils know that sixth-graders do not? What does a man know about his childhood that he cannot immediately recall? Does a nondirective discussion result in the absorption of more knowledge than a lecture on the same topic? Does the teacher really know which of his pupils are the most intelligent? etc. There are endless experiments of this kind done, none of which fall into difficulties over the term "know"; though, of course, some others do, just as in physics some experiments are doomed from the beginning owing to faulty logical analysis. Only the crypto-philosophical psychologist inflates his experimental results into epistomological conclusions, and he is usually somewhat short on logical training. Even though some important questions are not properly answered by experiment—amongst them legal, literary, and logical ones—it is not necessary to reject as nonexperimental all problems involving mentalistic concepts, as Skinner does. For every man who can talk a language understands very well how to use these words, and can almost always tell a proper question from a nonsense-statement involving them. The fact that we can all use this language with great efficiency shows that one cannot judge the utility of a language by the test of whether it is reducible to a specific list of specific statements in the observation language. Nor even its scientific utility, for the language of many sciences has this feature. Thus for proper psychological questions, we shall, I suggest, no more frequently find ourselves in difficulty understanding or formulating a problem about knowledge or belief in ordinary language than if we invent some *vaguely related* and *still imprecise* (if still useful) language of our own. Inventing new terms is too frequently a substitute for analyzing the old ones and a move which only postpones the difficulties, for at some stage we try to relate the discoveries formulated in the new language to the problems formulated in the old. We can have our Taylor Scale on which we define a psychological concept of anxiety, but we can't avoid the question, "Does this give a good measure of anxiety as we ordinarily use the term?" Because if it doesn't, we can't use it to find out whether students are made more anxious by subjective than objective examinations,

127

or patients less anxious by piped music in the waiting-room. The background concept and theory cannot be ignored, though they can nearly always be improved; they *have* to be studied. A similar study of scientific terms reveals, below that surface sheen of operationism, the same open texture or flexibility. The difference lies in the purpose, not the nature, of the definitions employed, or employable except for some variations of degree (which are not all in one direction).

The language of psychoanalysis, in particular, is very open-textured; it is a first approach. Being so, it runs the risk of becoming empirically meaningless, a ritual form of mental alchemy. But the approach is fully justifiable; and it is as wrong to suggest that Freud should have pinned his terms down to infant neurology (CPCT, p. 302) or, by the "simple expedient of an operational definition," to physical and biological science (CPCT, p. 305), as it would be to insist that the founders of radio astronomy should have early said whether a radio star was a solid body or a region of space. They introduced the term as a name for the hypothesized origin of short-wave electromagnetic radiation. It now appears they were justified in using a *name* (i.e., spatial location is well supported), but we cannot yet tell exactly what radio stars (physically speaking) are, what the name stands for. Freud introduced the concept of the ego-ideal or superego as the hypothesized repository of the learned censoring activities of the personality. It is less certain that he was justified in using a name and quite unclear what, if any, physical reference it will have. It certainly need have no observable or measurable referent (". . . the most unfortunate effect of all" those due to Freud's use of a "mental apparatus" approach [CPCT, p. 305]) to be respectable, though the hypothesis of its existence or operation must have observable consequences that are reliably identifiable. It was obvious to Freud that these consequences will have their neural counterpart if they exist and that the superego will thus, at least indirectly, have a neural counterpart; no one knew more than that. But everyone knew, or thought they knew, a great deal about conscience, anxiety, and guilt; and Freud discovered a great deal more, just as a psychologist might discover a great deal more about knowledge by an extension of the experiments described above. And just as the psychologist might quite accurately sum up some of his discoveries by distinguishing two types of knowledge (say kinesthetic and verbal), so Freud could distinguish two stages in the development of the superego. Should we argue whether both types of knowledge *exist* or are *real*? We can, and we know how to do it in terms of correlation coefficients and chi² values—but it's an odd way to put the question. Does the superego exist? is it real? Well, we can deal with those questions, too, by pointing out certain undeniable features of behavior and arguing for their correlation and common subsumption under this heading. This doesn't show that the superego is observable, nor does it show that it is an explanatory fiction: Skinner's dichotomy is unsound. But—if it can be done—it justifies *talking about the superego*, which is as near as we can get to showing that it's real. It isn't real like a brain tumor, but it is real rather like an electric field; and it's certainly not unreal or a "fiction" or a "myth" like the aether—unless the arguments for it can be met, as those for the aether were met, on their own ground.

The other way of throwing over a theory, and a common one in the history of science, is to produce a better one. This Skinner would not be anxious to describe himself as doing. But his account of psychotherapy in SHB is an illuminating one, and it is theoretical. It is still far from being capable of dealing with the strange complexities of neurosis at an explanatory level, and it has no therapeutic success to support any claims for its practical efficiency. In fact, we have argued that while Skinner belabors Freud (somewhat unfairly, I think) for failing to give "an explicit treatment of behavior as a datum, of probability of response as the principal quantifiable property of behavior . . ." (CPCT, p. 304), in short, for being too theoretical, Skinner is himself a little too upset by the idea of explanations involving mental states to do them justice, even in his own operational terms. It is sometimes these errors of emphasis, rather than of fact, that lead us to abandon an approach. In his discussion of early psychological theories, Skinner comments on the simple reflex approach with these words: "It is neither plausible nor expedient to conceive of the organism as a complicated jack-in-the-box with a long list of tricks, each of which may be evoked by pressing the proper button" (SHB, p. 49). Reading Skinner, one sometimes wonders whether it is any more plausible or expedient to conceive of the organism as a complicated (but transparent) marionette with a long list of tricks, each of which may be evoked by pulling the proper string.

129

Michael Scriven

REFERENCES

1. Feigl, Herbert. "Some Remarks on the Meaning of Scientific Explanation," in H. Feigl and W. Sellars (eds.), Readings in Philosophical Analysis, pp. 510–14. New York: Appleton-Century-Crofts, 1949.
2. Feigl, Herbert. "Principles and Problems of Theory Construction in Psychology," in W. Dennis (ed.), Current Trends in Psychological Theory, pp. 179–213. Pittsburgh: University of Pittsburgh Press, 1951.
3. Ginsberg, Arthur. "Operational Definitions and Theories," Journal of General Psychology, 52:223–45 (1955).
4. Kendler, H. H. "What Is Learned—A Theoretical Blind Alley," Psychological Review, 59:269–77 (1952).
5. Meehl, P. E., and Kenneth MacCorquodale. "Edward C. Tolman," in William K. Estes et al. (eds.), Modern Learning Theory, pp. 177–266. New York: Appleton-Century-Crofts, 1954.
6. Skinner, B. F. The Behavior of Organisms. New York: Appleton-Century-Crofts, 1938.
7. Skinner, B. F. Review of Hull's "Principles of Behavior," American Journal of Psychology, 57:276–81 (1944).
8. Skinner, B. F. "Are Theories of Learning Necessary?" Psychological Review, 57: 193–216 (1950).
9. Skinner, B. F. Science and Human Behavior. New York: Macmillan, 1953.
10. Skinner, B. F. "Critique of Psychoanalytic Concepts and Theories," Scientific Monthly, 79:300–5 (1954).
11. Verplanck, W. S. "Burrhus F. Skinner," in William K. Estes et al. (eds.), Modern Learning Theory, pp. 267–316. New York: Appleton-Century-Crofts, 1954.

An Operational Reformulation of Some of the Basic Principles of Psychoanalysis

THERE have been surprisingly few attempts to reformulate the main tenets of psychoanalysis in operational language, although many writers, including the present author (8, 9), have said that this can be done. Several theorists, such as Brown and Farber (4), Frenkel-Brunswik (19), Reid (41), Seeman (47), and Skinner (49), have attempted to translate a few psychoanalytic or psychodynamically oriented concepts into more operational terms, but a systematic reformulation of a good many of the Freudian principles does not as yet seem to have been attempted. Other theorists, such as Sullivan (51), have actually reworded much of the Freudian hypotheses in more precise terminology; but they have been systematic neither in their operationism nor in their inclusion of Freudian constructs; and they have often been more concerned with criticizing and modifying than with restating orthodox psychoanalytic concepts.

What Operationism Is

If psychoanalytic (or any other psychological) theory is to be reformulated in operational terms, the question must immediately arise: What is meant by *operational?* As originally presented by Bridgman (3), operationism seemed to be a relatively clear-cut method of research. But much ensuing comment and discussion has shown that, especially

NOTE: This paper was an outgrowth of a Conference on Psychoanalysis and the Philosophy of Science, held at the University of Minnesota, June 14–16, 1954, under the auspices of the Minnesota Center for the Philosophy of Science, directed by Dr. Herbert Feigl. Grateful acknowledgment is made for discussions with and comments by Drs. Herbert Feigl, Else Frenkel-Brunswik, Starke R. Hathaway, Paul E. Meehl, John Reid, William Schofield, W. S. Sellars, and Henry Winthrop. Extensive correspondence with Michael Scriven in regard to the first draft of this paper has been especially helpful. All responsibility for the views expressed herein, however, is the author's.

as it relates to psychological theory, it presents many serious problems (12, 25, 28, 31, 34, 39). Before we attempt to restate some of the basic principles of psychoanalysis in "operational" terms, therefore, it is best to define some of the main elements in a modified or revisionist operationism that today will philosophically and scientifically stand up.

1. To be operationally meaningful, a statement must be confirmable at least in principle: that is to say, a scientific theory must be tied to observables at some point. It may be part of a whole network of other statements or theories; but eventually, somewhere along the line, it must be related to observables (15, 32).

2. Strict operationism, as originally presented by Bridgman (3), may be unduly restrictive when applied to theory-making (34, 35, 50). It may be modified, as Feigl (12) has aptly shown, by requiring that scientific theories be, in some final analysis, linked to operations that are logically consistent, definite, empirically rooted, possible to execute, intersubjective and repeatable, and aimed at the creation of concepts which will function in laws or theories of greater predictiveness.

3. In modern operationism or empiricism we can no longer demand full verifiability or full falsifiability of scientific statements since, as Hempel (25), Scriven (43, 44), and others have recently shown, it is more realistic to demand only confirmability or partial verifiability. Modern physics, as Reichenbach (15) shows, accepts a statement as meaningful if it is verifiable as true, false, or indeterminate; and all scientists must today recognize what Feigl (15) calls the incompleteness and indirectness of the verification of practically all statements.

4. So-called intervening variables or dispositional concepts—that is, concepts which are fairly directly abstracted from or closely tied to observables and whose definition is given by the empirical laws in which they occur, which they imply, or which they presuppose—are legitimate and fruitful in scientific theorizing, but they have distinct limitations. In addition, modern operationists or empiricists may, and indeed should, make use of higher-order abstractions, or hypothetical constructs—which, as Ginsberg (22) and MacCorquodale and Meehl (33) point out, are highly abstract and general systems of concepts which are only indirectly rather than explicitly related or reducible to observational facts or empirical terms. Where intervening variables are of limited usefulness in scientific theorizing (30, 33), hypothetical constructs take in the widest

range of relevant phenomena, lead to maximum success in the prediction and explanation of behavior, and are heuristically necessary because the human intellect is so limited that it cannot very well get along without them (15, 22, 23, 24, 25, 30, 32, 38, 40, 44, 50). At the same time, the dangers of cavalierly employing hypothetical constructs must be acknowledged, as they are frequently used in an indefinite, vague, overspeculative, and rigid manner (5, 11, 15, 21, 24, 35, 44).

5. While almost all leading psychological theorists today, including Hull (27), Skinner (49), and Tolman (52), are known as Behaviorists, Skinner in particular has gone to extremes in insisting that the so-called inner states of the organism, such as the idea of "emotion" or "wish," or even physiological formulations like "neuron" or "engram," may actually exist but are not relevant in the functional analysis of behavior. Skinner also states that events affecting an organism must be capable of description in the language of physical science. Theorists like Frenkel-Brunswik (19) and Rapaport (40), on the other hand, insist that only partial explanations of human behavior are ever offered by the behavioral-operational approach. Although strict operationism would probably require a fairly strict Behaviorism in psychological theorizing, a modified operational approach leaves room for a less strict, non-Skinnerian form of psychological theory.

6. Many psychological theorists, including Hebb (24), Krech (30), and Tolman (53), have recently favored the use of hypothetical constructs in psychological theorizing, but at the same time have asked that, whenever possible, these constructs be stated in neurophysiological terms. At the same time, other psychologists, such as Lindzey (32), Skinner (49), and Spiker and McCandless (50), have been sceptical of the neurophysiological approach. From the standpoint of a modified operationism or empiricism it may be pointed out that although it is highly probable that many neurophysiological constructs are isomorphically related to many behavioral ones (Feigl (14, 15)), and although it would be highly desirable if constructs which apply to behavior could be stated in physiological terms, at the present time this is neither necessary nor, to a large degree, possible. Therefore operational reformulations of psychoanalytic (or other psychological) theory need not presently be stated in neurophysiological language.

7. The question has been raised by various writers, including Lundberg and Sarbin (quoted in Meehl (37), Maze (36), and Pratt (39)),

as to whether hypothetical constructs are not, at bottom, arrived at by essentially inductive methods, and are therefore actually closely related to so-called intervening variables. Meehl (37), attacking this view, points out that although the process of hypothesis creation is not entirely outside the rules of inductive logic, and must eventually conform to these rules; and while it is theoretically possible to arrive at hypothetical constructs by amassing so much experiential data and intercorrelating these data so thoroughly that the hypotheses will almost automatically arise out of the collected data and their intercorrelations; this, in point of fact, is *not* the way in which hypothetical constructs are ordinarily formulated. Instead, humans arrive at such hypotheses by employing exceptionally incomplete data and intercorrelations; and the human process of thereby formulating hypotheses, or of unconsciously inferring from relatively few facts and partial correlations, may be called creative imagination or clinical intuition and is indispensable to scientific thinking. Whether Meehl or Lundberg and Sarbin are strictly correct or not, a modified operationism or empiricism may, with Kneale (15), extend the use of the word "induction" to cover the hypothetical method but at the same time, perhaps, distinguish this new application of the term by adding the adjective "secondary." This usage would permit us to retain, as an integral part of the scientific method, creative hypothesizing, while recognizing that it is, in the last analysis, a form of unconscious or secondary induction.

8. Assuming that a modified operationism may encompass both higher-order and lower-order theories, or hypothetical constructs as well as intervening variables, the following question arises: With what degree of simplicity or parsimony shall we attempt to state our psychological theories? A fairly rigorous adherence to simple or parsimonious statements of scientific theories has, as Feigl (13, 14), Ginsberg (22), and Scriven (45) demonstrate, the advantage of insuring against inconsistency, superfluity, confusion, and mysticism. At the same time, as Dittmann and Rausch (6), Beck (15) and Reichenbach (15) indicate, simplicity, in itself, cannot carry too much of the burden of adequate theorizing since it may lead to a surrendering of plausibility or specificity of prediction. It would appear, then, that simplicity is a desirable but not essential requisite of scientific theorizing; that it often serves a useful purpose; but that, in itself, it does not guarantee the formulation of the best kind of theory.

9. It has often been contended—as by Feigl (13), Frank (18), Lindsay (31) and Seeger (46)—that although some scientific theories, particularly those stated in the form of hypothetical constructs, may seem vague, inconsistent, or even mistaken, they may have distinct heuristic value: that is to say, they stimulate further scientific investigation and ultimately lead to the formulation of better theories. Rudner (42), Wigner (15), and others have also noted that value decisions are inevitably involved in scientific conclusions, and that it is foolish to deny that this is so. On the other hand, as the present author (8, 10) and Skinner (48) have observed, it is difficult to prove or disprove the notion that theories postulated in the early days of science, such as theories of "essences," "phlogistons," "ethers," "ids," or "libidos," were essential to the historical process or that they have actually advanced scientific thinking. It could well be that such "heuristically desirable" theories actually have done more harm than good, and that some of them are still hindering our thinking. From the standpoint of a modified operationism or empiricism, it is legitimate to formulate speculative theories; but it is questionable whether they should be defended on "heuristic" grounds, since it is virtually impossible accurately to define or confirm what is or is not "heuristic."

In the light of the foregoing description of what modified operationism or empiricism is, it can be seen that it is a highly liberal, open-minded, scientific viewpoint, which includes, and even encourages, considerable speculative, creative hypothesizing. Modern empiricism, in fact, seems to have only one invariant requisite: namely, that in some final analysis, albeit most indirectly and through a long network of intervening constructs, a statement or hypothesis must in some manner (or in principle) be confirmable—that is, significantly tie-able to or correlatable with some kind of observable. It thereby rules out sheer metaphysical speculation but keeps the door widely open for all other hypotheses.

This, then, is modern operationism or empiricism. As applied to psychoanalysis, it means that psychoanalytic principles should be stated in terms so that they are, in some final analysis, in principle confirmable in terms of some ultimate observables. In the following paragraphs, however, we shall attempt to be even more strictly operational than this in translating psychoanalytic principles into scientific language. For as Joseph Zubin (personal communication) stated in commenting upon

Robert Oppenheimer's plea for scientific open-mindedness in his address to the American Psychological Association at its 1955 annual convention: modern physicists, because they have already brilliantly established many factual findings, can afford to be liberal in their scientific hypothesizing today. But can, as yet, modern psychologists also afford this when, in the realm of personality theory, they have factually established very little?

In the formulations of psychoanalytic principles that follow, then, a deliberate attempt will be made to avoid hypothetical constructs and higher-order abstractions and to remain, instead, on the so-called intervening variable, lower-order level of theorizing. No attempt will be made to use physiological constructs, on the one hand, nor strictly behavioral terms, on the other hand, though a moderately behavioral terminology will be employed.

The main reasons for adhering, in the following psychoanalytic reformulations, to lower-order theorizing are these:

A. The existing orthodox Freudian principles make use of many vague terms like "libido," "id," "mental life," "energy cathexis," etc., which may be legitimate hypothetical constructs but are most difficult to pin down to earth and experimentally validate or disprove.

B. The science of psychoanalysis, because of the complexities involved in examining human perceptions and responses, is difficult enough to confirm empirically when it is stated in lower-order terms, and tends to be considerably less easily confirmable when stated in the form of hypothetical constructs.

C. It has never been shown that the use of hypothetical constructs in psychoanalytic theory is necessary or desirable.

D. Stating analytic hypotheses in lower-order terms may have the practical advantages of eliminating dogmatism and fuzzy thinking, encouraging new psychoanalytic hypotheses and experiments, making for a closer rapprochement between general psychological theory and psychoanalysis, and making analytic principles more acceptable to practicing therapists and their patients.

E. By restating psychoanalytic views in terms of lower-order theorizing, some of the more speculative, and perhaps erroneous, physiological hypothetical constructs originated by Freud may be eliminated as being redundant.

It should not be denied that psychoanalytic principles can be scientifically, and quite legitimately, formulated in terms of hypothetical constructs, including physiological constructs. It is the present writer's contention, however, that these principles can be presented so that they become more easily empirically confirmable, clearer, less tautological, and more practical. To this end, a more operational reformulation of psychoanalytic theories will now be attempted.

A Basic Operational Vocabulary

In any set of psychodynamic principles a basic vocabulary is necessary. Such a vocabulary will now be operationally derived from two observables or "facts"—perception and response. It will be assumed that every human organism (a) *perceives* (observes, sees, senses, or feels) and (b) *responds* (acts, performs, or behaves). Perception and response would appear to be basic, unarguable characteristics of living organisms because, first, they are intrinsic to the definition of life (an organism that in some way did not perceive and respond could hardly be called living); and, second, perceiving and responding to stimuli can be as directly observed as almost anything else in this world.

In the empirical concepts of perception and response we can easily anchor all the other constructs necessary and useful to a psychodynamic set of principles of human behavior. Consider the following:

1. *Conscious and unconscious perception.* The individual *consciously perceives* when he perceives that he perceives. He *unconsciously perceives* when he perceives but does not perceive that he perceives. We can observe an individual's conscious perception by (a) asking him if he perceives that he is perceiving; or (b) observing his other behavior— e.g., observing that he is alert, that he is performing a difficult task, that he speaks as if he were conscious of what he is doing, that he is not drunk, dazed, or asleep, etc.

We can confirm the hypothesis that an individual is unconsciously perceiving by observing that he acts *as if* he perceives, although he may tell us that he is not aware that he is perceiving (41). Thus, if he suddenly swerves his car to avoid a log in the road, but tells us that he does not know why he swerved, we may infer that he unconsciously did see the log. Or if he tells us that he consciously sees his wife as a most desirable sex partner, but we observe that, in practice, he continually has sex relations with other women and rarely with his wife, we may infer that he unconsciously perceives his wife as an unsatisfactory sex partner.

Unconscious behavior, then, is merely behavior which occurs without the individual's perceiving that it occurs. Unconscious perception occurs without his perceiving that he perceives; unconscious responding occurs without his perceiving that he responds. There is nothing mysterious about this, since there is no reason why an individual should not fail to observe events, either outside himself or part of his own behavior, even though they are conspicuous and important. If a man can fail to report the details of an accident or a robbery accurately, he can certainly also fail to note correctly his own perceptions or responses.

2. *Thinking and learning.* The individual *thinks* or *discriminates* when he organizes or reorganizes his perceptions—when he labels or distinguishes among the things he perceives. More specifically, he thinks when he perceives two or more of his sensations as being integrally or causally related so that he can make accurate predictions about one or more of them. The individual *remembers* when he perceives again something that he has previously perceived. He *learns* (adjusts, adapts) when he organizes or reorganizes his perceptions and changes his behavior as a result of this reorganizing.

The individual's thinking, learning, and remembering may be observed by asking him to verbalize about his perceptions; or the hypothesis that he thinks may be confirmed by observing his nonverbal behavior. Thus, if we observe that a child who, on several occasions, is given a basket containing rotten and good apples, soon begins consistently to disregard the rotten and eat only the good ones, we may conclude that (a) he has organized or discriminated among his perceptions of the apples—that is, he has thought about them; (b) he has reperceived—or remembered—the apples from occasion to occasion; and (c) he has adjusted or changed his behavior—learned—in regard to the apples on the basis of his organizing his perceptions.

An individual unconsciously remembers, thinks, and learns when he organizes or reorganizes his perceptions *as if* he consciously remembered, thought, or learned. Thus, if we observe a child invariably throwing away rotten apples and eating good ones, but he tells us that he doesn't realize what he is doing, we may conclude that he has unconsciously learned to make this kind of a selection.

3. *Evaluating, emoting, and desiring.* An individual *evaluates* (atti-

tudinizes, becomes biased) when he perceives something as being "good" or "bad," "pleasant" or "unpleasant," "beneficial" or "harmful" and when, as a result of his perceptions, he responds positively or negatively to this thing. Evaluating is a fundamental characteristic of human organisms and seems to work in a kind of closed circuit with a feedback mechanism, since perception biases response and then response tends to bias subsequent perception. Also, prior perceptions appear to bias subsequent perceptions, and prior responses to bias subsequent responses.

Evaluating always seems to involve both perceiving and responding, not merely one or the other. It also appears to be a fundamental, virtually definitional, property of humans, since if they did not have some way of favoring or reacting positively to "good" or "beneficial" stimuli and of disfavoring or reacting negatively to "bad" or "harmful" stimuli, they could hardly survive.

An individual *emotes* when he evaluates something strongly—when he clearly perceives it as being "good" or "bad," "beneficial" or "harmful," and strongly responds to it in a negative or positive manner. Emoting usually, probably always, involves some kind of bodily sensations which, when perceived by the emoting individual, may then reinforce the original emotion. Emotions may therefore simply be evaluations which have a strong bodily component, while so-called nonemotional attitudes may be evaluatings with a relatively weak bodily component.

Evaluatings and emotions are consciously experienced when the individual perceives that he is experiencing them. They are unconsciously experienced when he acts as *if* he evaluates or emotes but does not perceive that he does so. Thus, he may consciously perceive that he hates another; or may bristle, glower, and make nasty remarks, so that everyone else perceives that he hates this other, even though he does not perceive or admit this himself.

Some of the more important human evaluations and emotions may be defined as follows:

A. An individual *desires* (wishes, wants, likes, loves) when he evaluates something positively—perceives it as being "good" or "beneficial" and usually moves toward or tries to possess it.

B. He *needs* (has a *drive* toward) something when he strongly evaluates it in a positive manner—perceives it as being vitally important or necessary to him.

C. An individual *fears* something when he evaluates it negatively, perceives it as being "bad" or "harmful," and tries to prevent its occurrence or to get away from it.

D. He *is anxious* when he perceives that something he does or may do will be disapproved by himself and/or others and is uncomfortably expecting something dreadful to happen because of this action.

E. He *becomes angry* when he perceives something as being "bad" or "harmful" and strongly wants to annihilate this thing.

F. He *is guilty* when he perceives that some aspects of his behavior are "bad" or socially disapprovable and agrees that he should be punished or disapproved for acting in this way.

An individual becomes unconsciously fearful, anxious, angry, or guilty when, without perceiving that he perceives something as "bad" or socially reprehensible, he acts *as if* he so perceived it and consequently avoids it, is uncomfortably expectant about it, wants to annihilate it, or wants to punish himself because of it. When an individual is unconsciously fearful, anxious, angry, or guilty, he tends to express his unperceived emotions in psychosomatic and psychomotor reactions, such as muscular tensions, vasomotor reactions, respiratory effects, etc.

Reformulating Psychoanalytic Principles

The foregoing definitions of human (conscious and unconscious) perceiving, responding, thinking, learning, and evaluating are meant to be operational formulations in that they are solidly anchored to observable events or things. Using these definitions, we shall now take some of Freud's main hypotheses, as stated by him in his last work, *An Outline of Psychoanalysis* (20), and restate these in more operational terms.

The id. Freud: "The id . . . contains everything that is inherited, that is present at birth, that is fixed in the constitution—above all, therefore, the instincts, which originate in the somatic organization and which find their first mental expression in the id in forms unknown to us" (20, p. 14).*

Operational reformulation: Human beings have certain basic needs or drives, such as hunger, sex, and thirst needs, toward the expression of which they inherit tendencies, but which can be considerably modi-

* All quotations from Sigmund Freud's *An Outline of Psychoanalysis*, published by W. W. Norton & Co. (New York, 1949), are made with the permission of the publisher.

fied by experiential reinforcement or social learning. The existence of these needs is confirmable by our observing—e.g., in the course of the famous University of Minnesota experiments in semistarvation (29)—how aberrated, distorted, and frenzied the behavior of most humans becomes when some of their basic needs are frustrated.

The ego. Freud: "The ego . . . has the task of self-preservation. As regards *external* events, it performs that task by becoming aware of the stimuli from without, by storing up experience of them (in the memory), by avoiding excessive stimuli (through flight), by dealing with moderate stimuli (through adaptation) and, finally, by learning to bring about appropriate modifications in the external world to its own advantage (through activity). As regards *internal* events, in relation to the id, it performs that task by gaining control over the demands of the instincts, by deciding whether they shall be allowed to obtain satisfaction, by postponing that satisfaction to times and circumstances favorable in the external world or by suppressing their excitations completely" (20, p. 15).

Operational reformulation: The individual perceives, remembers, thinks, learns, and evaluates. The entire network comprising his perceptions, memories, thoughts, and evaluations may be called his *ego* or *self.* To say that an individual has a self or ego has also come to mean that he has self-evaluating attitudes, or concepts of himself. That is to say, just as he evaluates outside persons and things, he also comes to view himself as "good" or "bad." If he has consistently favorable self-evaluations, we say he has a "strong" ego or "good" self-concept; if he has unfavorable self-evaluations, we say he has a "poor" ego structure.

The individual's ego or self is self-protective in that in order to maintain his physical and mental well-being he acts to protect himself from threatening external events, such as fire, flood, and attack, and from social disapproval. Out of fear of external danger or social disapproval he will also frequently control some of his internal needs, such as his hunger and sex needs. He may decide whether these needs shall be allowed outlets at certain times and may even, on occasion, completely suppress their excitations.

The individual's tendency to protect himself and his self-evaluating concepts from external and internal threat may be confirmed by experimental and clinical observation, as Hilgard, Kubie, and Pumpian-Mindlin (26), Skinner (48), and other authors have shown.

The superego. Freud: "The long period of childhood, during which the growing human being lives in dependence upon his parents, leaves behind it a precipitate, which forms within his ego a special agency in which this parental influence is prolonged. It has received the name of superego" (20, p. 16).

Operational reformulation: Just as individuals learn to evaluate external objects, they also, largely through the teachings of their parents, come to evaluate their own behavior as being "good" or "bad." When they perceive their own acts as "bad" or socially reprehensible, and when they agree that they should be reprimanded or punished for these acts, we say that they have a poor conscience, or a strong superego, or are guilty. Like all other thoughts and emotions, feelings of guilt may be consciously perceived; or they may be unconsciously perceived, as shown by an individual's acting as *if* he perceived them.

Eros and the death instinct. Freud: "After long doubts and vacillations we have decided to assume the existence of only two basic instincts, *Eros and the destructive instinct.* . . . We may suppose that the final aim of the destructive instinct is to reduce living things to an inorganic state. For this reason we also call it the *death instinct*" (20, p. 20).

Operational reformulation: All important desires and needs of human beings may be grouped under two main headings: (a) the erotic, life, or self-preservative needs; (b) the destructive or death needs. If only these two basic needs exist (as few of even the most orthodox Freudians today seem to agree) confirmation of their existence may be found through empirical observation and experimentation.

The sexual life. Freud: "Sexual life does not begin only at puberty, but starts with clear manifestations soon after birth. It is necessary to distinguish sharply between the concepts of 'sexual' and 'genital.' The former is the wider concept and includes many activities that have nothing to do with the genitals. Sexual life comprises the function of obtaining pleasures from zones of the body . . ." (20, p. 26).

Operational reformulation: Since the word "sexual" normally connotes "genital" in our culture, it is perhaps best to use it as a synonym for "genital" and to use another word, "sensual," to describe the function of obtaining pleasures from all zones of the body, genital and non-genital. Sensual life, especially that comprising oral and anal sensations, begins soon after an infant's birth. Sexual or genital activity also to some degree begins in infancy.

Confirmation of this hypothesis may be obtained from (clinically and experimentally) observing infants, most of whom appear to act as if they perceive and respond to stimulation of their oral, anal, and genital areas.

Oral eroticism. Freud: "The baby's obstinate persistence in sucking gives evidence at an early stage of a need for satisfaction which, although it originates from and is stimulated by the taking of nourishment, nevertheless seeks to obtain pleasure independently of nourishment and for that reason may and should be described as 'sexual' " (20, p. 28).

Operational reformulation: Babies, through their oral perceptions, appear to obtain satisfaction independently of nourishment. We may describe this tendency of infants to seek oral stimulation as oral sensuality and may find confirmation of it through observing the behavior of infants in relation to their oral zones.

Anal sadism. Freud: "Sadistic impulses already begin to occur sporadically during the oral phase along with the appearance of the teeth. Their extent increases greatly during the second phase, which we describe as the sadistic-anal phase, because satisfaction is then sought in aggression and in the excretory function" (20, p. 28).

Operational reformulation: Children, through their anal perceptions, appear to obtain satisfaction, at least on some occasions, when they are anally stimulated. We may describe their tendency to obtain, and sometimes actively seek, anal stimulation as anal sensuality. Some children discover that their excretory functions are a means through which they may express hostility; and some of these children become anal sadistic.

The phallic phase. Freud: "The third phase is the so-called phallic one, which is, as it were, a forerunner of the final shape of sexual life, and already greatly resembles it" (20, p. 29).

Operational reformulation: Children often have sex desires and activities which are quite similar to those experienced by adults. Childhood sex experiences may have important influences on adult sex and other behavior.

These hypotheses may be confirmed by observing the verbal and nonverbal behavior of children and adults in relation to their sex activities and calculating appropriate correlations between childhood and adult sex feelings and behavior.

Repression. Freud: "During this development the young and feeble ego dropped and pushed back into the unconscious condition certain material which it had already taken in, and behaved similarly in regard to many new impressions which it *might* have taken in, so that these were rejected and were able to leave traces in the id only. In consideration of its origin, we term this portion of the id the *repressed*" (20, p. 43).

Operational reformulation: When the human individual perceives something, particularly something that he himself has done or helped bring about, as being "bad" or socially reprehensible, he often protects himself by trying not to reperceive or remember this thing. In these instances, he sometimes manages to forget the thing entirely, or to remember it in a vague or distorted way; and he thus protects his feelings of self-esteem (i.e., his ego or his perception of himself). When he consciously misperceives or forgets significant occurrences, we say that he *suppresses* them; when he unconsciously does so, we say that he *represses* them.

If we consider an individual's inherited needs or action-tendencies, some of which he may never have been conscious of and some of which he may have once perceived and then have suppressed or repressed; and if we add to these his socially learned thoughts and evaluations, some of which he also may have once perceived but later suppressed or repressed; we may call the totality of his never-conscious and once-conscious thoughts and evaluations his *id.*

The hypothesis of the individual's repressing some of his perceptions may be confirmed (or denied) by our (a) observing that he remembers things in certain situations when he is off guard—e.g., when he is relaxed, in psychotherapeutic interviews, during dreams, in hypnotic or sodium amytal interviews, etc.; and by our (b) observing that he sometimes acts as *if* he were making an effort *not* to remember some embarrassing fact—e.g., when we observe him staring at pretty girls but insisting that he has never done such a thing.

Dreams. Freud: "With the help of the unconscious, every dream in the process of formation makes a demand upon the ego for the satisfaction of an instinct (if it originates from the id) or for the solution of a conflict, the removal of a doubt, or the making of a decision (if it originates from a residue of preconscious activity in waking life). The sleeping ego, however, is focused upon the wish to maintain sleep; it regards this demand as a disturbance and seeks to get rid of the disturbance. The ego achieves this by what appears to be an act of compliance: it meets the demand with what is, in the circumstances, the innocent fulfillment of a wish and thus disposes of the demand. This replacement of a demand by the fulfillment of a wish remains the essential function of dream-work" (20, pp. 54–55).

Operational reformulation: The human individual frequently dreams and appears to use many of his dreams as an outlet for the direct or symbolic satisfaction of some of his needs and desires. Thus, he may employ a dream to prevent himself from waking; to continue certain lines of thought he has had during the day; to express pent-up emotions; and to satisfy some of his "good" and "bad" wishes. In his dream thoughts, particularly when they pertain to socially tabooed desires, he may protect his self-esteem (his ego) by resorting to distortion, condensation, displacement of affect, censorship, symbolism, and various other techniques of disguising his dream thoughts and desires.

If this hypothesis concerning human dream processes is true it may be confirmed by having individuals describe a series of their dreams and correlating the contents of these dreams with other important things known about the dreamers—e.g., their life events preceding the dreams; their associations; the mores of their culture; etc. The hypothesis that dream contents are related to underlying wishes and desires of the dreamer may be tested by predicting that certain kinds of dreams represent certain kinds of desires and then probing into the dreamers' present and past experiences to discover whether or not they have or have had the predicted desires.

The libido. Freud: "We may picture an initial state of things by supposing that the whole available energy of Eros, to which we shall henceforward give the name of *libido,* is present in the as yet undifferentiated ego-id and serves to neutralize the destructive impulses which are simultaneously present . . . It is difficult to say anything of the behavior of the libido in the id and in the superego. Everything that we know about it relates to the ego, in which the whole available amount of libido is at first stored up. We call this state of things absolute, primary narcissism. It continues until the ego begins to cathect the presentation of objects with libido—to change narcissistic libido into *object libido.* Throughout life the ego remains the great reservoir from which libidinal cathexes are sent out onto objects and into which they are also once more withdrawn, like the pseudopodia of a body of protoplasm. It is only when someone is completely in love that the main quantity of libido is transferred onto the object and the object to some extent takes the place of the ego. A characteristic of libido which is important in life is its *mobility*, the ease with which it passes from one object to another. This must be contrasted with the *fixation* of libido to particular objects, which often persists through life. There can be no question that the libido has somatic sources, that it streams into the ego from various organs and parts of the body" (20, pp. 22–24).

Operational reformulation: The human individual has self-preservative and sex needs which partly originate in his biological make-up and partly stem from his social learning. When he is young, the individual tends to concentrate almost exclusively on himself and his own self-preservative needs and to view objects in his environment in a non-differentiated manner, as extensions of himself. At this time, we may say that he is in a state of primary narcissism.

As he grows older, the individual begins to differentiate other objects from himself and to discriminate among outside objects. In accordance with his perceptual discrimination and the satisfactions he derives from outside objects, he begins to evaluate them positively or negatively, as "good" or "bad" objects. He may thereby become interested in outside persons or things in their own right and forgo much of his primary narcissism. But unless he falls completely in love with some outside person or thing he never surrenders a considerable amount of his narcissism or self-interest.

Once an individual becomes significantly interested in, or positively evaluates, objects outside himself, he is usually able to transfer his interest easily from one object to another. Occasionally, however, he becomes so strongly attached to a certain object or thing that his interest becomes fixated on it; and this kind of fixation may sometimes persist through life.

The individual's propensity to become interested, and in particular amatively and sexually interested, in other people and things we may call his *libido*. While many aspects of the expression of his libidinous drives are learned, his underlying tendencies to become vitally interested in outside things, or to display libido, would appear to be biologically rooted.

The sexual libido. Freud: A "portion of the libido . . . from its instinctual aim, is known as sexual excitation. The most prominent of the parts of the body from which this libido arises are described by the name of erotogenic zones, though strictly speaking the whole body is an erotogenic zone. The greater part of what we know about Eros— that is, about its exponent, the libido—has been gained from the study of the sexual function, which, indeed, in the popular view, if not in our theory, coincides with Eros. We have been able to form a picture of the way in which the sexual impulse, which is destined to exercise a decisive influence on our life, gradually develops out of successive contributions from a number of the component instincts, which represent particular erotogenic zones" (20, p. 24).

Operational reformulation: Sexual excitation stems from (a) our biological drives, which appear to be hormonally activated; and (b) our social learning or conditioning. Sexual impulses seem to be closely related to, and in part compounded of, sensual excitations—e.g., oral, anal, urethral, and other tactile sensations. In some instances, human beings never clearly differentiate their sexual or genital sensations from some of their sensual sensations; or they become sexually fixated on an oral, anal, or urethral level because, originally, there was a close association between their genital and oral, anal, or urethral sensations.

The Oedipus complex. Freud: "When a boy, from about the age of two or three, enters upon the phallic phase of his libidinal development, feels pleasurable sensations in his sexual organ and learns to procure these at will by manual stimulation, he becomes his mother's lover. He desires to possess her physically in the ways which he has divined from his observations and intuitive surmises of sexual life and tries to seduce her by showing her the male organ of which he is the proud owner. In a word, his early awakened masculinity makes him seek to assume, in relation to her, the place belonging to his father . . . At last his mother adopts the severest measures: she threatens to take away from him the thing he is defying her with. As a rule, in order to make the threat more terrifying and more credible, she delegates its carrying out to the boy's father, saying that she will tell him and that he will cut the penis off" (20, pp. 91–92).

Operational reformulation: When, in a small family system such as normally exists in our culture, a boy learns that his father assumes an all-important position in regard to his mother, he frequently wishes that he could usurp this position for himself. When, in addition, a boy's early sex drives are denied easy outlet, as they usually are in our society, he often becomes sexually obsessed, and intensely desires to have sex

147

relations with a great many women, including his own mother. As a result of his nonsexual and sexual jealousy of his father, complicated by his guilt about his incestuous desires, a boy in our society may develop an incest complex and may desire to kill his father and/or fear that his father is going to castrate him. This complex will tend to be even greater if his parents make an issue over masturbation and sexually threaten him because of it.

Confirmation of the Freudian hypothesis of incest and castration complexes may be sought by (a) questioning boys about their sex desires and attitudes and about their relations with their parents; and (b) by observing the sexual behavior of boys and men and correlating their early and later sex desires and attitudes.

The ego defenses. Freud: "The ego often enough finds itself in the position of warding off some claims from the external world which it feels as painful and . . . this is effected by denying the perceptions that bring to knowledge such a demand on the part of reality. Denials of this kind often occur, and not only with fetishists; and whenever we are in a position to study them, they turn out to be half-measures, incomplete attempts at detachment from reality." (20, p. 118)

Operational reformulation: When an individual's perception of himself—that is, his self-esteem or ego-strength—is threatened, he frequently tends to perceive reality in such a distorted way as to convince himself that he is still a "good" or socially approved individual and that his behavior is justified. His techniques of distorting his perceptions may include repressing or denying painful occurrences; displacing or transferring embarrassing affects; becoming fixated or fetishistically attached to an early form of behavior that he views as pleasant or safe; compensating for his deficiencies in one area by becoming proficient in another; rationalizing or excusing his presumed deficiencies; projecting his own failings onto others; insisting that the world is acting unfairly against him; compulsively resorting to magical notions and rituals; resorting to asocial or antisocial behavior; masochistically expiating his "sins" by resorting to self-punishment; using alcohol or drugs as an escape from anxiety; etc.

The hypothesis that human beings tend to protect their self-esteem by consciously or unconsciously becoming defensive may be tested by observing their verbal and nonverbal behavior and correlating their perceptions of threat with the defense techniques they employ.

Neurosis and psychosis. Freud: "The necessary conditions for the pathological states we have mentioned can only be a relative or absolute weakening of the ego which prevents it from performing its tasks. The severest demand upon the ego is probably the keeping down of the instinctual claims of the id, and for this end the ego is obliged to maintain great expenditures of energy upon anti-cathexes. But the claims made by the superego, too, may become so powerful and so remorseless that the ego may be crippled, as it were, for its other tasks. We may suspect that, in the economic conflicts which now arise, the id and the superego often make common cause against the hard-pressed ego, which, in order to retain its normal state, clings onto reality. But if the other two are too strong, they may succeed in loosening the organization of the ego and altering it so that its proper relation to reality is disturbed or even abolished" (20, p. 62).

Operational reformulation: The so-called normal or well adjusted individual learns to like himself sufficiently (i.e., to perceive his behavior as being "good" enough and to have confidence that he will consistently continue to behave in a socially approved manner) to face his own desires and the demands of the external world even when conditions are rough and he is having a hard time making his way. But if his own unsatisfied needs become too great (e.g., he becomes continually cold, hungry, or sex-starved) or if he perceives many of his desires or actions as being "bad" or socially reprehensible, he tends to become hostile toward the world and himself and to lose confidence in himself.

If what the individual perceives as reality—that is, his picture of himself and the world around him—becomes too threatening, his perceptions of this reality may become distorted and he may see many things as he would like them to be rather than as they actually are. Such a distorted view of reality by the over-frustrated or over-guilty individual we call a neurosis or a psychosis.

Confirmation or disproof of the hypothesis that individuals become neurotic or psychotic when they are over-threatened by external events or by their own guilt feelings may be sought by correlating their verbal and nonverbal behavior relating to feelings of threat with their neurotic or psychotic symptoms.

Psychoanalytic therapy. Freud: "To begin with, we induce the patient's thus enfeebled ego to take part in the purely intellectual work of interpretation, which aims at provisionally filling the gaps in his mental resources, and to transfer to us the authority of his super-ego; we stimulate his ego to take up the struggle over each individual demand made by the id and to defeat the resistances which arise in connection with it. At the same time, we restore order in his ego, by detecting the material and impulses which have forced their way from the unconscious, and expose them to criticism by tracing them back to their origin. We serve the patient in various functions as an authority and a substitute for his parents, as a teacher and educator; and we have done the best for him if, as analysts, we raise the mental processes in his ego to a normal level, transform what has become unconscious and repressed into preconscious material and thus return it once more to the possession of his ego" (20, pp. 76–77).

Operational reformulation: The psychoanalyst helps the emotionally disturbed individual in several ways: (a) He accepts the patient and shows that he likes and approves him, thus reducing the patient's notion that he is socially reprehensible. (b) He helps the patient tolerate some of his ungratified needs—that is, accept the fact that obtaining certain advantages in life also entails accepting some disadvantages. (c) He helps the patient gratify some of his ungratified needs—e.g., to work more effectively and thereby get a better-paying position. (d) He enables the patient to understand why he behaves in an irrational, disorganized way, and how to stop this irrational behavior. (e) He becomes something of a parent-substitute and authority-figure to the patient, and thereby serves as a good model for the patient and encourages him, out of love for the analyst, to surrender some of his neurotic symptoms. (f) He acts as a teacher and educator to the patient, often giving him useful information, such as sex information. (g) He gives the patient the possibility of greater conscious, and more effective, control over his behavior by making him aware of many things which he did not previously consciously perceive but which were seriously affecting him. He thus enables the patient to be honest with himself and to forgo time- and energy-consuming self-deceptions.

Limitations of the Operational Reformulation
of Freudian Principles

In the foregoing sections of this paper we have defined the keywords needed for psychodynamic formulations by operationally anchoring them in human perception and response. We have then translated some of the most important Freudian theories into this operationally derived language. In so doing, we have been able to state the essentials of Freudian theory in molar terms, on a so-called intervening variable level. We have not actually proven or empirically verified any of the restated psychoanalytic hypotheses; but we have indicated how they may be confirmed or disproved by clinical or experimental observation.

We have made no attempt to show that all scientific theories can or should be operationally stated in terms of lower-order constructs; and, in fact, have shown that, at the present time, setting such a limitation on scientific theorizing is neither practical nor desirable. But we have tried to demonstrate that it is practical, and probably quite desirable, to state the essentials of analytic theory in considerably more operational terms than those in which they are usually stated.

We have not, in this paper, made any attempt to translate all Freudian hypotheses into operational terms: since that would be too space-consuming. It is hoped, however, that a sufficient number of the main Freudian principles have been operationally reformulated so that it will be obvious that virtually all the psychoanalytic theories omitted in this paper may also be, with relatively little trouble, reformulated along similar lines.

There has been no attempt in this paper to rephrase two of Freud's more debatable concepts: (a) that of the psyche, mental life, and mental qualities; and (b) that of mental energy and energy cathexes. These are hypothetical constructs which are in part based on nineteenth-century notions of physics which are no longer tenable and in part confirmable only in terms of neurophysiological findings which have not yet been made. They also appear to be redundant in that all the necessary and valuable psychodynamic principles which are involved in the hypotheses of mental life and energy cathexes can easily be stated, as we have shown in the previous sections of this paper, in terms of behavioral intervening variables, without resorting to these vague and debatable hypothetical constructs.

Summary

Some of the main problems involved in scientific theorizing are considered. It is concluded that theories should not be strictly limited to

151

Albert Ellis

observational, intervening variable, dispositional, strictly inductive, or lower-order terms, since this kind of rigid operationism would, at the present time, unduly restrict scientific thinking and investigation. It is nonetheless felt that, for a variety of reasons, the reformulation of Freudian psychoanalytic principles into more operational, observational, and intervening variable terminology is desirable at present. Accordingly, many of the basic Freudian hypotheses are quoted and then restated in operational terms.

REFERENCES

1. Ayer, A. J. *Language, Truth and Logic*. New York: Dover, 1947.
2. Bergmann, G. "Sense and Nonsense in Operationism," *Scientific Monthly*, 79: 210–14 (1954).
3. Bridgman, P. W. "Some General Principles of Operational Analysis," *Psychological Review*, 52:246–49 (1945).
4. Brown, J. S., and I. E. Farber. "Emotions Conceptualized as Intervening Variables—With Suggestions Toward a Theory of Frustration," *Psychological Bulletin*, 48:465–95 (1951).
5. Dallenbach, K. M. "The Place of Theory in Science," *Psychological Review*, 60: 33–39 (1953).
6. Dittmann, A. T., and H. L. Rausch. "The Psychoanalytic Theory of Conflict: Structure and Methodology," *Psychological Review*, 61:386–400 (1954).
7. Ellis, A. "Towards the Improvement of Psychoanalytic Research," *Psychoanalytic Review*, 36:123–43 (1949).
8. Ellis, A. "An Introduction to the Principles of Scientific Psychoanalysis," *Genetic Psychology Monograph*, 41:147–212 (1950).
9. Ellis, A. "A Critique of Systematic Theoretical Foundations in Clinical Psychology," *Journal of Clinical Psychology*, 8:11–15 (1952).
10. Ellis, A. *The American Sexual Tragedy*. New York: Twayne, 1954.
11. Eysenck, H. J. "The Organization of Personality," *Journal of Personality*, 20: 101–17 (1951).
12. Feigl, H. "Operationism and Scientific Method," *Psychological Review*, 52:250–59 (1945).
13. Feigl, H. "Principles and Problems of Theory Construction in Psychology," in W. Dennis (ed.), *Current Trends in Psychological Theory*, pp. 174–213. Pittsburgh: Univ. of Pittsburgh Pr., 1951.
14. Feigl, H. "Aims of Education for Our Age of Science: Reflections of a Logical Empiricist," in Nelson B. Henry (ed.), *Modern Philosophies and Education, 1955*, pp. 304–41. Chicago: National Society for the Study of Education, 1955.
15. Feigl, H., and M. Brodbeck (eds.). *Readings in the Philosophy of Science*. New York: Appleton-Century-Crofts, 1953.
16. Feigl, H., and W. Sellars (eds.). *Readings in Philosophical Analysis*. New York: Appleton-Century-Crofts, 1949.
17. Flew, A. "Motives and the Unconscious." Paper delivered at the Conference on Psychoanalysis and Science, University of Minnesota, June 1954. Also reprinted in this volume.
18. Frank, P. G. "The Variety of Reasons for the Acceptance of Scientific Theories," *Scientific Monthly*, 79:139–45 (1954).
19. Frenkel-Brunswik, Else. "Psychoanalysis and the Unity of Science," *Proceedings of the American Academy of Arts and Sciences*, 80:271–350 (1954).

20. Freud, S. *An Outline of Psychoanalysis*. New York: Norton, 1949.
21. George, F. H. "Logical Constructs and Psychological Theory," *Psychological Review*, 60:1–6 (1953).
22. Ginsberg, A. "Hypothetical Constructs and Intervening Variables," *Psychological Review*, 61:119–31 (1954).
23. Halstead, W. C. "Biological Intelligence," *Journal of Personality*, 20:118–29 (1951).
24. Hebb, D. O. "The Role of Neurological Ideas in Psychology," *Journal of Personality*, 20:39–55 (1951).
25. Hempel, C. G. "A Logical Appraisal of Operationism," *Scientific Monthly*, 79: 215–23 (1954).
26. Hilgard, E. R., L. S. Kubie, and E. Pumpian-Mindlin. *Psychoanalysis as Science*. Stanford: Stanford Univ. Pr., 1952.
27. Hull, C. L. *Principles of Behavior*. New York: Appleton-Century, 1943.
28. Israel, H. E. "Two Difficulties in Operational Thinking," *Psychological Review*, 52:260–61 (1945).
29. Keys, A., J. Brozek, A. Henschel, O. Mickelson, and H. L. Taylor. *The Biology of Human Starvation*. Minneapolis: Univ. of Minn. Pr., 1950.
30. Klein, G., and D. Krech. "The Problem of Personality and Its Theory," *Journal of Personality*, 20:2–23 (1951).
31. Lindsay, R. B. "Operationalism in Physics Re-assessed," *Scientific Monthly*, 79: 221–23 (1954).
32. Lindzey, G. "Hypothetical Constructs, Conventional Constructs, and the Use of Physiological Data in Psychological Theory," *Psychiatry*, 16:27–34 (1953).
33. MacCorquodale, K., and P. E. Meehl. "Hypothetical Constructs and Intervening Variables," *Psychological Review*, 55:95–107 (1948).
34. Margenau, H. "On Interpretations and Misinterpretations of Operationalism," *Scientific Monthly*, 79:209–10 (1954).
35. Marx, M. H. "Intervening Variable or Hypothetical Construct," *Psychological Review*, 58:235–47 (1951).
36. Maze, J. R. "Do Intervening Variables Intervene?", *Psychological Review*, 61: 226–34 (1954).
37. Meehl, P. E. *Clinical Versus Statistical Prediction*. Minneapolis: Univ. of Minn. Pr., 1954.
38. Miller, N. E. "Comments on Theoretical Models," *Journal of Personality*, 20: 82–100 (1951).
39. Pratt, C. C. "Operationism in Psychology," *Psychological Review*, 52:262–69 (1945).
40. Rapaport, D. "The Conceptual Model of Psychoanalysis," *Journal of Personality*, 20:56–81 (1951).
41. Reid, J. R. "The Concept of Unconscious Anxiety and Its Use in Psychotherapy." Paper delivered at the Conference on Psychoanalysis and Science, University of Minnesota, June 1954.
42. Rudner, R. "Remarks on Value Judgments in Scientific Validation," *Scientific Monthly*, 79:151–53 (1954).
43. Scriven, M. "The Age of the Universe," *British Journal for the Philosophy of Science*, 5:181–90 (1954).
44. Scriven, M. "Notes on the Discussion Between Frenkel-Brunswik and Skinner," *Scientific Monthly*, 79:309–10 (1954).
45. Scriven, M. "The Principle of Inductive Simplicity," *Philosophical Studies*, February 1955.
46. Seeger, R. J. "Beyond Operationalism," *Scientific Monthly*, 79:226–27 (1954).
47. Seeman, W. "The Freudian Theory of Daydreams: An Operational Analysis," *Psychological Bulletin*, 48:369–82 (1951).

Albert Ellis

48. Skinner, B. F. "Critique of Psychoanalytic Concepts and Theories," *Scientific Monthly*, 79:300–5 (1954).
49. Skinner, B. F. *Science and Human Behavior*. New York: Macmillan, 1953.
50. Spiker, C. C., and B. R. McCandless. "The Concept of Intelligence and the Philosophy of Science," *Psychological Review*, 61:255–66 (1954).
51. Sullivan, H. S. *Conceptions of Modern Psychiatry*. Washington: William Alanson White Psychiatric Foundation, 1947.
52. Tolman, E. C. *Purposive Behavior in Animals and Men*. New York: Appleton-Century, 1932.
53. Tolman, E. C. "Discussion," *Journal of Personality*, 18:48–50 (1949).

Motives and the Unconscious

> There is, for instance, a lack of trained clarifiers, who
> might properly co-ordinate the various propositions with
> each other or try to eliminate the inequities of language in
> psychoanalysis.
>
> Ernst Kris (24)

I

I WANT to do two main things: first, to reformulate, to explain, and, as
far as is then necessary, to defend a thesis about the logical status of
the discovery of the unconscious mind; and second, to point one or
two morals which are implicit in this thesis. It is one salvaged from a
controversy which began in the journal, *Analysis*, in which it was inadequately and inaccurately formulated, and unfortunately entangled
with various curiously misguided side issues (33, 7, 12, 28, 29, 34, 18,
and 9). But for the present, without any refinements of qualification,
it is simply that the kernel of Freud's discovery was this: if you are
prepared so to extend such notions as *motive, intention, purpose, wish,*
and *desire* that it becomes proper to speak of motives and so forth which
are not known to, and the behavior resulting from which is not under
the immediate control of, the person who harbors them, then you can
interpret (and even guide) far more of human behavior in terms of
concepts of this sort than any sophisticated adult had previously realized. The morals all arise from the peculiarities of the notions which
are being thus extended; these peculiarities are such as to ensure that
their central and basic place in psychoanalysis must give this discipline
a logical status different from, though not of course for that reason

NOTE: A first version of this paper was originally delivered in June, 1954 at a conference on the philosophy of psychoanalysis, sponsored by the Center for Philosophy
of Science of the University of Minnesota. I wish to thank the Center for their
generosity in making it possible for me to attend that conference and for their
permission to publish this paper.

155

either inferior or superior to, that of sciences concerned with things other than human beings, and even from that of sciences concerned with less distinctively human aspects of human beings.

I shall draw most of my evidence from those of Freud's works which are classical and fundamental. It may be suggested that these are all out of date. But first, it is more than doubtful whether in the relevant respects this is true, because they are still regarded as essential in the training of analysts; and because we have been able to find plenty of parallel passages in recent works by orthodox Freudians. And, second, even if they did represent a closed incident in the history of thought, Freud's stature was sufficient to justify the study of his ideas in their own right.

II

1. a. The degree of extension required to allow us to speak of motives, etc., which are unrecognized or even honestly repudiated by their 'owners' varies from case to case. It is perhaps least of a stretch with motives and wishes: for, without benefit of Freud, people have come to admit underlying motives which they had not recognized (34, pp. 185–86); while notoriously some are as slow to realize as others are swift to mistake themselves to be in love. The stretch seems to be greatest with intentions; for surely before Freud we ought to have been at the very least extremely uneasy about talk of intentions which had never been consciously formulated, and which would not even be admitted by the intender if the question were raised and he gave an ingenuous answer after reflection. Of course Freud himself was at considerable pains to point out, particularly in *The Psychopathology of Everyday Life* but also elsewhere in his more apologetic works, that here he was continuing and systematizing extensions to which many sensitive observers of human nature, as well as plain men in their more percipient moments, were already considerably inclined.* But, in developing techniques for bringing to consciousness motives which had been buried much more deeply than any previously recognized, he achieved something which, if it was to be described in this way, demanded an extension much greater in degree than these, inasmuch as the time, trouble, and understanding of people needed to get a patient

* The historian of ideas might like to notice the following, for instance: "the real motives impelling him remain unknown to him . . . hence he imagines false or apparent motives" (10, p. 511, letter to Mehring).

to recognize deeply unconscious material is so immeasurably more than that needed with an ordinary unrecognized but unrepressed desire (12, pp. 12–13 [144–45] *).

b. A second extension required by Freud's conception of the unconscious is more disturbing and apparently less obvious, for it was not remarked in the earlier discussions. The first involved that bits of a person's behavior could be said to be motivated (etc., *mutatis mutandis*) in such and such a way, although he either did not know they were motivated, or did not know what the motive was, or was mistaken as to what it was.† The second allowed this, even of items which were beyond his voluntary control. Now, in general, before a piece of behavior can correctly be said to be motivated (etc.) in the ordinary (conscious) sense, the behaver must be unable honestly to deny his motive (etc.), and *the behavior must be voluntary*. These two things are quite different: but they go together so regularly that we have evolved a large vocabulary of terms whose criteria of applicability involve both; and the terms which Freud is stretching all belong, with greater or less degrees of definiteness, to this group. All the members of the group have their idiosyncrasies. Usage is not as precise as one could wish. Nor is membership completely determinate at the edges. But at least in the most typical cases the general rule applies: (consciously) motivated behavior is voluntary. On the other hand, where Freud wants to speak of unconscious motives, particularly for errors, dreams, and obsessive actions, typically this is precisely not the case. Again there may be some exceptions, and certainly the range and complexity both of the human situations and of the language in which responsibility may be ascribed or disclaimed is fabulously greater than is allowed for in this present rough-and-ready dichotomy between those performances which a person could and those which he could not have helped. Nevertheless, the general position is clear.

2. That Freud and his followers are concerned, in these extended senses of the words, with *motives, wishes, intentions, purposes, desires,* and the like is abundantly obvious from even a cursory examination of the elementary and classical texts of psychoanalysis. It is words such

* The first pages listed refer to the original article, the bracketed pages to the reprinted article. This procedure will be followed throughout this paper.

† By the way, the term "behavior" is quite properly used to cover dreams here; for Freud stipulated that "exactly what the dreamer tells is to count as the dream" (14, p. 68).

as these which are constantly employed (12, especially pp. 8–9 [144–45]): any suggestion that they are being systematically misused may be rebutted by considering typical illustrations. Take, for instance, that of the obsessional behavior which no longer seems mad when the story of the patient's traumatic wedding night has been uncovered, and we think of all her performances as repetitions and representations of her husband's ineffective efforts, ending in a bizarre attempt to convince the maid that he had not in fact proved impotent; and of these and the illness which they constitute as motivated by the desire "to shield him from malicious gossip, to justify her separation from him, and to make a comfortable existence apart from her possible for him" (14, p. 220, pp. 221–24). Further evidence of the same sort might be cited indefinitely. We labor the point only because there was some inclination in the *Analysis* discussion to overlook the fact that examination of psychoanalytic literature is a prerequisite for doing philosophy about this discipline, and even cavalierly to dismiss all such evidence.*

3. Freud himself showed inklings that the introduction of the conception of the unconscious involved changes in the notions of *motive*, etc., as when he wrote of "the psychoanalytical definition of the mind," defending the dispute about this innovation against the charge of being "an empty wrangle over words" (14, pp. 16–17). Or again he attacks as "thoroughly unpractical," in his metapsychological study *The Unconscious*, "the conventional identification of the mental with the conscious" (17, Vol. IV, p. 100: "conventional" here definitely refers to a "convention of nomenclature"; whereas "metapsychology" is not being used in what would be the philosopher's sense, *Ibid.*, p. 7). He is thoroughly aware of the main justifications for these conceptual innovations: that, obviously, the notion of the unconscious provides the theoretical basis for psychoanalytic therapy †; and that, not quite so

---

* "Many articles could be written showing that Freud was not overconscious of verbal and methodological niceties and I have no intention of replying in detail to Mr. Flew's onslaught" (2, p. 105 [51]). Well, perhaps; but it would be extraordinarily interesting to have even one article designed to prove the radical thesis that the regular and consistent use of terms like "motive" by Freud and his followers has been systematically misguided, though Peters himself is unlikely to produce such a paper, being inclined to dismiss out of hand "the vagaries of 'ordinary language'" (2, p. 145) in favor of a newfangled concept taking over the word "motive." Urmson has argued that this particular new conception has little if any present application (34, p. 189).

† E.g., "the assumption of the unconscious helps us to construct a highly successful practical method . . ." (17, Vol. IV, p. 99).

obviously, it makes possible a large expansion both of the frontiers of psychology * and of the understanding of phenomena within these in psychological terms.† In speaking of "psychological terms" Freud usually seems to have had in mind primarily and in the first instance just such terms as *motive, purpose, desire, wish, want, intention,*‡ and, standing rather apart, *meaning* **; but of course it must not be mistakenly supposed that this commits him to expelling from the empire of psychology any other phenomena previously subject to its jurisdiction.

4. All this brings out that the unconscious starts as almost a paradigm case of a logical construction, or 'intervening variable' (25); and shows out of what the construction is made, between what the variable intervenes.†† That is to say that talk of the unconscious starts as simply a particular shorthand way of talking about unconscious *motives*, etc. But it has not always been allowed to retain that status. Having formed a new noun from an adjective, Freud occasionally fell for the temptation to think that it was the word for a thing: not "*une façon de parler*" but "something actual and tangible" which can "produce something so real and palpable as an obsessive action" (14, pp. 234–35).‡‡ It has

* E.g., "We have widened the domain of mental phenomena to a very considerable extent and have won for psychology phenomena which were never before accredited to it" (14, p. 47).

† E.g., "All these conscious acts remain disconnected and unintelligible if we are determined to hold fast to the claim that every single mental act performed within us must be consciously experienced . . ." (17, Vol. IV, p. 99; cf. also Vol. V, p. 382).

‡ I cannot find a suitable single nutshell text: but consider the sort of evidence he brings to prove that, for example, "dreams are not a somatic, but a mental, phenomenon," which is explained as meaning that "they are a performance and an utterance on the part of the dreamer" (14, p. 82; cf. also 17 Vol. V, pp. 377 ff.). And compare, though this is no sort of evidence as to what Freud thought, MacDougall's remark: "Purposive action is the most fundamental category of psychology; just as the motion of a material particle . . . has long been the fundamental category of physical science."

** The importance of this notion has not previously been noted either here or in the *analysis* controversy. It would repay special examination: for what is involved seems to range through a spectrum of cases shading from, at one extreme, mere relevance, through the general possibility of motivational interpretation, to the other extreme where the claim is that the performances, dreams, are elements in a full-blown language.

†† "For to say that a chair is a logical construction out of appearances of a chair is to say that a chair is related to its appearances *not* as a thing is related to the images of it in a mirror, *not* as a member of parliament to his constituents, but as the average plumber to plumbers, as a family to its members, as energy to its manifestations, as electrons to the evidence for electrons" (36, p. 205).

‡‡ It was partly to dispose of this sort of thing that I introduced the notion of efficient causes into the original discussion, though mainly in the hope thus to bring

been regarded as the name of a region of the mind: the elusive scene of many colorful proceedings, a country in diplomatic and topographical relations with others, such as the preconscious which was early separated from it. Again it has been given another sense, that in which it is abbreviated to ucs, and is defined as referring to a system: I am unsure how much solid content is to be given to the word translated "system"; but if the new sense is to have any point it must have *some*, and insofar as it has, there is need for some justification for the employment of the term (17, Vol. IV, pp. 104–9). All of which is no doubt perfectly well so long as no one forgets how empty of literal meaning such metaphorical talk about a logical construction may become (9, pp. 193–94).

5. We have noticed two conceptual changes involved in the introduction of the idea of the unconscious (1.a. and 1.b.); and we do not say, for we are disinclined to believe, that there are not others. The second of these two calls for two remarks.

a. First, this conceptual change is obviously important for assessing the ethical implications of Freud's discoveries. In his paper on "Moral Responsibility for the Content of Dreams," Freud failed to note that no one can stop himself from dreaming (in the non-behaviorist sense of "dream" into which he had here inevitably lapsed). So he concludes too easily that "the problem of responsibility for the immoral content of dreams no longer exists for us as it formerly did for writers who knew nothing of latent dream-thoughts and the repressed part of our mental life . . . one must hold oneself responsible for the evil impulses of one's dreams" (17, Vol. V, p. 156).* This is all very well, providing that it is clearly understood to mean no more than that insofar as we accept the Freudian theory, we must accept that the unconscious desires (etc.) revealed in our dreams, like the recognized desires (etc., *mutatis mutandis*), of our waking hours, provide indications of the sort of people we are. But it will not do at all if it is to be taken as implying

out the peculiarity of the motivational concepts which are so fundamental in psychoanalysis (12, pp. 8–15 [143–48]). But Urmson showed that this move was misconceived (34, *passim*). By the way, responsibility for certain of the remarks and illustrations attributed by Gardiner to Toulmin belongs in fact to me (18, p. 13n).

* The historian of ideas may enjoy noticing Hume's remark: "Several moralists have recommended it as an excellent method of becoming acquainted with our own hearts, and knowing our progress in virtue, to recollect our dreams in a morning, and examine them with the same rigour that we would our most serious and most deliberate actions" (21, I.4, p. 219).

that a man can as fairly be praised or blamed, rewarded or punished, for the activities of his dreams as for the deliberate actions of his waking life, precisely because the former are not, whereas the latter are, under his control.*

b. Second, this conceptual change can throw light on Toulmin's extraordinary thesis that "if a fully-fledged analytic explanation is not part of a successful cure, we do not regard it as a 'correct' explanation: therapeutic failure is as fatal to an explanation in psychoanalysis as predictive failure is to an explanation in physics" (33, p. 29 [p. 138]). Against this Dingle argued simply that "the reasons why an abnormally large proportion of the phenomena with which psychoanalysis is concerned is associated with cures are clear enough" (7, p. 65); it is a purely contingent matter of humanitarianism and the practical needs to secure the cooperation of subjects and the payment of analysts. (This Freud said in 14, p. 217. He showed the same thing by his unfortunate willingness to analyze Moses posthumously and primitive peoples at a distance and, one might add, both on the basis of evidence which was quite inadequate and/or unreliable. For in these cases there could be no question of cure.) Further, Peters quoted devastatingly a passage from Freud to rebuke Toulmin's apparent ignorance of the toil, stress of soul, and conflict involved in the struggle for a cure; and provided a framework of relevant distinctions between diagnostic, therapeutic, and two different theoretical functions. The same passage shows that Freud distinguished between, on the one hand, the discovery by the analyst and, on the other, the acceptance by the patient of an explana-

* For the purposes of this paper we can generally afford to neglect the differences between *desires, wishes, motives, intentions* and *purposes,* which might for other purposes be crucial. But perhaps we should just notice here one obvious point which applies to *wishes* and *desires* but not to *purposes* and *intentions;* namely, that even conscious *wishes* and *desires,* and a fortiori unconscious ones, are not under immediate control in the sense that we can start or stop ourselves wanting at will; what we meant above by desires being "under the immediate control of the person who harbours them" is that he can control their expression in action. I cannot, at least in the short run, help devoutly *wishing* for some consummation; but I can, usually at any rate, help *doing* anything about it (9, p. 179). It is all very well to echo Christ in saying "Everyone that looketh on a woman to lust after her hath committed adultery with her already in his heart" (Matt. 5:28), so long as you do not permit this inspired paradox of assimilation to mislead you to overlook pedestrian but vital distinctions: between what a person can, and what he cannot, help; and between thinking of doing something, and actually doing it. Freud elsewhere quotes Plato as saying "that the good are those who content themselves with dreaming of what others, the wicked, actually do" (14, p. 122).

Antony Flew

tion; and that it is this latter which "is often enough to relieve mental illness" (33, p. 24 [133]). It is easy, if only one goes a little beyond the first volume of the *Collected Papers*, to find further examples to show what is actually the accepted usage of analysts.* This is the sort of evidence which is appropriate here, and it must be decisive (13 *passim*), unless Toulmin can show that analysts have been misled by some radical misconception. Furthermore, not only do analysts not in fact insist that association with a cure is a necessary condition of "a 'correct' explanation," but non- and rival analysts notoriously and rightly refuse to concede that it is even a sufficient one (see, e.g., 11, Chaps. 10–12 *passim*).

But still, why should Toulmin think that the identification of explanation with cure, combined with a recognition of the distinctive concern of psychoanalysis with motives and desires, shows that there "need be nothing mysterious . . . about the therapeutic success of psychoanalysis" (33, p. 27 [p. 138])? This might be explained partly by direct reference to our distinction above between two sorts of extension necessary to make it proper to speak of *unconscious* motives, etc.: the one to allow of motives, etc. (more deeply) concealed from their 'owners' (than any usually recognized before); the other to enable us to attribute motives to behavior beyond our control. For if there were no distinction to be made between the recognition of one's motive for, and the ability to control, behavior, then indeed there would be no problem of why hysterical and obsessional symptoms (sometimes) vanish when their unconscious motives are recognized. Another part of the explanation might be this. Supposing it were to have been the case that "revealing to the mentally ill the contents of their unconscious minds" was simply a matter of offering them "the . . . psychoanalytic explanation . . . as presented by an analyst at the end of a series of consultations" (33, p. 24, p. 27 [133, 138]); and supposing also that association with a cure were part of what analysts *meant* by "a 'correct' ex-

---

* E.g.: "Even if psychoanalysis showed itself as unsuccessful with all other forms of nervous and mental disease as with delusions, it would still remain justified as an irreplaceable instrument of scientific research" (14, p. 217, and cf. pp. 252–53, 366–67, 373–74 and the case already quoted, at p. 221. Also 17, Vol. V, p. 124–25, in which the most categorical claims are made of an advance in understanding combined with therapeutic impotence.). Or, from a contemporary: "More often than not insight satisfies the therapist's rather than the patient's emotional needs" (8, p. 11). Surely, by the way, Peters should not, in view of his views on Freud's carelessness in methodology (see preceding note, p. 158) have been satisfied with only one citation.

planation": then indeed it might have *appeared* that the correlation
between presentations and recoveries required no explanation. But
Toulmin, accepting the two protases, is still in fact wrong to maintain the apodosis: for no manoeuvres with the meaning of the word
"explanation" could really explain the brute fact of this correlation;
they could at most force us to reword our questions. In fact both protases are false and there thus remains not merely one but a whole
range of empirical problems which can be grouped under the head
"Why do psychoanalytic cures work at all?" (33, pp. 23–24 [133]). And
these are not to be brushed away, along with two paragraphs of other
assorted questions, by any a priori broom, however bright and new.

I have here to admit, though this may well be merely a confession of
ignorance or ineptitude or both, that I have not found either Freud's
own writings or later analytic literature at all illuminating about the
alleged one/one correlation between recognition of the motivation of,
and the attaining of control over, symptoms (14, pp. 236–37). And
I say "the attaining of control over," not "the disappearance of," deliberately; because it is logically possible that a cured patient might
choose to indulge voluntarily in the performances which formerly had
been compulsive.* Often in the literature it seems that no distinction
is being made between the problems of why and under what conditions
people come to recognize unconscious desires (etc.) and the logically
independent problems of why and under what conditions behavior becomes or ceases to be voluntary;† and the theories then offered to deal
with the two sets as if they were one in any case leave a great deal to
be desired. When occasionally, the alleged one/one correlation seems
to be recognized as such, it is apparently regarded as a fundamental
brute fact in terms of which other facts are to be explained; ‡ and
though it may be that we shall have so to accept some very general

* Consider here the theme of Arthur Koestler's *Arrival and Departure*; and consider also some actual cases in which analysis is discontinued because analyst or patient
comes to believe that in the circumstances of the patient's life the illness is for him
a lesser evil (14, pp. 319–20; 17, Vol. II, pp. 294–95).

† ". . . the transformation of this unconscious material in the mind of the patient
into conscious material must have the result . . . of lifting the compulsion . . .
For conscious will-power governs only the conscious mental processes, and every
mental compulsion is rooted in the unconscious" (17, Vol. I, p. 261, italics mine).
Even if it governed not *only* but *all*, our problem would remain; for why should
there be this correlation?

‡ ". . . you must recognize it as a fundamentally new fact, by means of which
much else becomes explicable" (14, p. 236).

fact of the form 'people just are able to control the movements of such and such parts of themselves under such and such conditions,' this present alleged one/one correlation is surely too particular to be easily accepted as thus ultimate. Maybe it is premature to raise such questions, which certainly do not concern analysis only; but if I am right in thinking that little light has so far been thrown on the problem by analytic thinking, then at least this fact should be recognized before the problem is filed for the future.

III

1. Important implications of our main thesis emerge as soon as we recognize the peculiarity of those notions whose range Freud was systematically extending. For these are all distinctively human. They are thus radically different from the notions of rat-oriented experimental psychology. They are all, at least most typically, purposive—not in any weak 'as if' sense which would assimilate the purposive to the merely teleological, which involves no more than, as a matter of brute fact, either moving toward an end or fulfilling a function, but in the primary strong one, which involves either having an aim in mind or at least the present possibility of bringing it to mind (3, *passim*). They all, at least most typically, imply on the behavioral side a capacity to operate with words (18, pp. 123–24). (The qualification "at least most typically" must never be forgotten; for recognized usage of such mental terms is not quite as clear-cut as it appears in the precisified representations of philosophers.) They are precisely the notions in terms of which rational agents give accounts of the voluntary and deliberate conduct of themselves and of other rational agents. And they cannot be logically "reduced" to physicalistic terms.*

a. It is wrong to present Freud's "doctrine of 'psychic determinism' '" as "simply that *mental phenomena are causally determined*" (26, p. 229, italics his); † and it is wrong to cite, as if it were either equivalent to—

* "We can neither assert nor deny discontinuity between the human and subhuman fields so long as we know so little about either. If, nevertheless, the author of a book of this sort is expected to hazard a guess publicly, I may say that the only differences I expect to see revealed between the behavior of a rat and a man (aside from enormous differences of complexity) lie in the field of verbal behaviour" (32, p. 442). No doubt experiments on rats are as essential as they are practically convenient; but to write "only" here is like excusing the omission of the Prince of Denmark on the grounds that he is only one character in *Hamlet*.

† And wrong again to attribute this mistaken interpretation to Horney (see 19, p. 18).

or at least sufficient to establish that—"all behaviour is motivated," the claim that "everyday activities are all causally determined" (37, p. 1). These textbooks fail to do justice to Freud's originality: long before his time it was a commonplace in the most tough-minded medical scientific circles that all human behavior, and hence presumably parapraxes, dreams, and obsessive actions, must be explicable in terms of physiological causes; what was new was to suggest that these were "explainable through purposive ideas" (16, p. 148)—in terms, that is, of ideas such as *motive, desire, purpose, intention,* and so forth, all suitably extended. Notice, by way of contrast to such textbook misrepresentations, that Sears undertook his survey at the instigation of the "Subcommittee on Motivation" (31, p. vii); and he writes, "Boiled down to an acceptable terminology the wish-fulfillment hypothesis becomes a statement that dreams are motivated" (*Ibid.,* p. 129; see 33, p. 28 [138]).

b. These purposive and motivational concepts which are central and fundamental in psychoanalysis are all distinctively human. Any application of any of them below the human level is at best atypical and at worst a logical solecism. It is not a matter of special snobbery, analogous to the social snobbery which bids us substitute "perspires," or even "feels uncomfortably hot," for "sweats" when speaking of a lady. The solid basis of justification for this prerogative is that the human animal is the only one which has what it takes; and what it takes is the developed capacity to use words and symbols. Any psychologists who may "have the impression that the concept of motivation has some esoteric monopoly on explanation in psychology" (23, p. 26) are surely wrong (see III, 2 below). Yet even from the most radically behavioristic point of view there is no mystery that and why we have a monopoly on motivation of behavior. This is a straightforward corollary of our effective corner in language.

These claims to human uniqueness might be challenged by students of animal behavior. Now of course there are analogies between most aspects even of the verbal and verbally-dependent behavior of human beings and some aspects of the behavior of some other animals; between the burglar intending to break into the farmhouse and the fox intending to raid the henhouse; between the pilot of the reconnaissance aircraft reporting back orally and the bee "reporting back in the sign language of the dance." And presumably all the differences between men and the other animals are differences of degree: in the sense that it would be possible to construct spectra of actual or possible cases stretching between the distinctively human and the indisputably subhuman with no sharp breaks at which the dividing line must naturally and inevitably be drawn. But the enormous development of language in man and the vast behavioral ramifications which it makes possible nevertheless justify us, when they are considered together, in speaking as we have done of "man's unique capacity" and of "distinctively human prerogatives." For two reasons. First, because it is, in any case, quite wrong to dismiss all differences of degree as *mere* differences of degree; the difference between sanity and insanity is certainly, in the sense defined above, a difference of degree, and yet for Neville Clively Heath on trial for murder it was, in the most literal sense, a matter of life and death. Secondly, because, in this particular case, we are concerned not with any single difference of degree, however great, but with a massive accumulation. It is this accumulation of substantial differences of degree, rather than the possession of one component of a unique sort, which in general provides sufficient justification for an insistence on the uniqueness of man; and it is a justification which does not conflict with evolutionary theory by postulating any special creations.* Similarly, it is an accumulation of substantial differences of degree, rather than the possession of some single capacity or range of capacities altogether without parallel, which in particular entitles us to claim that man has "an effective corner in language" and "a monopoly on motivation of behaviour."

We are not committed by these claims to a pedantic refusal ever to tolerate the application of any purposive or motivational term to animals below the human level. No doubt it is all right to say of a dog (though not perhaps of an earthworm) that it *wants* to get in or to get out, to eat or to drink, to sleep or to chase rabbits, even though it cannot formulate these wants or express them to others in words. But we surely ought to feel very uneasy indeed at any attribution to a dog (and a fortiori to an earthworm) of purposes or *intentions*,

---

* Contrast: (a) Descartes (6, pp. 44–47) on the two supposedly knock-down tests for humanity and on the allegedly unique capacities of the soul which "must be expressly created"; and (b) the Encyclical *Humani Generis* (Catholic Truth Society, 1950, p. 30) also (5, § 3027) "Thus the Teaching of the Church leaves the doctrine of evolution an open question, as long as it confines its speculations to the development, from other living matter already in existence, of the human body. (That souls are immediately created by God is a view which the Catholic faith imposes on us)."

for here the capacity to formulate is absolutely crucial (see 18, p. 115).*
Nevertheless, the standard employments of all these terms are so
elaborately and multiply connected with the use of a developed language, and with the complex behavioral possibilities which this opens
up,† that we are entitled to draw sharp lines in thought here between
the human and the nonhuman. "Without symbols we could not make-
believe, dissimulate, or lie; we could not form plans for our future; nor
hold those schemata in mind that make possible consistency in moral
conduct" (1, p. 167). When Russell wrote "A desire is 'conscious' when
we have told ourselves that we have it . . . it only differs from an
'unconscious' desire by the presence of appropriate words, which is by
no means a fundamental difference" (30, p. 31), he was ignoring not
only that there was at least one other important difference (see II. 1.b.
above) but also that all these elaborate and manifold connections are
of fundamental importance for most human interests and purposes.

c. The fact that psychoanalysis puts these purposive concepts in a
central and fundamental position has much wider implications than
a mere stressing of the importance for human psychology of verbal as
opposed to nonverbal behavior. The concepts which psychoanalytic
theory seeks to extend are precisely those in terms of which rational
agents give account of their own conduct and of that of other rational
agents. And that they do this is not a contingent but a necessary fact:
for a person is a rational agent, as opposed, not to an irrational agent
but to a nonrational creature, only and precisely insofar as he (logically)
can give account of his motives for (reasons for) acting thus and thus,

* Compare the sharp criticism which has been made of the use of the expression
"trial and error" in connection with animal learning; which does indeed become seriously misleading if we ever forget that animals which cannot use words lack the
necessary qualifications for this method of investigation (4, pp. 122–26).

† The variety and the importance of these it is almost impossible to exaggerate.
Those who defined "man" as "the rational animal" and those who named our species
homo sapiens were not always and only, as Russell and many lesser men have sar-
castically suggested, flattering the whole human race with attributes of reasonableness
and good sense which are attained only by some men some of the time. Usually and
primarily, though perhaps in an obscure and old-fashioned way, they were picking
out and underlining this uniquely human characteristic, by which alone men are able
to be any sort, good or bad, of arguers, makers of statements, planners, moral agents,
or a thousand other distinctively human things. Consider again, for example, Descartes' "two most certain tests" whereby "if there were machines bearing the image
of our bodies, and capable of imitating our actions as far as that is morally possible"
these might be distinguished from men; and the whole context in which they were
given.

and state the purposes, plans, and intentions which he had in mind; and it is only rational agents in this sense, as opposed to nonrational objects like animals and sticks and stones, which are (logically) capable of being irrational—by formulating or adopting foolish, inconsistent, and self-frustrating plans and attitudes. The object of psychoanalysis as a therapy is so to educate the patient that he becomes able *both* to recognize formerly unconscious desires *and* to inhibit their expression in action if he so chooses. "To strengthen the ego, to make it more in-dependent of the superego, to widen its field of vision and so to extend its organization that it can take over new portions of the id. *Where id was, there shall ego be*" (15, p. 106, italics mine). To do this is to extend the (factually) possible area of rationality (and therefore of irrationality too), to replace compulsive and uncontrollable behavior by voluntary and deliberate conduct (20, *passim*). It is these features of the theory and the therapy which make psychoanalysis inherently a peculiarly rational enterprise, an educative force of liberation and enlightenment.* This is so despite the fact that the standards of verifi-cation and of theory construction acceptable to the psychoanalytic pro-fession, compared with those achieved in many other disciplines which are not in this peculiar way rational, leave much to be desired. (See 9, *passim*; 11, Chaps. 10–12; 31, *passim*.) And it would remain true of the logical nature of the whole enterprise even if it turned out that in fact the theory is wholly unsound and the therapy quite ineffective.

d. It would surely be a mistake to try to 'reduce' these notions, at least in their standard and typical applications, to behavioristic terms.† First, because in these cases, as so often, meaning cannot be made out

---

* See, as texts to illustrate these points: (a) ". . . the physician makes it possible for him to do this by suggestions which are in the *nature of an education*. It has been truly said therefore, that psychoanalytic treatment is a kind of re-education" (14, p. 377); (b) "The making conscious of repressed sexual desires in analysis makes it possible . . . to obtain a mastery over them which previous repression had been unable to achieve" (17, Vol. V, p. 128); and (c) "But above all, all the energies which are today consumed in the production of neurotic symptoms to serve the purposes of a world of phantasy out of touch with reality, will . . . help to strengthen the outcry for those changes in our civilization from which alone we can hope for better things for our descendants" (17, Vol. II, p. 295).

And here is another, not from Freud but from a disciple, "The aim of psycho-analytical method is to achieve permanent eradication of the very root of the illness, and at the same time to put its psychic energies at the disposal of the ego or reason" (2, p. 229).

† Previously I argued that motive-propositions could not be reduced to cause-propositions, thus confounding a defensible anti-physicalist thesis about the peculiarity

to be equivalent to verification, verdict to evidence (35, pp. 181 ff.), what is being said to a conjunction of good reasons for saying it. Second, because behavioristic evidence is not all we have; for in the case of ourselves we have our own 'experiences'; while in the case of other people we can get some idea of their 'experiences' from knowing what ours are or would be like in analogous circumstances (18, especially Chap. 2, Sect. 4, and Chap. 4). This most necessary technique of putting ourselves in other people's places has the most serious dangers and limitations, of which the literature of psychoanalysis provides most abundant illustration (27, passim). Third, because these notions are all, most typically, applied to creatures endowed with a capacity for, and surely involve some sort of reference to, self-consciousness (in that peculiar and elusive sense not equivalent to that of "embarrassed" or "shy"). Here consider Descartes' second test of humanity "from which it could be discovered that they did not act from knowledge, but solely from the disposition of their organs" (6, p. 45). Fourth, for a reason less hackneyed than the first three but which alone would be decisive. Every verbal performance has two aspects, one of which can and one of which cannot be comprehended in purely physicalist terms. Suppose a man emits noises from his mouth within the range of variety which could be rendered in the notation of the English language as "I wanted to do something to spite her." This event has a purely physical aspect, about which we may ask such questions as "What were the physiological and environmental preconditions of the emission of these sounds?" But it also has another aspect, about which we may ask such radically different questions as "Does this utterance make sense?" "Is it true?" or "Does it follow from, is it even compatible with, what has been said before?" (Incidentally, both sorts of question are different from a third sort, such as "What possible reason or motive can he have had for making such a confession?" And, pace Socrates [see Phaedo 98B7-99D3], answers to questions of this third sort are not necessarily rival answers to questions of the first, physiological, sort. A great deal of misguided popular debunking, which often involves throwing out babies with precious little accompanying bath water, depends on confounding these

of the former with some forced and misguided ideas about the latter (12, pp. 13–14). But it is strange that Cohen, concluding "it is an error to assimilate purposive explanations to 'ordinary causal' ones," should find it necessary to add a footnote dissociating himself from this, surely equivalent, thesis (3, p. 267).

three sorts of question.) Any account of motives and purposes in exclusively physicalist terms must neglect this vital aspect of the linguistic capacities and performances which are essential to them.

2. The scope of psychoanalysis could perhaps be defined—with no more than the amount of distortion customary in such definitions—as encompassing *motives, purposes, desires, wishes,* and *intentions*.

a. This sets the elucidation of these notions as the fundamental task in the philosophy of psychoanalysis. It involves studying the logic of both the pre-Freudian and the extended uses of the terms concerned, and comparing those of each pair, just as a fundamental, but excessively elementary, task of the philosophy of physics is to elucidate the ordinary and the physical use of terms such as "work"; and to compare the two.

The job to be done here is not at all elementary, as can be seen by considering what heavy weather was made in the *Analysis* discussion even over the pre-Freudian uses. Toulmin started with a small schema of sentence types but straightway committed two howlers in explaining them. First, "if I call out 'I want you to come here' it makes no sense for you to ask 'How do you know?' or 'Are you sure?' . . ." But it makes perfectly good sense to ask "Are you sure?" Second, "Over S 2 [the example given is 'He is in pain'] it makes sense to talk of 'evidence' and of 'mistakes'; but what the person himself says constitutes conclusive evidence" (33, pp. 25, 26). But it does not; for he may be lying.

Furthermore, it is a job which is bound to have some repercussions on analytic theory. For instance, what distinction in the unconscious field could really parallel the distinction, at the conscious level, between a desire adopted as a motive and a desire felt but not allowed to determine any action?

b. The same definition suggests that we might find illuminating comparisons by looking toward other disciplines concerned with men and their motives, particularly perhaps to history, as I have tried to suggest by frequent references to Gardiner's study, *The Nature of Historical Explanation*. Just one example. To understand a piece of history, a battle or some negotiations, it is essential to understand what the participants *believed* the situation to be; for it is in accordance with these *beliefs* that they shaped their plans, adopted attitudes, and, at a less deliberate level, became mollified or resentful. But the historian needs also to master what the situation actually was—possibly a very different matter indeed. Perhaps this is an analogy which, developed, might be of some help in elucidating the desperately involved problem of the relations between what the patient says, and presumably, usually, believes, about past influences and experiences (or, for that matter, about present ones outside the analytic hour) and what he actually did experience and what in fact did influence him. 'Psychical reality' is all very well when we want to understand the present, conscious and unconscious, motivation of behavior. But a knowledge of this can be at best suggestive when what we want is to find what sorts, if any, of adult traits are causally related with what sorts of toilet training.

c. To say that psychoanalysis deals with these things, that these are its fundamental notions, that it tries in the first instance to provide explanations in terms of them, and that they are not logically reducible to physiological or any other sort of physicalist terms, is not to deny either the possibility or the need to push beyond explanations in terms of conscious and unconscious motives and so forth. Once we reach the limit of explanation of this sort, in these terms, we can and should go on to ask why, in another sense of "why," people have the basic desires which they do have and why these have in different people different relative strengths. The answer will presumably have to be physiological, telling us what are the physiological preconditions and mechanics of desire and its satisfaction, and what are the genetic determinants of physiological difference; and at this level and after, nothing more will be said about purposes, except by theologians. Freud himself, having been reared in the tough-minded epiphenomenalism of a medical school, always expected that "all our provisional ideas in psychology will some day be based on an organic substructure" (17, Vol. IV, p. 36). Yet his own effort to push beyond particular desires and to try to explain their origin and relative strengths was not physiological but introduced a 'hypothetical construct,' the protean libido (17, Vol. I, Chap. V.) with its baffling combination of electrical (17, Vol. IV, p. 75) and hydraulic (25, pp. 105–6) characteristics with those of a horde—a construct which will probably "have to remain only a metaphor" because of the apparent impossibility of connecting it with anything physiological (25, p. 106).

IV

To repeat, my main thesis has been that the kernel of Freud's discovery was this: If you are prepared so to extend such notions as motive, intention, purpose, wish, and desire that it becomes proper to speak of motives and so forth which are not known to, and the behavior resulting from which is not under the immediate control of, the person who harbors them, then you can interpret (and even guide) far more of human behavior in terms of concepts of this sort than any sophisticated adult had previously realized. I drew attention especially to the second sort of change involved in this conceptual innovation, which has perhaps been understressed. Among the many implications which I suggested were carried by this thesis were these: that the fundamental concepts of psychoanalysis are distinctively human because they can only be applied to creatures possessed of our unique capacity to employ a developed language; that these are precisely the notions which rational agents employ to give account of their own conduct and that of other rational agents qua rational agents; that their place in psychoanalysis necessarily makes this a peculiarly rational enterprise, though in a sense which makes this assertion quite compatible with a claim that the methods of analysts are unscientific and their conclusions ill-founded; that it would be a mistake to attempt a logical reduction of these notions to physicalistic terms; that the elucidation of these notions in their pre-Freudian and Freudian senses and a study of their differences and interrelations constitute a prime task of the philosophy of psychoanalysis; that comparisons between psychoanalysis and other disciplines dealing with men and their motives—history for example—might help to illuminate some of the dark places of the former; and that nothing we have urged, not even our anti-reductionist thesis, commits us to saying that these notions must be taken as explanatory ultimates. Finally, it must be emphasized that I have not been concerned here either with the truth of analytic theories or with the quality of the evidence deployed in their support.

REFERENCES

1. Allport, G. W. "Emphasis on Molar Problems," in M. H. Marx (ed.), *Psychological Theory*, pp. 156–70. New York: Macmillan, 1951.
2. Berg, Charles. *War in the Mind*. London: Macauley, 1941.
3. Cohen, L. J. "Teleological Explanation," *Proceedings of the Aristotelian Society*, 51:255–92 (1950).
4. Collingwood, R. G. *Essay on Metaphysics*. London: Oxford Univ. Pr., 1940.
5. Denzinger, H. *Enchiridion Symbolorum*. Freiberg: Herden, 1953.
6. Descartes, R. *Discourse on Method*. London: Everyman, 1912.
7. Dingle, H. "The Logical Status of Psychoanalysis," *Analysis*, 9:63–66 (1949).

8. Ehrenwald, Jan. "Cause, Purpose and Meaning in Psychosomatic Medicine," *Journal of Clinical Psychopathology*, 11:164–73 (1950).
9. Ellis, Albert. "An Introduction to the Principles of Scientific Psychoanalysis," *Genetic Psychology Monographs*, 41:147–212 (1950).
10. Engels, Friedrich. *Marx-Engels Correspondence*. London: Martin Lawrence, 1934.
11. Eysenck, J. J. *Uses and Abuses of Psychology*. London: Pelican, 1954.
12. Flew, Antony. "Psychoanalytic Explanation," *Analysis*, 10:8–15 (1950). Revised version reprinted in M. Macdonald (ed.), *Philosophy and Analysis*. Oxford: Blackwell, 1954.
13. Flew, Antony. "Philosophy and Language," *Philosophical Quarterly*, 5:21–36 (1955).
14. Freud, Sigmund. *Introductory Lectures on Psychoanalysis*. London: Allen & Unwin, 1929 (2nd edition).
15. Freud, Sigmund. *New Introductory Lectures*. London: Hogarth, 1933.
16. Freud, Sigmund. *Psychopathology of Everyday Life*. London: Pelican, 1938.
17. Freud, Sigmund. *Collected Papers*. London: Hogarth, Vols. I–IV, 1924–25, Vol. V, 1950.
18. Gardiner, P. L. *The Nature of Historical Explanation*. London: Oxford Univ. Pr., 1952.
19. Horney, Karen. *New Ways in Psychoanalysis*. London: Kegan Paul, 1939.
20. Hospers, John. "Psychoanalysis and Ethics," in W. Sellars and J. Hospers (eds.), *Readings in Ethical Theory*, p. 560 ff. New York: Appleton-Century-Crofts, 1952.
21. Hume, David. *A Treatise of Human Nature*. London: Oxford Univ. Pr., 1896.
22. Huxley, Julian. *The Process of Evolution*. London: Chatto & Windus, 1953.
23. Koch, Sigmund. "The Logical Character of the Motivation Concept," *Psychological Review*, 48:15–37 (1941).
24. Kris, Ernst. "Psychoanalytic Propositions," in M. H. Marx (ed.), *Psychological Theory*, pp. 332–51 (quotation, p. 333). New York: Macmillan Company, 1951.
25. MacCorquodale, Kenneth, and P. E. Meehl. "On a Distinction Between Hypothetical Constructs and Intervening Variables," *Psychological Review*, 55:95–107 (1948).
26. McKellar, T. P. *A Textbook of Human Psychology*. London: Cohen & West, 1952.
27. Orlansky, Harold. "Infant Care and Personality," *Psychological Bulletin*, 46:1–48 (1949).
28. Peters, R. S. "Cause, Cure and Motive," *Analysis*, 10:103–9 (1950). Revised version reprinted in M. Macdonald (ed.), *Philosophy and Analysis*. Oxford: Blackwell, 1954.
29. Peters, R. S. "Motives and Causes," in *Proceedings of the Aristotelian Society*, Supplement, 26:139–62 (1952).
30. Russell, B. A. W. *The Analysis of Mind*. London: Allen & Unwin, 1921.
31. Sears, R. R. *Survey of Objective Studies of Psychoanalytic Concepts* (Social Science Research Council Bulletin, No. 51), 1943.
32. Skinner, B. F. *The Behavior of Organisms*. New York: Appleton-Century-Crofts, 1938.
33. Toulmin, S. E. "The Logical Status of Psychoanalysis," *Analysis*, 9:23–29 (1949). Revised version reprinted in M. Macdonald (ed.), *Philosophy and Analysis*. Oxford: Blackwell, 1954.
34. Urmson, J. O. "Motives and Causes," in *Proceedings of the Aristotelian Society*, Supplement, 26:179–94 (1952).
35. Warnock, G. J. *Berkeley*. London: Pelican, 1953.
36. Wisdom, John. *Philosophy and Psychoanalysis*. Oxford: Blackwell, 1953.
37. Young, P. T. *The Motivation of Behaviour*. New York: Wiley, 1936.

Construct Validity in Psychological Tests

VALIDATION of psychological tests has not yet been adequately conceptualized, as the APA Committee on Psychological Tests learned when it undertook (1950–54) to specify what qualities should be investigated before a test is published. In order to make coherent recommendations the Committee found it necessary to distinguish four types of validity, established by different types of research and requiring different interpretation. The chief innovation in the Committee's report was the term *construct validity*.* This idea was first formulated by a subcommittee (Meehl and R. C. Challman) studying how proposed recommendations would apply to projective techniques, and later modified and clarified by the entire Committee (Bordin, Challman, Conrad, Humphreys, Super, and the present writers). The statements agreed upon by the Committee (and by committees of two other associations) were published in the *Technical Recommendations* (59). The present interpretation of construct validity is not "official" and deals with some areas in which the Committee would probably not be unanimous. The present writers are solely responsible for this attempt to explain the concept and elaborate its implications.

Identification of construct validity was not an isolated development. Writers on validity during the preceding decade had shown a great deal of dissatisfaction with conventional notions of validity, and introduced new terms and ideas, but the resulting aggregation of types of

---

* Referred to in a preliminary report (58) as *congruent validity*.

NOTE: The second author worked on this problem in connection with his appointment to the Minnesota Center for Philosophy of Science. We are indebted to the other members of the Center (Herbert Feigl, Michael Scriven, Wilfrid Sellars), and to D. L. Thistlethwaite of the University of Illinois, for their major contributions to our thinking and their suggestions for improving this paper. The paper first appeared in *Psychological Bulletin*, July 1955, and is reprinted here, with minor alterations, by permission of the editor and of the authors.

validity seems only to have stirred the muddy waters. Portions of the distinctions we shall discuss are implicit in Jenkins' paper, "Validity for What?" (33), Gulliksen's "Intrinsic Validity" (27), Goodenough's distinction between tests as "signs" and "samples" (22), Cronbach's separation of "logical" and "empirical" validity (11), Guilford's "factorial validity" (25), and Mosier's papers on "face validity" and "validity generalization" (49, 50). Helen Peak (52) comes close to an explicit statement of construct validity as we shall present it.

Four Types of Validation

The categories into which the *Recommendations* divide validity studies are: predictive validity, concurrent validity, content validity, and construct validity. The first two of these may be considered together as *criterion-oriented* validation procedures.

The pattern of a criterion-oriented study is familiar. The investigator is primarily interested in some criterion which he wishes to predict. He administers the test, obtains an independent criterion measure on the same subjects, and computes a correlation. If the criterion is obtained some time after the test is given, he is studying *predictive validity*. If the test score and criterion score are determined at essentially the same time, he is studying *concurrent validity*. Concurrent validity is studied when one test is proposed as a substitute for another (for example, when a multiple-choice form of spelling test is substituted for taking dictation), or a test is shown to correlate with some contemporary criterion (e.g., psychiatric diagnosis).

Content validity is established by showing that the test items are a sample of a universe in which the investigator is interested. Content validity is ordinarily to be established deductively, by defining a universe of items and sampling systematically within this universe to establish the test.

Construct validation is involved whenever a test is to be interpreted as a measure of some attribute or quality which is not "operationally defined." The problem faced by the investigator is, "What constructs account for variance in test performance?" Construct validity calls for no new scientific approach. Much current research on tests of personality (9) is construct validation, usually without the benefit of a clear formulation of this process.

Construct validity is not to be identified solely by particular investigative procedures, but by the orientation of the investigator. Criterion-oriented validity, as Bechtoldt emphasizes (3, p. 1245), "involves the acceptance of a set of operations as an adequate definition of whatever is to be measured." When an investigator believes that no criterion available to him is fully valid, he perforce becomes interested in construct validity because this is the only way to avoid the "infinite frustration" of relating every criterion to some more ultimate standard (21). In content validation, *acceptance* of the universe of content as defining the variable to be measured is essential. Construct validity must be investigated whenever no criterion or universe of content is accepted as entirely adequate to define the quality to be measured. Determining what psychological constructs account for test performance is desirable for almost any test. Thus, although the MMPI was originally established on the basis of empirical discrimination between patient groups and so-called normals (concurrent validity), continuing research has tried to provide a basis for describing the personality associated with each score pattern. Such interpretations permit the clinician to predict performance with respect to criteria which have not yet been employed in empirical validation studies (cf. 46, pp. 49–50, 110–11).

We can distinguish among the four types of validity by noting that each involves a different emphasis on the criterion. In predictive or concurrent validity, the criterion behavior is of concern to the tester, and he may have no concern whatsoever with the type of behavior exhibited in the test. (An employer does not care if a worker can manipulate blocks, but the score on the block test may predict something he cares about.) Content validity is studied when the tester is concerned with the type of behavior involved in the test performance. Indeed, if the test is a work sample, the behavior represented in the test may be an end in itself. Construct validity is ordinarily studied when the tester has no definite criterion measure of the quality with which he is concerned, and must use indirect measures. Here the trait or quality underlying the test is of central importance, rather than either the test behavior or the scores on the criteria (59, p. 14).

Construct validation is important at times for every sort of psychological test: aptitude, achievement, interests, and so on. Thurstone's statement is interesting in this connection:

In the field of intelligence tests, it used to be common to define validity as the correlation between a test score and some outside criterion. We have reached a stage of sophistication where the test-criterion correlation is too coarse. It is obsolete. If we attempted to ascertain the validity of a test for the second space-factor, for example, we would have to get judges [to] make reliable judgments about people as to this factor. Ordinarily their [the available judges'] ratings would be of no value as a criterion. Consequently, validity studies in the cognitive functions now depend on criteria of internal consistency . . . (60, p. 3).

Construct validity would be involved in answering such questions as: To what extent is this test of intelligence culture-free? Does this test of "interpretation of data" measure reading ability, quantitative reasoning, or response sets? How does a person with A in Strong Accountant, and B in Strong CPA, differ from a person who has these scores reversed?

Example of construct validation procedure. Suppose measure X correlates .50 with Y, the amount of palmar sweating induced when we tell a student that he has failed a Psychology I exam. Predictive validity of X for Y is adequately described by the coefficient, and a statement of the experimental and sampling conditions. If someone were to ask, "Isn't there perhaps another way to interpret this correlation?" or "What other kinds of evidence can you bring to support your interpretation?" we would hardly understand what he was asking because no interpretation has been made. These questions become relevant when the correlation is advanced as evidence that "test X measures anxiety proneness." Alternative interpretations are possible; e.g., perhaps the test measures "academic aspiration," in which case we will expect different results if we induce palmar sweating by economic threat. It is then reasonable to inquire about other *kinds* of evidence.

Add these facts from further studies: Test X correlates .45 with fraternity brothers' ratings on "tenseness." Test X correlates .55 with amount of intellectual inefficiency induced by painful electric shock, and .68 with the Taylor Anxiety Scale. Mean X score decreases among four diagnosed groups in this order: anxiety state, reactive depression, "normal," and psychopathic personality. And palmar sweat under threat of failure in Psychology I correlates .60 with threat of failure in mathematics. Negative results eliminate competing explanations of the X score; thus, findings of negligible correlations between X and social class, vocational aim, and value-orientation make it fairly safe to reject the suggestion that X measures "academic aspiration." We can have substantial confidence that X does measure anxiety proneness if the current theory of anxiety can embrace the variates which yield positive correlations, and does not predict correlations where we found none.

Kinds of Constructs

At this point we should indicate summarily what we mean by a construct, recognizing that much of the remainder of the paper deals with this question. A construct is some postulated attribute of people, assumed to be reflected in test performance. In test validation the attribute about which we make statements in interpreting a test is a construct. We expect a person at any time to possess or not possess a qualitative attribute (amnesia) or structure, or to possess some degree of a quantitative attribute (cheerfulness). A construct has certain associated meanings carried in statements of this general character: Persons who possess this attribute will, in situation X, act in manner Y (with a stated probability). The logic of construct validation is invoked whether the construct is highly systematized or loose, used in ramified theory or a few simple propositions, used in absolute propositions or probability statements. We seek to specify how one is to defend a proposed interpretation of a test; *we are not recommending any one type of interpretation.*

The constructs in which tests are to be interpreted are certainly not likely to be physiological. Most often they will be traits such as "latent hostility" or "variable in mood," or descriptions in terms of an educational objective, or "ability to plan experiments." For the benefit of readers who may have been influenced by certain exegeses of MacCorquodale and Meehl (40), let us here emphasize: Whether or not an interpretation of a test's properties or relations involves questions of construct validity is to be decided by examining the entire body of evidence offered, together with what is asserted about the test in the context of this evidence. Proposed identifications of constructs allegedly measured by the test with constructs of other sciences (e.g., genetics, neuroanatomy, biochemistry) make up only one class of construct-validity claims, and a rather minor one at present. Space does not permit full analysis of the relation of the present paper to the MacCorquodale-Meehl distinction between hypothetical constructs and intervening variables. The philosophy of science pertinent to the present paper is set forth later in the section entitled, "The nomological network."

178

The Relation of Constructs to "Criteria"

CRITICAL VIEW OF THE CRITERION IMPLIED

An unquestionable criterion may be found in a practical operation, or may be established as a consequence of an operational definition. Typically, however, the psychologist is unwilling to use the directly operational approach because he is interested in building a theory about a generalized construct. A theorist trying to relate behavior to "hunger" almost certainly invests that term with meanings other than the operation "elapsed-time-since-feeding." If he is concerned with hunger as a tissue need, he will not accept time lapse as *equivalent* to his construct because it fails to consider, among other things, energy expenditure of the animal.

In some situations the criterion is no more valid than the test. Suppose, for example, that we want to know if counting the dots on Bender-Gestalt figure five indicates "compulsive rigidity," and that we take psychiatric ratings on this trait as a criterion. Even a conventional report on the resulting correlation will say something about the extent and intensity of the psychiatrist's contacts and should describe his qualifications (e.g., diplomate status? analyzed?).

Why report these facts? Because data are needed to indicate whether the criterion is any good. "Compulsive rigidity" is not really intended to mean "social stimulus value to psychiatrists." The implied trait involves a range of behavior-dispositions which may be very imperfectly sampled by the psychiatrist. Suppose dot-counting does not occur in a particular patient and yet we find that the psychiatrist has rated him as "rigid." When questioned the psychiatrist tells us that the patient was a rather easy, free-wheeling sort; however, the patient *did* lean over to straighten out a skewed desk blotter, and this, viewed against certain other facts, tipped the scale in favor of a "rigid" rating. On the face of it, counting Bender dots may be just as good (or poor) a sample of the compulsive-rigidity domain as straightening desk blotters is.

Suppose, to extend our example, we have four tests on the "predictor" side, over against the psychiatrist's "criterion," and find generally positive correlations among the five variables. Surely it is artificial and arbitrary to impose the "test-should-predict-criterion" pattern on such data. The psychiatrist samples verbal content, expressive pattern, voice, posture, etc. The psychologist samples verbal content, perception, expressive pattern, etc. Our proper conclusion is that, from this evidence, the four tests and the psychiatrist all assess some common factor.

The asymmetry between the "test" and the so-designated "criterion" arises only because the terminology of predictive validity has become a commonplace in test analysis. In this study where a construct is the central concern, any distinction between the merit of the test and criterion variables would be justified only if it had already been shown that the psychiatrist's theory and operations were excellent measures of the attribute.

Inadequacy of Validation in Terms of Specific Criteria

The proposal to validate constructual interpretations of tests runs counter to suggestions of some others. Spiker and McCandless (57) favor an operational approach. Validation is replaced by compiling statements as to how strongly the test predicts other observed variables of interest. To avoid requiring that each new variable be investigated completely by itself, they allow two variables to collapse into one whenever the properties of the operationally defined measures are the same: "If a new test is demonstrated to predict the scores on an older, well-established test, then an evaluation of the predictive power of the older test may be used for the new one." But accurate inferences are possible only if the two tests correlate so highly that there is negligible reliable variance in either test, independent of the other. Where the correspondence is less close, one must either retain all the separate variables operationally defined or embark on construct validation.

The practical user of tests must rely on constructs of some generality to make predictions about new situations. Test X could be used to predict palmar sweating in the face of failure without invoking any construct, but a counselor is more likely to be asked to forecast behavior in diverse or even unique situations for which the correlation of test X is unknown. Significant predictions rely on knowledge accumulated around the generalized construct of anxiety. The *Technical Recommendations* state:

It is ordinarily necessary to evaluate construct validity by integrating evidence from many different sources. The problem of construct validation becomes especially acute in the clinical field since for many of the constructs dealt with it is not a question of finding an imperfect criterion but of finding any criterion at all. The psychologist interested in construct validity for clinical devices is concerned with making an estimate of a hypothetical internal process, factor, system, structure, or state and cannot expect to find a clear unitary behavioral criterion. An attempt to identify any one criterion measure or any composite as the criterion aimed at is, however, usually unwarranted (59, pp. 14–15).

This appears to conflict with arguments for specific criteria prominent at places in the testing literature. Thus Anastasi (2) makes many statements of the latter character: "It is only as a measure of a specifically defined criterion that a test can be objectively validated at all . . . To claim that a test measures anything over and above its criterion is pure speculation" (p. 67). Yet elsewhere this article supports construct validation. Tests can be profitably interpreted if we "know the relationships between the tested behavior . . . and other behavior samples, none of these behavior samples necessarily occupying the preeminent position of a criterion" (p. 75). Factor analysis with several partial criteria might be used to study whether a test measures a postulated "general learning ability." If the data demonstrate specificity of ability instead, such specificity is "useful in its own right in advancing our knowledge of behavior; it should not be construed as a weakness of the tests" (p. 75).

We depart from Anastasi at two points. She writes, "The validity of a psychological test should not be confused with an analysis of the factors which determine the behavior under consideration." We, however, regard such analysis as a most important type of validation. Second, she refers to "the will-o'-the-wisp of psychological processes which are distinct from performance" (2, p. 77). While we agree that psychological processes are elusive, we are sympathetic to attempts to formulate and clarify constructs which are evidenced by performance but distinct from it. Surely an inductive inference based on a pattern of correlations cannot be dismissed as "pure speculation."

SPECIFIC CRITERIA USED TEMPORARILY: THE "BOOTSTRAPS" EFFECT

Even when a test is constructed on the basis of a specific criterion, it may ultimately be judged to have greater construct validity than the criterion. We start with a vague concept which we associate with certain observations. We then discover empirically that these observations co-vary with some other observation which possesses greater reliability or is more intimately correlated with relevant experimental changes than

181

is the original measure, or both. For example, the notion of temperature arises because some objects feel hotter to the touch than others. The expansion of a mercury column does not have face validity as an index of hotness. But it turns out that (a) there is a statistical relation between expansion and sensed temperature; (b) observers employ the mercury method with good interobserver agreement; (c) the regularity of observed relations is increased by using the thermometer (e.g., melting points of samples of the same material vary little on the thermometer; we obtain nearly linear relations between mercury measures and pressure of a gas). Finally, (d) a theoretical structure involving unobservable microevents—the kinetic theory—is worked out which explains the relation of mercury expansion to heat. This whole process of conceptual enrichment begins with what in retrospect we see as an extremely fallible "criterion"—the human temperature sense. That original criterion has now been relegated to a peripheral position. We have lifted ourselves by our boostraps, but in a legitimate and fruitful way.

Similarly, the Binet scale was first valued because children's scores tended to agree with judgments by schoolteachers. If it had not shown this agreement, it would have been discarded along with reaction time and the other measures of ability previously tried. Teacher judgments once constituted the criterion against which the individual intelligence test was validated. But if today a child's IQ is 135 and three of his teachers complain about how stupid he is, we do not conclude that the test has failed. Quite to the contrary, if no error in test procedure can be argued, we treat the test score as a valid statement about an important quality, and define our task as that of finding out what other variables—personality, study skills, etc.—modify achievement or distort teacher judgment.

Experimentation to Investigate Construct Validity

VALIDATION PROCEDURES

We can use many methods in construct validation. Attention should particularly be drawn to Macfarlane's survey of these methods as they apply to projective devices (41).

Group differences. If our understanding of a construct leads us to expect two groups to differ on the test, this expectation may be tested directly. Thus Thurstone and Chave validated the Scale for Measuring

Attitude Toward the Church by showing score differences between church members and nonchurchgoers. Churchgoing is not the criterion of attitude, for the purpose of the test is to measure something other than the crude sociological fact of church attendance; on the other hand, failure to find a difference would have seriously challenged the test.

Only coarse correspondence between test and group designation is expected. Too great a correspondence between the two would indicate that the test is to some degree invalid, because members of the groups are expected to overlap on the test. Intelligence test items are selected initially on the basis of a correspondence to age, but an item that correlates .95 with age in an elementary school sample would surely be suspect.

Correlation matrices and factor analysis. If two tests are presumed to measure the same construct, a correlation between them is predicted. (An exception is noted where some second attribute has positive loading in the first test and negative loading in the second test; then a low correlation is expected. This is a testable interpretation provided an external measure of either the first or the second variable exists.) If the obtained correlation departs from the expectation, however, there is no way to know whether the fault lies in test A, test B, or the formulation of the construct. A matrix of intercorrelations often points out profitable ways of dividing the construct into more meaningful parts, factor analysis being a useful computational method in such studies.

Guilford (26) has discussed the place of factor analysis in construct validation. His statements may be extracted as follows: "The personnel psychologist wishes to know 'why his tests are valid.' He can place tests and practical criteria in a matrix and factor it to identify 'real dimensions of human personality.' A factorial description is exact and stable; it is economical in explanation; it leads to the creation of pure tests which can be combined to predict complex behaviors." It is clear that factors here function as constructs. Eysenck, in his "criterion analysis" (18), goes farther than Guilford, and shows that factoring can be used explicitly to test hypotheses about constructs.

Factors may or may not be weighted with surplus meaning. Certainly when they are regarded as "real dimensions" a great deal of surplus meaning is implied, and the interpreter must shoulder a substantial burden of proof. The alternative view is to regard factors as defining a working reference frame, located in a convenient manner in the "space" defined by all behaviors of a given type. Which set of factors from a given matrix is "most useful" will depend partly on predilections, but in essence the best construct is the one around which we can build the greatest number of inferences, in the most direct fashion.

Studies of internal structure. For many constructs, evidence of homogeneity within the test is relevant in judging validity. If a trait such as *dominance* is hypothesized, and the items inquire about behaviors subsumed under this label, then the hypothesis appears to require that these items be generally intercorrelated. Even low correlations, if consistent, would support the argument that people may be fruitfully described in terms of a generalized tendency to dominate or not dominate. The general quality would have power to predict behavior in a variety of situations represented by the specific items. Item-test correlations and certain reliability formulas describe internal consistency.

It is unwise to list uninterpreted data of this sort under the heading "validity" in test manuals, as some authors have done. High internal consistency may *lower* validity. Only if the underlying theory of the trait being measured calls for high item intercorrelations do the correlations support construct validity. Negative item-test correlations may support construct validity, provided that the items with negative correlations are believed irrelevant to the postulated construct and serve as suppressor variables (31, pp. 431–36; 44).

Study of distinctive subgroups of items within a test may set an upper limit to construct validity by showing that irrelevant elements influence scores. Thus a study of the PMA space tests shows that variance can be partially accounted for by a response set, a tendency to mark many figures as similar (12). An internal factor analysis of the PEA Interpretation of Data Test shows that in addition to measuring reasoning skills, the test score is strongly influenced by a tendency to say "probably true" rather than "certainly true," regardless of item content (17). On the other hand, a study of item groupings in the DAT Mechanical Comprehension Test permitted rejection of the hypothesis that knowledge about specific topics such as gears made a substantial contribution to scores (13).

Studies of change-over occasions. The stability of test scores ("retest reliability," Cattell's "N-technique") may be relevant to construct validation. Whether a high degree of stability is encouraging or discouraging for the proposed interpretation depends upon the theory defining the construct.

More powerful than the retest after uncontrolled intervening experiences is the retest with experimental intervention. If a transient influence swings test scores over a wide range, there are definite limits on the extent to which a test result can be interpreted as reflecting the typical behavior of the individual. These are examples of experiments which have indicated upper limits to test validity: studies of differences associated with the examiner in projective testing, of change of score under alternative directions ("tell the truth" vs. "make yourself look good to an employer"), and of coachability of mental tests. We may recall Gulliksen's distinction (27): When the coaching is of a sort that improves the pupil's intellectual functioning in school, the test which is affected by the coaching has validity as a measure of intellectual functioning; if the coaching improves test-taking but not school performance, the test which responds to the coaching has poor validity as a measure of this construct.

Sometimes, where differences between individuals are difficult to assess by any means other than the test, the experimenter validates by determining whether the test can detect induced intra-individual differences. One might hypothesize that the Zeigarnik effect is a measure of ego involvment, i.e., that with ego involvement there is more recall of incomplete tasks. To support such an interpretation, the investigator will try to induce ego involvement on some task by appropriate directions and compare subjects' recall with their recall for tasks where there was a contrary induction. Sometimes the intervention is drastic. Porteus finds (53) that brain-operated patients show disruption of performance on his maze, but do not show impaired performance on conventional verbal tests and argues therefrom that his test is a better measure of planfulness.

Studies of process. One of the best ways of determining informally what accounts for variability on a test is the observation of the person's process of performance. If it is supposed, for example, that a test measures mathematical competence, and yet observation of students' errors shows that erroneous reading of the question is common, the implications of a low score are altered. Lucas in this way showed that the Navy Relative Movement Test, an aptitude test, actually involved two different abilities: spatial visualization and mathematical reasoning (39).

Mathematical analysis of scoring procedures may provide important negative evidence on construct validity. A recent analysis of "empathy" tests is perhaps worth citing (14). "Empathy" has been operationally defined in many studies by the ability of a judge to predict what responses will be given on some questionnaire by a subject he has observed briefly. A mathematical argument has shown, however, that the scores depend on several attributes of the judge which enter into his perception of any individual, and that they therefore cannot be interpreted as evidence of his ability to interpret cues offered by particular individuals, or of his intuition.

THE NUMERICAL ESTIMATE OF CONSTRUCT VALIDITY

There is an understandable tendency to seek a "construct validity coefficient." A numerical statement of the degree of construct validity would be a statement of the proportion of the test score variance that is attributable to the construct variable. This numerical estimate can sometimes be arrived at by a factor analysis, but since present methods of factor analysis are based on linear relations, more general methods will ultimately be needed to deal with many quantitative problems of construct validation.

Rarely will it be possible to estimate definite "construct saturations," because no factor corresponding closely to the construct will be available. One can only hope to set upper and lower bounds to the "loading." If "creativity" is defined as something independent of knowledge, then a correlation of .40 between a presumed test of creativity and a test of arithmetic knowledge would indicate that at least 16 per cent of the reliable test variance is irrelevant to creativity as defined. Laboratory performance on problems such as Maier's "hatrack" would scarcely be an ideal measure of creativity, but it would be somewhat relevant. If its correlation with the test is .60, this permits a tentative estimate of 36 per cent as a lower bound. (The estimate is tentative because the test might overlap with the irrelevant portion of the laboratory measure.) The saturation seems to lie between 36 and 84 per cent; a cumulation of studies would provide better limits.

It should be particularly noted that rejecting the null hypothesis does not finish the job of construct validation (35, p. 284). The problem is not to conclude that the test "is valid" for measuring the construct variable. The task is to state as definitely as possible the degree of validity the test is presumed to have.

The Logic of Construct Validation

Construct validation takes place when an investigator believes that his instrument reflects a particular construct, to which are attached certain meanings. The proposed interpretation generates specific testable hypotheses, which are a means of confirming or disconfirming the claim. The philosophy of science which we believe does most justice to actual scientific practice will now be briefly and dogmatically set forth. Readers interested in further study of the philosophical underpinning are referred to the works by Braithwaite (6, especially Chapter III), Carnap (7; 8, pp. 56–69), Pap (51), Sellars (55, 56), Feigl (19, 20), Beck (4), Kneale (37, pp. 92–110), Hempel (29; 30, §7).

THE NOMOLOGICAL NET

The fundamental principles are these:

1. Scientifically speaking, to "make clear what something *is*" means to set forth the laws in which it occurs. We shall refer to the interlocking system of laws which constitute a theory as a *nomological network*.

2. The laws in a nomological network may relate (a) observable properties or quantities to each other; or (b) theoretical constructs to observables; or (c) different theoretical constructs to one another. These "laws" may be statistical or deterministic.

3. A necessary condition for a construct to be scientifically admissible is that it occur in a nomological net, at least some of whose laws involve observables. Admissible constructs may be remote from observation, i.e., a long derivation may intervene between the nomologicals which implicitly define the construct, and the (derived) nomologicals of type a. These latter propositions permit predictions about events. The construct is not "reduced" to the observations, but only combined with other constructs in the net to make predictions about observables.

4. "Learning more about" a theoretical construct is a matter of elaborating the nomological network in which it occurs, or of increasing the definiteness of the components. At least in the early history of a construct the network will be limited, and the construct will as yet have few connections.

5. An enrichment of the net such as adding a construct or a relation to the theory is justified if it generates nomologicals that are confirmed by observation or if it reduces the number of nomologicals required to

predict the same observations. When observations will not fit into the network as it stands, the scientist has a certain freedom in selecting where to modify the network. That is, there may be alternative constructs or ways of organizing the net which for the time being are equally defensible.

6. We can say that "operations" which are qualitatively very different "overlap" or "measure the same thing" if their positions in the nomological net tie them to the same construct variable. Our confidence in this identification depends upon the amount of inductive support we have for the regions of the net involved. It is not necessary that a direct observational comparison of the two operations be made—we may be content with an intra-network proof indicating that the two operations yield estimates of the same network-defined quantity. Thus, physicists are content to speak of the "temperature" of the sun and the "temperature" of a gas at room temperature even though the test operations are nonoverlapping because this identification makes theoretical sense.

With these statements of scientific methodology in mind, we return to the specific problem of construct validity as applied to psychological tests. The preceding guide rules should reassure the "toughminded," who fear that allowing construct validation opens the door to nonconfirmable test claims. *The answer is that unless the network makes contact with observations, and exhibits explicit, public steps of inference, construct validation cannot be claimed.* An admissible psychological construct must be behavior-relevant (59, p. 15). For most tests intended to measure constructs, adequate criteria do not exist. This being the case, many such tests have been left unvalidated, or a finespun network of rationalizations has been offered as if it were validation. Rationalization is not construct validation. One who claims that his test reflects a construct cannot maintain his claim in the face of recurrent negative results because these results show that his construct is too loosely defined to yield verifiable inferences.

A rigorous (though perhaps probabilistic) chain of inference is required to establish a test as a measure of a construct. To validate a claim that a test measures a construct, a nomological net surrounding the concept must exist. When a construct is fairly new, there may be few specifiable associations by which to pin down the concept. As research proceeds, the construct sends out roots in many directions, which attach it to more and more facts or other constructs. Thus the electron has more accepted properties than the neutrino; *numerical ability* has more than *the second space factor.*

"Acceptance," which was critical in criterion-oriented and content validities, has now appeared in construct validity. Unless substantially the same nomological net is accepted by the several users of the construct, public validation is impossible. If A uses *aggressiveness* to mean overt assault on others, and B's usage includes repressed hostile reactions, evidence which convinces B that a test measures *aggressiveness* convinces A that the test does not. Hence, the investigator who proposes to establish a test as a measure of a construct must specify his network or theory sufficiently clearly so that others can accept or reject it (cf. 41, p. 406). A consumer of the test who rejects the author's theory cannot accept the author's validation. He must validate the test for himself, if he wishes to show that it represents the construct as *he* defines it.

Two general qualifications are in order with reference to the methodological principles 1–6 set forth at the beginning of this section. Both of them concern the amount of "theory," in any high-level sense of that word, which enters into a construct-defining network of laws or lawlike statements. We do not wish to convey the impression that one always has a very elaborate theoretical network, rich in hypothetical processes or entities.

Constructs as inductive summaries. In the early stages of development of a construct or even at more advanced stages when our orientation is thoroughly practical, little or no theory in the usual sense of the word need be involved. In the extreme case the hypothesized laws are formulated entirely in terms of descriptive (observational) dimensions although not all of the relevant observations have actually been made.

The hypothesized network "goes beyond the data" only in the limited sense that it purports to *characterize* the behavior facets which belong to an observable but as yet only partially sampled cluster; hence, it generates predictions about hitherto unsampled regions of the phenotypic space. Even though no unobservables or high-order theoretical constructs are introduced, an element of inductive extrapolation appears in the claim that a cluster including some elements not-yet-observed has been identified. Since, as in any sorting or abstracting task involving a finite set of complex elements, several nonequivalent bases of categorization are available, the investigator may choose a hypothesis which generates erroneous predictions. The failure of a supposed, hitherto untried, member of the cluster to behave in the manner said to be characteristic of the group, or the finding that a nonmember of the postulated cluster does behave in this manner, may modify greatly our tentative construct.

For example, one might build an intelligence test on the basis of his background notions of "intellect," including vocabulary, arithmetic calculation, general information, similarities, two-point threshold, reaction time, and line bisection as subtests. The first four of these correlate, and he extracts a huge first factor. This becomes a second approximation of the intelligence construct, described by its pattern of loadings on the four tests. The other three tests have negligible loading on any common factor. On this evidence the investigator reinterprets intelligence as "manipulation of words." Subsequently it is discovered that test-stupid people are rated as unable to express their ideas, are easily taken in by fallacious arguments, and misread complex directions. These data support the "linguistic" definition of intelligence and the test's claim of validity for that construct. But then a block design test with pantomime instructions is found to be strongly saturated with the first factor. Immediately the purely "linguistic" interpretation of Factor I becomes suspect. This finding, taken together with our initial acceptance of the others as relevant to the background concept of intelligence, forces us to reinterpret the concept once again.

If we simply *list* the tests or traits which have been shown to be saturated with the "factor" or which belong to the cluster, no construct is employed. As soon as we even *summarize the properties* of this group of indicators, we are already making some guesses. Intensional characterization of a domain is hazardous since it selects (abstracts) properties and implies that new tests sharing those properties will behave as do the known tests in the cluster, and that tests not sharing them will not.

The difficulties in merely "characterizing the surface cluster" are strikingly exhibited by the use of certain special and extreme groups for purposes of construct validation. The P_d scale of MMPI was originally derived and cross-validated upon hospitalized patients diagnosed "Psychopathic personality, asocial and amoral type" (42). Further research shows the scale to have a limited degree of predictive and concurrent validity for "delinquency" more broadly defined (5, 28). Several studies show associations between P_d and very special "criterion" groups which it would be ludicrous to identify as "*the* criterion" in the traditional sense. If one lists these heterogeneous groups and tries to characterize them intensionally, he faces enormous conceptual difficulties. For example, a recent survey of hunting accidents in Minnesota showed that hunters who had "carelessly" shot someone were significantly elevated on P_d when compared with other hunters (48). This is in line with one's theoretical expectations; when you ask MMPI "experts" to predict for such a group they invariably predict P_d or M_a or both. The finding seems therefore to lend some slight support to the construct validity of the P_d scale. But of course it would be nonsense to define the P_d component "operationally" in terms of, say, accident proneness. We might try to subsume the original phenotype and the hunting-accident proneness under some broader category, such as "Disposition to violate society's rules, whether legal, moral, or just sensible." But now we have ceased to have a neat operational criterion, and are using instead a rather vague and wide-range class. Besides, there is worse to come. We want the class specification to cover a group trend that (nondelinquent) high school students judged by their peer group as least "responsible" score over a full sigma higher on P_d than those judged most "responsible" (23, p. 75). Most of the behaviors contributing to such sociometric choices fall well within the range of socially permissible action; the proffered criterion specification is still too restrictive. Again, any clinician familiar with MMPI lore would predict an elevated P_d on a sample of (nondelinquent) professional actors. Chyatte's confirmation of this prediction (10) tends to support both: (a) the theory sketch of "what the P_d factor is, psychologically"; and (b) the claim of the P_d scale to construct validity for this hypothetical factor. Let the reader try his hand at writing a brief phenotypic criterion specification that will cover both trigger-happy hunters and Broadway actors! And if he should be ingenious enough to achieve this, does his definition also encompass Hovey's report that high P_d predicts the judgments "not shy" and "unafraid of mental patients" made upon nurses by their supervisors (32, p. 143)? And then we have Gough's report that low P_d is associated with ratings as "good-natured" (24, p. 40), and Roessell's data showing that high P_d is predictive of "dropping out of high school" (54). The point is that all seven of these "criterion" dispositions would be guessed by any clinician having even superficial familiarity with MMPI interpretation; but to mediate these inferences explicitly requires quite a few hypotheses about dynamics, constituting an admittedly sketchy (but far from vacuous) network defining the genotype psychopathic deviate.

191

Vagueness of present psychological laws. This line of thought leads directly to our second important qualification upon the network schema. The idealized picture is one of a tidy set of postulates which jointly entail the desired theorems; since some of the theorems are coordinated to the observation base, the system constitutes an implicit definition of the theoretical primitives and gives them an indirect empirical meaning. In practice, of course, even the most advanced physical sciences only approximate this ideal. Questions of "categoricalness" and the like, such as logicians raise about pure calculi, are hardly even statable for empirical networks. (What, for example, would be the desiderata of a "well-formed formula" in molar behavior theory?) Psychology works with crude, half-explicit formulations. We do not worry about such advanced formal questions as "whether all molar-behavior statements are decidable by appeal to the postulates" because we know that no existing theoretical network suffices to predict even the *known* descriptive laws. Nevertheless, the sketch of a network is there; if it were not, we would not be saying *anything* intelligible about our constructs. We do not have the rigorous implicit definitions of formal calculi (which still, be it noted, usually permit of a multiplicity of interpretations). Yet the vague, avowedly incomplete network still gives the constructs whatever meaning they do have. When the network is very incomplete, having many strands missing entirely and some constructs tied in only by tenuous threads, then the "implicit definition" of these constructs is disturbingly loose; one might say that the meaning of the constructs is underdetermined. *Since the meaning of theoretical constructs is set forth by stating the laws in which they occur, our incomplete knowledge of the laws of nature produces a vagueness in our constructs* (see Hempel, 30; Kaplan, 34; Pap, 51). We will be able to say "what anxiety is" when we know all of the laws involving it; meanwhile, since we are in the process of discovering these laws, we do not yet know precisely what anxiety is.

Conclusions Regarding the Network after Experimentation

The proposition that x per cent of test variance is accounted for by the construct is inserted into the accepted network. The network then generates a testable prediction about the relation of the test scores to certain other variables, and the investigator gathers data. If prediction and result are in harmony, he can retain his belief that the test measures the construct. The construct is at best adopted, never demonstrated to be "correct."

We do not first "prove" the theory, and then validate the test, nor conversely. In any probable inductive type of inference from a pattern of observations, we examine the relation between the total network of theory and observations. The system involves propositions relating test to construct, construct to other constructs, and finally relating some of these constructs to observables. In ongoing research the chain of inference is very complicated. Kelly and Fiske (36, p. 124) give a complex diagram showing the numerous inferences required in validating a prediction from assessment techniques, where theories about the criterion situation are as integral a part of the prediction as are the test data. A predicted empirical relationship permits us to test all the propositions leading to that prediction. Traditionally the proposition claiming to interpret the test has been set apart as the hypothesis being tested, but actually the evidence is significant for all parts of the chain. If the prediction is not confirmed, any link in the chain may be wrong.

A theoretical network can be divided into subtheories used in making particular predictions. All the events successfully predicted through a subtheory are of course evidence in favor of that theory. Such a subtheory may be so well confirmed by voluminous and diverse evidence that we can reasonably view a particular experiment as relevant only to the test's validity. If the theory, combined with a proposed test interpretation, mispredicts in this case, it is the latter which must be abandoned. On the other hand, the accumulated evidence for a test's construct validity may be so strong that an instance of misprediction will force us to modify the subtheory employing the construct rather than deny the claim that the test measures the construct.

Most cases in psychology today lie somewhere between these extremes. Thus, suppose we fail to find a greater incidence of "homosexual signs" in the Rorschach records of paranoid patients. Which is more strongly disconfirmed—the Rorschach signs or the orthodox theory of paranoia? The negative finding shows the bridge between the two to be undependable, but this is all we can say. The bridge cannot be used unless one end is placed on solider ground. The investigator must decide which end it is best to relocate.

Numerous successful predictions dealing with phenotypically diverse "criteria" give greater weight to the claim of construct validity than do fewer predictions, or predictions involving very similar behaviors. In arriving at diverse predictions, the hypothesis of test validity is connected each time to a subnetwork largely independent of the portion previously used. Success of these derivations testifies to the inductive power of the test-validity statement, and renders it unlikely that an equally effective alternative can be offered.

IMPLICATIONS OF NEGATIVE EVIDENCE

The investigator whose prediction and data are discordant must make strategic decisions. His results can be interpreted in three ways:

1. The test does not measure the construct variable.

2. The theoretical network that generated the hypothesis is incorrect.

3. The experimental design failed to test the hypothesis properly. (Strictly speaking this may be analyzed as a special case of 2, but in practice the distinction is worth making.)

For further research. If a specific fault of procedure makes the third a reasonable possibility, his proper response is to perform an adequate study, meanwhile making no report. When faced with the other two alternatives, he may decide that his test does not measure the construct adequately. Following that decision, he will perhaps prepare and validate a new test. Any rescoring or new interpretative procedure for the original instrument, like a new test, requires validation *by means of a fresh body of data.*

The investigator may regard interpretation 2 as more likely to lead to eventual advances. It is legitimate for the investigator to call the network defining the construct into question, if he has confidence in the test. Should the investigator decide that some step in the network is unsound, he may be able to invent an alternative network. Perhaps he modifies the network by splitting a concept into two or more portions, e.g., by designating *types* of anxiety, or perhaps he specifies added conditions under which a generalization holds. When an investigator modifies the theory in such a manner, he is now required to gather a fresh body of data to test the altered hypotheses. This step should normally precede publication of the modified theory. If the new data are consistent with the modified network, he is free from the fear that his nomologicals were gerrymandered to fit the peculiarities of his first sample of observations. He can now trust his test to some extent, because his test results behave as predicted.

The choice among alternatives, like any strategic decision, is a gamble as to which course of action is the best investment of effort. Is it wise to modify the theory? That depends on how well the system is confirmed by prior data, and how well the modifications fit available observations. Is it worth while to modify the test in the hope that it will fit the construct? That depends on how much evidence there is—apart from this abortive experiment—to support the hope, and also on how much it is worth to the investigator's ego to salvage the test. The choice among alternatives is a matter of research planning and no routine policy can be stated.

For practical use of the test. The consumer can accept a test as a measure of a construct only when there is a strong positive fit between predictions and subsequent data. When the evidence from a proper investigation of a published test is essentially negative, it should be reported as a stop sign to discourage use of the test pending a reconciliation of test and construct, or final abandonment of the test. If the test has not been published, it should be restricted to research use until some degree of validity is established (1). The consumer can await the results of the investigator's gamble, with confidence that proper application of the scientific method will ultimately tell whether the test has value. Until the evidence is in, he has no justification for employing the test as a basis for terminal decisions. The test may serve, at best, only as a source of suggestions about individuals to be confirmed by other evidence (15, 47).

There are two perspectives in test validation. From the viewpoint of the psychological practitioner, the burden of proof is on the test. A test should not be used to measure a trait until its proponent establishes that predictions made from such measures are consistent with the best available theory of the trait. In the view of the test developer, however, both the test and the theory are under scrutiny. He is free to say *to himself privately,* "If my test disagrees with the theory, so much the worse for the theory." This way lies delusion, unless he continues his research using a better theory.

REPORTING OF POSITIVE RESULTS

The test developer who finds positive correspondence between his proposed interpretation and data is expected to report the basis for his validity claim. Defending a claim of construct validity is a major task, not to be satisfied by a discourse without data. The *Technical Recommendations* have little to say on reporting of construct validity. Indeed, the only detailed suggestions under that heading refer to correlations of the test with other measures, together with a cross reference to some other sections of the report. The two key principles, however, call for the most comprehensive type of reporting. The manual for any test "should report all available information which will assist the user in determining what psychological attributes account for variance in test scores" (59, p. 27). And, "The manual for a test which is used primarily to assess postulated attributes of the individual should outline the theory on which the test is based and organize whatever partial validity data there are to show in what way they support the theory" (59, p. 28). It is recognized, by a classification as "very desirable" rather than "essential," that the latter recommendation goes beyond present practice of test authors.

The proper goals in reporting construct validation are to make clear (a) what interpretation is proposed, (b) how adequately the writer believes this interpretation is substantiated, and (c) what evidence and reasoning lead him to this belief. Without (a) the construct validity of the test is of no use to the consumer. Without (b) the consumer must carry the entire burden of evaluating the test research. Without (c) the consumer or reviewer is being asked to take (a) and (b) on faith. The test manual cannot always present an exhaustive statement on these points, but it should summarize and indicate where complete statements may be found.

To specify the interpretation, the writer must state what construct he has in mind, and what meaning he gives to that construct. For a construct which has a short history and has built up few connotations, it will be fairly easy to indicate the presumed properties of the construct, i.e., the nomologicals in which it appears. For a construct with a longer history, a summary of properties and references to previous theoretical discussions may be appropriate. It is especially critical to distinguish proposed interpretations from other meanings previously given the same construct. The validator faces no small task; he must somehow communicate a theory to his reader.

To evaluate his evidence calls for a statement like the conclusions from a program of research, noting what is well substantiated and what alternative interpretations have been considered and rejected. The writer must note what portions of his proposed interpretation are speculations, extrapolations, or conclusions from insufficient data. The author has an ethical responsibility to prevent unsubstantiated interpretations from appearing as truths. A claim is unsubstantiated unless the evidence for the claim is public, so that other scientists may review the evidence, criticize the conclusions, and offer alternative interpretations.

The report of evidence in a test manual must be as complete as any research report, except where adequate public reports can be cited. Reference to something "observed by the writer in many clinical cases" is worthless as evidence. Full case reports, on the other hand, may be a valuable source of evidence so long as these cases are representative and negative instances receive due attention. The report of evidence must be interpreted with reference to the theoretical network in such a manner that the reader sees why the author regards a particular correlation or experiment as confirming (or throwing doubt upon) the proposed interpretation. Evidence collected by others must be taken into account fairly.

Validation of a Complex Test "As a Whole"

Special questions must be considered when we are investigating the validity of a test which is aimed to provide information about several constructs. In one sense, it is naive to inquire "Is this test valid?" One does not validate a test, but only a principle for making inferences. If a test yields many different types of inferences, some of them can be valid and others invalid (cf. Technical Recommendation C2: "The manual should report the validity of each type of inference for which a test is recommended"). From this point of view, every topic sentence in the typical book on Rorschach interpretation presents a hypothesis requiring validation, and one should validate inferences about each aspect of the personality separately and in turn, just as he would want information on the validity (concurrent or predictive) for each scale of MMPI.

There is, however, another defensible point of view. If a test is purely empirical, based strictly on observed connections between response to an item and some criterion, then of course the validity of one scoring key for the test does not make validation for its other scoring keys any less necessary. But a test may be developed on the basis of a theory which in itself provides a linkage between the various keys and the various criteria. Thus, while Strong's Vocational Interest Blank is developed empirically, it also rests on a "theory" that a youth can be expected to be satisfied in an occupation if he has interests common to men now happy in the occupation. When Strong finds that those with high Engineering interest scores in college are preponderantly in engineering careers nineteen years later, he has partly validated the proposed use of the Engineer score (predictive validity). Since the evidence is consistent with the theory on which all the test keys were built, this evidence alone increases the presumption that the *other* keys have predictive validity. How strong is this presumption? Not very, from the viewpoint of the traditional skepticism of science. Engineering interests may stabilize early, while interests in art or management or social work are still unstable. A claim cannot be made that the whole Strong approach is valid just because one score shows predictive validity. But if thirty interest scores were investigated longitudinally and all of them showed the type of validity predicted by Strong's theory, we would indeed be caviling to say that this evidence gives no confidence in the long-range validity of the thirty-first score.

Confidence in a theory is increased as more relevant evidence confirms it, but it is always possible that tomorrow's investigation will render the theory obsolete. The *Technical Recommendations* suggest a rule of reason, and ask for evidence for each type of inference for which a test is recommended. It is stated that no test developer can present predictive validities for all possible criteria; similarly, no developer can run all possible experimental tests of his proposed interpretation. But the recommendation is more subtle than advice that a lot of validation is better than a little.

Consider the Rorschach test. It is used for many inferences, made by means of nomological networks at several levels. At a low level are the simple unrationalized correspondences presumed to exist between certain signs and psychiatric diagnoses. Validating such a sign does nothing to substantiate Rorschach theory. For other Rorschach formulas an explicit a priori rationale exists (for instance, high F per cent interpreted as implying rigid control of impulses). Each time such a sign shows correspondence with criteria, its rationale is supported just a little. At a still higher level of abstraction, a considerable body of theory surrounds the general area of *outer control*, interlacing many different constructs. As evidence cumulates, one should be able to decide what specific inference-making chains within this system can be depended upon. One should also be able to conclude—or deny—that so much of the system has stood up under test that one has some confidence in even the untested lines in the network.

In addition to relatively delimited nomological networks surrounding *control* or *aspiration*, the Rorschach interpreter usually has an overriding theory of the test as a whole. This may be a psychoanalytic theory, a theory of perception and set, or a theory stated in terms of learned habit patterns. Whatever the theory of the interpreter, whenever he validates an inference from the system, he obtains some reason for added confidence in his overriding system. His total theory is not tested, however, by experiments dealing with only one limited set of constructs. The test developer must investigate far-separated, independent sections of the network. The more diversified the predictions the system is required to make, the greater confidence we can have that only minor parts of the system will later prove faulty. Here we begin to glimpse a logic to defend the judgment that the test and its whole interpretative system is valid at some level of confidence.

There are enthusiasts who would conclude from the foregoing paragraphs that since there is some evidence of correct, diverse predictions made from the Rorschach, the test as a whole can now be accepted as validated. This conclusion overlooks the negative evidence. Just one finding contrary to expectation, based on sound research, is sufficient to wash a whole theoretical structure away. Perhaps the remains can be salvaged to form a new structure. But this structure now must be exposed to fresh risks, and sound negative evidence will destroy it in turn. There is sufficient negative evidence to prevent acceptance of the Rorschach and its accompanying interpretative structures as a whole. So long as any aspects of the overriding theory stated for the test have been disconfirmed, this structure must be rebuilt.

Talk of areas and structures may seem not to recognize those who would interpret the personality "globally." They may argue that a test is best validated in matching studies. Without going into detailed questions of matching methodology, we can ask whether such a study validates the nomological network "as a whole." The judge does employ some network in arriving at his conception of his subject, integrating specific inferences from specific data. Matching studies, if successful, demonstrate only that each judge's interpretative theory has some validity, that it is not completely a fantasy. Very high consistency between judges is required to show that they are using the same network, and very high success in matching is required to show that the network is dependable.

If inference is less than perfectly dependable, we must know which aspects of the interpretative network are least dependable and which are most dependable. Thus, even if one has considerable confidence in a test "as a whole" because of frequent successful inferences, one still returns as an ultimate aim to the request of the *Technical Recommendations* for separate evidence on the validity of each type of inference to be made.

Recapitulation

Construct validation was introduced in order to specify types of research required in developing tests for which the conventional views on validation are inappropriate. Personality tests, and some tests of ability, are interpreted in terms of attributes for which there is no adequate criterion. This paper indicates what sorts of evidence can substantiate such an interpretation, and how such evidence is to be interpreted. The following points made in the discussion are particularly significant.

1. A construct is defined implicitly by a network of associations or propositions in which it occurs. Constructs employed at different stages of research vary in definiteness.

2. Construct validation is possible only when some of the statements in the network lead to predicted relations among observables. While some observables may be regarded as "criteria," the construct validity of the criteria themselves is regarded as under investigation.

3. The network defining the construct, and the derivation leading to the predicted observation, must be reasonably explicit so that validating evidence may be properly interpreted.

4. Many types of evidence are relevant to construct validity, including content validity, interitem correlations, intertest correlations, test-"criterion" correlations, studies of stability over time, and stability under experimental intervention. High correlations and high stability may constitute either favorable or unfavorable evidence for the proposed interpretation, depending on the theory surrounding the construct.

5. When a predicted relation fails to occur, the fault may lie in the proposed interpretation of the test or in the network. Altering the network so that it can cope with the new observations is, in effect, redefining the construct. Any such new interpretation of the test must be validated by a fresh body of data before being advanced publicly. Great care is required to avoid substituting a posteriori rationalizations for proper validation.

6. Construct validity cannot generally be expressed in the form of a single simple coefficient. The data often permit one to establish upper and lower bounds for the proportion of test variance which can be attributed to the construct. The integration of diverse data into a proper interpretation cannot be an entirely quantitative process.

7. Constructs may vary in nature from those very close to "pure description" (involving little more than extrapolation of relations among observation-variables) to highly theoretical constructs involving hypothesized entities and processes, or making identifications with constructs of other sciences.

8. The investigation of a test's construct validity is not essentially different from the general scientific procedures for developing and confirming theories.

Without in the least advocating construct validity as preferable to the other three kinds (concurrent, predictive, content), we do believe it imperative that psychologists make a place for it in their methodological thinking, so that its rationale, its scientific legitimacy, and its dangers may become explicit and familiar. This would be preferable to the widespread current tendency to engage in what actually amounts to construct validation research and use of constructs in practical testing, while talking an "operational" methodology which, if adopted, would force research into a mold it does not fit.

REFERENCES

1. American Psychological Association. *Ethical Standards of Psychologists*. Washington, D.C.: Amer. Psychological Assn., 1953.
2. Anastasi, Anne. "The Concept of Validity in the Interpretation of Test Scores," *Educational and Psychological Measurement*, 10:67–78 (1950).
3. Bechtoldt, H. P. "Selection," in S. S. Stevens (ed.), *Handbook of Experimental Psychology*, pp. 1237–67. New York: Wiley, 1951.
4. Beck, L. W. "Constructions and Inferred Entities," *Philosophy of Science*, 17: 74–86 (1950). Reprinted in H. Feigl and M. Brodbeck (eds.), *Readings in the Philosophy of Science*, pp. 368–81. New York: Appleton-Century-Crofts, 1953.

5. Blair, W. R. N. "A Comparative Study of Disciplinary Offenders and Non-Offenders in the Canadian Army," *Canadian Journal of Psychology*, 4:49–62 (1950).
6. Braithwaite, R. B. *Scientific Explanation.* Cambridge: Cambridge Univ. Pr., 1953.
7. Carnap, R. "Empiricism, Semantics, and Ontology," *Revue Internationale de Philosophie*, 2:20–40 (1950). Reprinted in P. P. Wiener (ed.), *Readings in Philosophy of Science*, pp. 509–21. New York: Scribner's, 1953.
8. Carnap, R. *Foundations of Logic and Mathematics.* International Encyclopedia of Unified Science, Vol. I, No. 3, pp. 56–69. Reprinted as "The Interpretation of Physics," in H. Feigl and M. Brodbeck (eds.), *Readings in the Philosophy of Science*, pp. 309–18. New York: Appleton-Century-Crofts, 1953.
9. Child, I. L. "Personality," *Annual Review of Psychology*, 5:149–71 (1954).
10. Chyatte, C. "Psychological Characteristics of a Group of Professional Actors," *Occupations*, 27:245–50 (1949).
11. Cronbach, L. J. *Essentials of Psychological Testing.* New York: Harper, 1949.
12. Cronbach, L. J. "Further Evidence on Response Sets and Test Design," *Educational and Psychological Measurement*, 10:3–31 (1950).
13. Cronbach, L. J. "Coefficient Alpha and the Internal Structure of Tests," *Psychometrika*, 16:297–335 (1951).
14. Cronbach, L. J. "Processes Affecting Scores on 'Understanding of Others' and 'Assumed Similarity,'" *Psychological Bulletin*, 52:177–93 (1955).
15. Cronbach, L. J. "The Counselor's Problems from the Perspective of Communication Theory," in Vivian H. Hewer (ed.), *New Perspectives in Counseling.* Minneapolis: Univ. of Minn. Pr., 1955.
16. Cureton, E. E. "Validity," in E. F. Lindquist (ed.), *Educational Measurement*, pp. 621–95. Washington, D. C.: Amer. Council on Education, 1950.
17. Damrin, Dora E. "A Comparative Study of Information Derived from a Diagnostic Problem-Solving Test by Logical and Factorial Methods of Scoring." Unpublished doctor's dissertation, University of Illinois, 1952.
18. Eysenck, H. J. "Criterion Analysis—An Application of the Hypothetico-Deductive Method in Factor Analysis," *Psychological Review*, 57:38–53 (1950).
19. Feigl, H. "Existential Hypotheses," *Philosophy of Science*, 17:35–62 (1950).
20. Feigl, H. "Confirmability and Confirmation," *Revue Internationale de Philosophie*, 5:1–12 (1951). Reprinted in P. P. Wiener (ed.), *Readings in Philosophy of Science*, pp. 522–30. New York: Scribner's, 1953.
21. Gaylord, R. H. "Conceptual Consistency and Criterion Equivalence: A Dual Approach to Criterion Analysis." Unpublished manuscript (Personnel Research Board, Research Note No. 17, 1953). Copies obtainable from Armed Services Technical Information Agency, Documents Service Center, Adjutant General's Office, AD-21 440.
22. Goodenough, Florence L. *Mental Testing.* New York: Rinehart, 1950.
23. Gough, H. G., H. McClosky, and P. E. Meehl. "A Personality Scale for Social Responsibility," *Journal of Abnormal and Social Psychology*, 47:73–80 (1952).
24. Gough, H. G., M. G. McKee, and R. J. Yandell. "Adjective Check List Analyses of a Number of Selected Psychometric and Assessment Variables." Unpublished manuscript. Berkeley: Institute for Personality Assessment and Research, 1953.
25. Guilford, J. P. "New Standards for Test Evaluation," *Educational and Psychological Measurement*, 6:427–39 (1946).
26. Guilford, J. P. "Factor Analysis in a Test-Development Program," *Psychological Review*, 55:79–94 (1948).
27. Gulliksen, H. "Intrinsic Validity," *American Psychologist*, 5:511–17 (1950).
28. Hathaway, S. R. and E. D. Monachesi. *Analyzing and Predicting Juvenile Delinquency With the MMPI.* Minneapolis: Univ. of Minn. Pr., 1953.

29. Hempel, C. G. "Problems and Changes in the Empiricist Criterion of Meaning," *Revue Internationale de Philosophie*, 4:41–63 (1950). Reprinted in L. Linsky (ed.), *Semantics and the Philosophy of Language*, pp. 163–85. Urbana: Univ. of Illinois Pr., 1952.

30. Hempel, C. G. *Fundamentals of Concept Formation in Empirical Science.* Chicago: Univ. of Chicago Pr., 1952.

31. Horst, P. "The Prediction of Personal Adjustment," *Social Science Research Council Bulletin*, No. 48, 1941.

32. Hovey, H. B. "MMPI Profiles and Personality Characteristics," *Journal of Consulting Psychology*, 17:142–46 (1953).

33. Jenkins, J. G. "Validity for What?" *Journal of Consulting Psychology*, 10:93–98 (1946).

34. Kaplan, A. "Definition and Specification of Meaning," *Journal of Philosophy*, 43:281–88 (1946).

35. Kelly, E. L. "Theory and Techniques of Assessment," *Annual Review of Psychology*, 5:281–311 (1954).

36. Kelly, E. L., and D. W. Fiske. *The Prediction of Performance in Clinical Psychology.* Ann Arbor: Univ. of Michigan Pr., 1951.

37. Kneale, W. *Probability and Induction.* Oxford: Clarendon Press, 1949. Pages 92-110 reprinted as "Induction, Explanation, and Transcendent Hypotheses," in H. Feigl and M. Brodbeck (eds.), *Readings in the Philosophy of Science*, pp. 353–67. New York: Appleton-Century-Crofts, 1953.

38. Lindquist, E. F. *Educational Measurement.* Washington, D.C.: Amer. Council on Education, 1950.

39. Lucas, C. M. "Analysis of the Relative Movement Test by a Method of Individual Interviews," *Bureau of Naval Personnel Research Report*, Contract Nonr-694 (00), NR 151-13, Educational Testing Service, March 1953.

40. MacCorquodale, K., and P. E. Meehl. "On a Distinction Between Hypothetical Constructs and Intervening Variables," *Psychological Review*, 55:95–107 (1948).

41. Macfarlane, Jean W. "Problems of Validation Inherent in Projective Methods," *American Journal of Orthopsychiatry*, 12:405–10 (1942).

42. McKinley, J. C., and S. R. Hathaway. "The MMPI: V. Hysteria, Hypomania, and Psychopathic Deviate," *Journal of Applied Psychology*, 28:153–74 (1944).

43. McKinley, J. C., S. R. Hathaway, and P. E. Meehl. "The MMPI: VI. The K Scale," *Journal of Consulting Psychology*, 12:20–31 (1948).

44. Meehl, P. E. "A Simple Algebraic Development of Horst's Suppressor Variables," *American Journal of Psychology*, 58:550–54 (1945).

45. Meehl, P. E. "An Investigation of a General Normality or Control Factor in Personality Testing," *Psychological Monographs*, 59, No. 4 (Whole No. 274), 1945.

46. Meehl, P. E. *Clinical Versus Statistical Prediction.* Minneapolis: Univ. of Minn. Pr., 1954.

47. Meehl, P. E., and A. Rosen. "Antecedent Probability and the Efficiency of Psychometric Signs, Patterns or Cutting Scores," *Psychological Bulletin*, 52:194–216 (1955).

48. *Minnesota Hunter Casualty Study.* St. Paul: Jacob Schmidt Brewing Co., 1954.

49. Mosier, C. I. "A Critical Examination of the Concepts of Face Validity," *Educational and Psychological Measurement*, 7:191–205 (1947).

50. Mosier, C. I. "Problems and Designs of Cross-Validation," *Educational and Psychological Measurement*, 11:5–12 (1951).

51. Pap, A. "Reduction-Sentences and Open Concepts," *Methodos*, 5:3–30 (1953).

52. Peak, Helen. "Problems of Objective Observation," in L. Festinger and D. Katz (eds.), *Research Methods in the Behavioral Sciences*, pp. 243–300. New York: Dryden, 1953.

53. Porteus, S. D. *The Porteus Maze Test and Intelligence.* Palo Alto: Pacific Bks., 1950.
54. Roessel, F. P. "MMPI Results for High School Drop-Outs and Graduates." Unpublished doctor's dissertation, University of Minnesota, 1954.
55. Sellars, W. S. "Concepts as Involving Laws and Inconceivable Without Them," *Philosophy of Science,* 15:287–315 (1948).
56. Sellars, W. S. "Some Reflections on Language Games," *Philosophy of Science,* 21:204–28 (1954). Also reprinted in this volume.
57. Spiker, C. C., and B. R. McCandless. "The Concept of Intelligence and the Philosophy of Science," *Psychological Review,* 61:255–67 (1954).
58. "Technical Recommendations for Psychological Tests and Diagnostic Techniques: Preliminary Proposal," *American Psychologist,* 7:461–76 (1952).
59. *Technical Recommendations for Psychological Tests and Diagnostic Techniques,* Psychological Bulletin Supplement, 51, 2, Part 2, 1–38 (1954).
60. Thurstone, L. L. "The Criterion Problem in Personality Research," *Psychometric Laboratory Report,* No. 78. Chicago: Univ. of Chicago Pr., 1952.

Problems in the Actuarial Characterization
of a Person

ONCE upon a time there was a young fellow who, as we say, was "vocationally maladjusted." He wasn't sure just what the trouble was, but he knew that he wasn't happy in his work. So, being a denizen of an urban, sophisticated, psychologically-oriented culture, he concluded that what he needed was some professional guidance. He went to the counseling bureau of a large midwestern university (according to some versions of the tale, it was located on the banks of a great river), and there he was interviewed by a world-famous vocational psychologist. When the psychologist explained that it would first be necessary to take a fourteen-hour battery of tests, the young man hesitated a little; after all, he was still employed at his job and fourteen hours seemed like quite a lot of time. "Oh well," said the great psychologist reassuringly, "don't worry about that. If you're too busy, you can arrange to have my assistant take these tests for you. I don't care who takes them, just so long as they come out in quantitative form."

Lest I, a Minnesotan, do too great violence to your expectations by telling this story of the dust-bowl empiricism with which we Minnesotans are traditionally associated, let me now tell you a true story having the opposite animus. Back in the days when I was a teaching assistant, my colleague, Kenneth MacCorquodale was grading a young lady's elementary laboratory report on an experiment which involved a correlation problem. At the end of an otherwise flawless report, this particular bobby-soxer had written "The correlation was seventy-five, with a standard error of ten, which is significant. However, I do not

NOTE: This paper appeared, under the title "Wanted—A Good Cookbook," in the *American Psychologist* for November 1956 and is reprinted here, with minor alterations, by permission of the American Psychological Association and of the author.

think these variables are related." MacCorquodale wrote a large red "FAIL" and added a note: "Dear Miss Fisbee: The correlation coefficient was devised expressly to relieve you of all responsibility for deciding whether these two variables are related."

If you find one of these anecdotes quite funny, and the other one rather stupid (I don't care which), you are probably suffering from a slight case of bias. Although I have not done a factor-analysis with these two stories in the matrix, my clinical judgment tells me that a person's spontaneous reactions to them reflect his position in the perennial conflict between the tough-minded and the tender-minded, between those for whom the proper prefix to the word "analysis" is "factor" and those for whom it is "psycho," between the groups that Lord Russell once characterized as the "simple-minded" and the "muddle-headed." In a recent book (10), I have explored one major facet of this conflict, namely the controversy over the relative merits of clinical and statistical methods of prediction. Theoretical considerations, together with introspections as to my own mental activities as a psychotherapist, led me to conclude that the clinician has certain unique, practically unduplicable powers by virtue of being himself an organism like his client; but that the domain of straight prediction would not be a favorable locus for displaying these powers. Survey of a score of empirical investigations in which the actual predictive efficiency of the two methods could be compared, gave strong confirmation to this latter theoretical expectation. After reading these studies, one would think that the first rule to follow in trying to predict the subsequent course of a student's or patient's behavior is carefully to avoid talking to him, and that the second rule is to avoid thinking about him.

Statisticians (and rat men) with castrative intent toward clinicians should beware of any temptation to overextend these findings to a generalization that "clinicians don't actually add anything to the clinical process." Apart from the clinician's therapeutic efforts—the power of which is a separate issue and also a matter of current dispute—a glance at a sample of clinical diagnostic documents, such as routine psychological reports submitted in a Veterans' Administration installation, shows that a kind of mixed predictive-descriptive statement, which is different from the type of gross prediction considered in the aforementioned survey, predominates. (I hesitate to propose a basic distinction here, having learned that proposing a distinction between two classes of concepts is a sure road to infamy.) Nevertheless, I suggest that we distinguish between (a) the clinician's predictions of such gross, outcome-type, "administrative" dimensions as recovery from psychosis, survival in a training program, persistence in therapy, and the like; and (b) a rather more detailed and ambitious enterprise roughly characterizable as "describing the person." (It might be thought that (a) always presupposes (b), but a moment's reflection shows this to be false; since there are empirical prediction systems in which the sole property ascribed to the person is the disposition to a predicted gross outcome.) A very considerable fraction of the typical clinical psychologist's time seems to be spent in giving tests or semi-tests, the intention being to come out with some kind of characterization of the individual. In part this characterization is "phenotypic," attributing to the patient such behavior-dispositions as "hostile," "relates poorly," "loss in efficiency," "manifest anxiety," or "depression"; in part it is "genotypic," inferring as the causes of the phenotype certain inner events, states, or structures, e.g., "latent n Aggression," "oral-dependent attitudes," "severe castration anxiety," and the like. While the phenotypic-genotypic question is itself deserving of careful methodological analysis, in what follows I shall use the term "personality description" to cover both phenotypic and genotypic inferences, i.e., statements of all degrees of internality or theoreticalness. I shall also assume, while recognizing that at least one group of psychologists has made an impressive case to the contrary, that the description of a person is a worth-while stage in the total clinical process. Granted, then, that we wish to use tests as a means of securing a description of the person, how shall we go about it? Here we sit, with our Rorschach and Multiphasic results spread out before us. From this mess of data we have to emerge with a characterization of the person from whose behavior these profiles are a highly abstracted, much-reduced distillation. How shall we proceed?

Some readers are no doubt wondering, "What is the fellow talking about? You look at the profiles, you call to mind what the various test dimensions mean for dynamics, you reflect on other patients you have seen with similar patterns, you think of the research literature; then you combine these considerations to make inferences. Where's the problem?" The problem is whether or not this is the most efficient *way to do it.* We ordinarily do it this way, in fact the practice is so universal that most clinicians find it shocking, if not somehow sinful, to imagine any other. We feed in the test data and let that rusty digital computer in our heads go to work until a paragraph of personality description emerges. It requires no systematic study, although some quantitative data have begun to appear in the literature (2, 3, 6, 7, 8, 9), to realize that there is a considerable element of vagueness, hit-or-miss and personal judgment involved in this approach. Because explicit rules are largely lacking, and hence the clinician's personal experience, skill, and creative artistry play so great a role, I shall refer to this time-honored procedure for generating personality descriptions from tests as the "rule-of-thumb method."

I wish now to contrast this rule-of-thumb method with what I shall call the "cookbook method." In the cookbook method, any given configuration (holists please note—I said "configuration," not "sum"!) of psychometric data is associated with each facet (or configuration) of a personality description, and the closeness of this association is explicitly indicated by a number. This number need not be a correlation coefficient; its form will depend upon what is most appropriate to the circumstances. It may be a correlation, or merely an ordinary probability-of-attribution, or (as in the empirical study I shall report upon later in my remarks) an average Q-sort placement. Whatever its form, the essential point is that the transition from psychometric pattern to personality description is an automatic, mechanical, "clerical" kind of task, proceeding by the use of explicit rules set forth in the cookbook. I am quite aware that the mere prospect of such a method will horrify some of my readers; in my weaker moments it horrifies me. All I can say is that many clinicians are also horrified by the cookbook method as applied in the crude prediction situation; whereas the studies reported to date indicate this horror to be quite groundless (10, Chap. 8). As B. F. Skinner once said, some men are less curious about nature than about the accuracy of their guesses (15, p. 44). Our responsibility to our patients and to the taxpayer obliges us to decide between the rule-of-thumb and the cookbook methods on the basis of their empirically demonstrated efficiency, rather than upon which one is more exciting, more "dynamic," more like what psychiatrists do, or more harmonious with the clinical psychologist's self-concept.

Let us sneak up the clinician's avoidance gradient gradually to prevent the negative therapeutic reaction. Consider a particular complex attribute, say "strong dependency with reaction-formation." Under what conditions should we take time to give a test of moderate validity as a basis for inferring the presence or absence of this complex attribute? Putting it negatively, it appears to me pretty obvious that there are two circumstances under which we should *not* spend much skilled time on testing even with a moderately valid test because we stand to lose if we let the test finding influence our judgments. First, when the attribute is found in almost all our patients; and second, when it is found in almost none of our patients. (A third situation, which I shall not consider here, is one in which the attribute makes no practical difference anyhow.) A disturbingly large fraction of the assertions made in routine psychometric reports or uttered by psychologists in staff conferences fall into one of these classes.

It is not difficult to show that when a given personality attribute is almost always or almost never present in a specified clinical population, rather severe demands are made upon the test's validity if it is to contribute in a practical way to our clinical decision-making. A few simple manipulations of Bayes' Rule for calculating inverse probability lead to rather surprising (and depressing) results. Let me run through some of these briefly. In what follows,

P = Incidence of a certain personality characteristic in a specified clinical population. ($Q = 1 - P$, $P > Q$)

p_1 = Proportion of "valid positives" (i.e., incidence of positive test findings among cases who actually have the characteristic). ($q_1 = 1 - p_1$)

p_2 = Proportion of "false positives" (i.e., incidence of positive test findings among cases who actually lack the characteristic). ($q_2 = 1 - p_2$)

1. When is a positive assertion (attribution of the characteristic) on the basis of a positive test finding more likely to be correct than incorrect?

When

$$\frac{P}{Q} > \frac{p_2}{p_1}$$

Example: A test correctly identifies 80 per cent of brain-damaged patients at the expense of only 15 per cent false positives, in a neuropsychiatric population where one tenth of all patients are damaged. The decision "brain damage present" on the basis of a positive test finding is more likely to be false than true, since the inequality is unsatisfied.

2. When does the use of a test improve over-all decision-making?
When

$$P < \frac{q_2}{q_1 + q_2}$$

If $P < Q$ this has the form $Q < \dfrac{p_1}{p_1 + p_2}$.

Example: A test sign identifies 85 per cent of "psychotics" at the expense of only 15 per cent of false positives among the "non-psychotic." It is desired that a decision be made on each case, and both kinds of errors are serious.* Only 10 per cent of the population seen in the given setting are psychotic. Hence, the use of the test yields more erroneous classifications than would proceeding without the test.

3. When does improving a sign, strengthening a scale, or shifting a cut improve decision-making?
When

$$\frac{\triangle p_1}{\triangle p_2} > \frac{Q}{P}$$

Example: We improve the intrinsic validity of a "schizophrenic index" so that it now detects 20 per cent more schizophrenics than it formerly did, at the expense of only a 5 per cent rise in the false positive rate. This surely looks encouraging. However, we work with an outpatient clientele only one tenth of whom are actually schizophrenic. Since these values violate the inequality, "improvement" of the index will result in an increase in the proportion of erroneous diagnoses.
N.B. *Sampling errors are not involved in the above.* The values are assumed to be parameter values, and the test sign is valid (i.e., $p_1 > p_2$ in the population).

Further inequalities and a more detailed drawing out of their pragmatic implications can be found in a recent paper by Dr. Albert Rosen and myself (12). The moral to be drawn from these considerations, which even we clinicians can follow because they involve only high school algebra, is that a great deal of skilled psychological effort is probably being wasted in going through complex, skill-demanding, time-

---

* Inequalities (2) and (3) are conditions for improvement if there is no reason to see one kind of error as worse than the other. In trait attribution this is usually true; in prognostic and diagnostic decisions it may or may not be. If one is willing to say how many errors of one kind he is prepared to tolerate in order to avoid one of the other kind, these inequalities can be readily corrected by inserting this ratio. A more general development can be found in an unpublished paper by Ward Edwards.

consuming test procedures of moderate or low validity, in order to arrive at conclusions about the patient which could often be made with high confidence without the test, and which in other cases ought not to be made (because they still tend to be wrong), even with the test indications positive. Probably most surprising is the finding that there are certain quantitative relations between the base-rates and test-validity parameters such that the use of a "valid" test will produce a net rise in the frequency of clinical mistakes. The first task of a good clinical cookbook would be to make explicit quantitative use of the inverse probability formulas in constructing efficient "rules of attribution" when test data are to be used in describing the personalities of patients found in various clinical populations.

For example, I know of an outpatient clinic which has treated, by a variety of psychotherapies, approximately 5,000 patients in the course of the past eight years not one of whom has committed suicide. If the clinical psychologists in this clinic have been spending much of their time scoring suicide keys on the Multiphasic or counting suicide indicators in Rorschach content, either these test indicators are close to infallible (which is absurd), or else the base-rate is so close to zero that the expenditure of skilled time is of doubtful value. Suicide is an extreme case, of course (14); but the point reflected there so dramatically is valid, with suitable quantitative modifications, over a wider range of base-rates. To take some examples from the high end of the base-rate continuum, it is not very illuminating to say of a known psychiatric patient that he has difficulty in accepting his drives, experiences some trouble in relating emotionally to others, and may have problems with his sexuality. Many psychometric reports bear a disconcerting resemblance to what my colleague, Donald G. Paterson, calls "personality description after the manner of P. T. Barnum" (13). I suggest—and I am quite serious—that we adopt the phrase "Barnum effect" to stigmatize those pseudosuccessful clinical procedures in which personality descriptions from tests are made to fit the patient largely or wholly by virtue of their triviality; and in which any non-trivial (but perhaps erroneous) inferences are hidden in a context of assertions or denials which carry high confidence simply because of the population base-rates, regardless of the test's validity. I think this fallacy is at least as important and frequent as others for which we have familiar labels ("halo effect," "leniency error," "contamination," etc.). One of the best ways to increase the general sensitivity to such fallacies is to give them a name. We ought to make our clinical students as acutely aware of the Barnum effect as they are of the dangers of countertransference or the standard error of r.

The preceding mathematical considerations, while they should serve as a check upon some widespread contemporary forms of tea-leaf reading, are unfortunately not very "positive" by way of writing a good cookbook. "Almost anything needs a little salt for flavor" or "It is rarely appropriate to put ketchup on the dessert" would be sound advice but largely negative and not very helpful to an average cook.

I wish now to describe briefly a piece of empirical research, reported in a thesis just completed at the University of Minnesota by Dr. Charles C. Halbower, which takes the cookbook method 100 per cent seriously; and which seems to show, at least in one clinical context, what can be done in a more constructive way by means of a cookbook of even moderate trustworthiness.* By some geographical coincidence, the psychometric device used in this research was a structured test consisting of a set of 550 items, commonly known as the MMPI. Let me emphasize that the MMPI is not here being compared with anything else, and that the research does not aim to investigate Multiphasic validity (although the general order of magnitude of the obtained correlations does give some incidental information in that respect). What Dr. Halbower asked was this: Given a Multiphasic profile, how arrive at a personality description from it? Using the rule-of-thumb method, a clinician familiar with MMPI interpretation looks at the profile, thinks a while, and proceeds to describe the patient he imagines would have produced such a pattern. Using the cookbook method, we don't need a clinician; instead, a $230-per-month clerk-typist in the outer office simply reads the numbers on the profile, enters the cookbook, locates the page on which is found some kind of "modal description" for patients with such a profile. And this description is then taken as the best available approximation to the patient.

We know, of course, that every patient is unique—absolutely, unqualifiedly unique. Therefore, the application of a cookbook description will inevitably make errors, some of them perhaps serious ones. If we knew *which* facets of the cookbook sketch needed modification as

---

* I am indebted to Dr. Halbower for permission to present this summary of his thesis data in advance of his own more complete publication.

applied to the present unique patient, we would, of course, depart from the cookbook at these points; but we don't know this. If we start monkeying with the cookbook recipe in the hope of avoiding or reducing these errors, we will in all likelihood improve on the cookbook in some respects but, unfortunately, will worsen our approximation in others. Given a finite body of information, such as the thirteen two-digit numbers of a Multiphasic profile, there is obviously *in fact* (whether we have yet succeeded in *finding* it or not) a "most probable" value for any personality facet, and also for any configuration of facets, however complex or "patterned" (10, p. 131–34). It is easy to prove that a method of characterization which departs from consistent adherence to this "best guess" stands to lose. Keep in mind, then, that the raw data from which a personality description was to be inferred consisted of an MMPI profile. In other words, the Halbower study was essentially a comparison of the rule-of-thumb with the cookbook method, in which each method was, however, functioning upon the same information—an MMPI. We are in effect contrasting the validity of two methods of "reading" Multiphasics.

In order to standardize the domain to be covered, and to yield a reasonably sensitive quantification of the goodness of description, Dr. Halbower utilized Q-sorts. From a variety of sources he constructed a Q-pool of 154 items, the majority being phenotypic or intermediate and a minority being genotypic. Since these items were intended for clinically expert sorters employing an "external" frame of reference, many of them were in technical language. Here are some sample items from his pool: "Reacts against his dependency needs with hostility"; "manifests reality distortions"; "takes a dominant, ascendant role in interactions with others"; "is rebellious toward authority figures, rules, and other constraints"; "is counteractive in the face of frustration"; "gets appreciable secondary gain from his symptoms"; "is experiencing pain"; "is naive"; "is impunitive"; "utilizes intellectualization as a defense mechanism"; "shows evidence of latent hostility"; "manifests inappropriate affect." The first step was to construct a cookbook based upon these 154 items as the ingredients; the recipes were to be in the form of directions as to the optimal Q-sort placement of each item.

How many distinguishable recipes will the cookbook contain? If we had infallible criterion Q-sorts on millions of cases, there would be as many recipes as there are possible MMPI profiles. Since we don't have this ideal situation, and never will, we have to compromise by introducing coarser grouping. Fortunately, we know that the validity of our test is poor enough so that this coarseness will not result in the sacrifice of much, if any, information. How coarsely we group—i.e., how different two Multiphasic curves have to be before we refuse to call them "similar" enough to be coordinated with the same recipe—is a very complicated matter involving both theoretical and practical considerations.

Operating within the limits of a doctoral dissertation, Halbower confined his study to four profile "types." These curve types were specified by the first two digits of the Hathaway code plus certain additional requirements based upon clinical experience. The four MMPI codes used were those beginning 123′, 13′, 27′, and 87′. (This is a compact method of representing a profile pattern. See 5.) The first three of these codes are the most frequently occurring in the population of the Minneapolis VA Mental Hygiene Clinic, and the fourth code, which is actually fifth in frequency of occurrence, was chosen in order to have a quasi-psychotic type in the study. It is worth noting that these four codes constitute 58 per cent of all MMPI curves seen in the given population; so that Halbower's gross recipe categories already cover the majority of such outpatients. The nature of the further stipulations, refining the curve criteria within each two-digit code class, is illustrated by the following specification for code 13′, the "hysteroid valley" or "conversion V" type: (1) Hs and Hy $\geq$ 70. (2) D < (Hs and Hy) by at least one sigma. (3) K or L > ? and F. (4) F $\leq$ 65. (5) Scales 4,5,6,7,8,9,0 all $\leq$ 70.

For each of these MMPI curve types, the names of nine patients were then randomly chosen from the list of those meeting the curve specifications. If the patient was still in therapy, his therapist was asked to do a Q-sort (11 steps, normal distribution) on him. The MMPI had been withheld from these therapists. If the patient had been terminated, a clinician (other than Halbower) did a Q-sort based upon study of the case folder, including therapist's notes and any available psychometrics (except, of course, the Multiphasic). This yields Q-sorts for nine patients of a given curve type. These 9 sorts were then pairwise intercorrelated, and by inspection of the resulting 36 coefficients, a subset of five patients was chosen as most representative of the curve type. The Q-sorts on these five "representative" patients were then averaged, and this average Q-sort was taken as the cookbook recipe to be used in describing future cases having the given MMPI curve. Thus, this modal, crystallized, "distilled-essence" personality description was obtained by eliminating patients with atypical sortings and pooling sortings on the more typical, in the hope that errors of both patient sampling and clinical judgment might be reduced. This rather complicated sequence of procedures may be summarized in the following manner.

Deriving cookbook recipe for a specified curve type, such as the "conversion V" above:

1. Sample of $N = 9$ patients currently or recently in therapy and meeting the MMPI specifications for conversion V curve.

2. 154-item Q-sort done on each patient by therapist or from therapist notes and case folder. (These sorts MMPI-uncontaminated.)

3. Pairwise Q-correlations of these 9 patients yields 36 intercorrelations.

4. Selection of subset $N = 5$ "modal" patients from this matrix by inspectional cluster method.

5. Mean of Q-sorts on these 5 "core" patients is the cookbook recipe for the MMPI curve type in question.

Having constructed one recipe, he started all over again with a random sample of nine patients whose Multiphasics met the second curve type specifications, and carried out these cluster-and-pooling processes upon them. This was done for each of the four curve types which were to compose the cookbook. If you have reservations about any of the steps in the construction of this miniature cookbook, let me remind you that this is all preliminary, i.e., *it is the means of arriving at the cookbook recipe.* The proof of the pudding will be in the eating, and any poor choices of tactics or patients up to this point should merely make the cookbook less trustworthy than it would otherwise be.

Having thus written a miniature cookbook consisting of only four recipes, Halbower then proceeded to cook some dishes to see how they would taste. For cross-validation he chose at random four new Mental Hygiene Clinic patients who met the four curve specifications and who had been seen in therapy for a minimum of ten hours. With an eye to validity generalization to a somewhat different clinical population (with different base-rates), he also chose four patients who were being seen as inpatients at the Minneapolis VA Hospital. None of the therapists involved had knowledge of the patients' Multiphasics. For purposes of his study, Halbower took the therapist's Q-sort, based upon all of the case-folder data (minus MMPI) plus his therapeutic contacts, as the best available criterion, although this "criterion" is acceptable only in the sense of construct validity (1). An estimate of its absolute level of trustworthiness is not important since it is being used as the common reference basis for a comparison of two methods of test-reading.

Given the 8 criterion therapist Q-sorts (two patients for each MMPI curve-type), the task of the cookbook is to predict these descriptions. Thus, for each of the two patients having MMPI code 123', we simply assign the Q-sort recipe found in the cookbook as the best available description. How accurate this description is can be estimated (in the sense of construct validity) by Q-correlating it with the criterion therapist's description. These 8 "validity" coefficients varied from .36 to .88 with a median of .69. As would be expected, the hospital inpatients yielded the lower correlations. The Mental Hygiene Clinic cases, for whom the cookbook was really intended, gave validities of .68, .69, .84, and .88. (See under 5 in Summary below.)

SUMMARY

Validation of the four cookbook descriptions on new cases, and comparative validities of the cookbook MMPI readings and rule-of-thumb readings by clinicians.

1. Four patients currently in therapy Q-described by the therapist (ten hours or more of therapy, plus case folder minus MMPI). This is taken as the best available criterion description of each patient.

2. MMPI cookbook recipe Q-correlated with this criterion description.

3. For each patient, four or five clinicians "read" his MMPI in usual rule-of-thumb way, doing Q-sorts.

4. These rule-of-thumb Q-sorts also Q-correlated with criterion description.

5. Cross-validation results in outpatient sample:

	MMPI Curve Type			
Validities	Code 123'	Code 27'	Code 13'	Code 87'
Cookbook	.88	.69	.84	.68
Rule-of-thumb (mean)	.75	.50	.50	.58
Range (4–5 readers)........ ..	.55 to .63	.29 to .54	.37 to .52	.34 to .58

Mean of 4 cookbook validities, through $z_r = .78$
Mean of 17 rule-of-thumb validities, through $z_r = .48$
Cookbook's superiority in validly predicted variance = 38%

6. Validity generalization to inpatient (psychiatric hospital) sample with different base-rates; hence, an "unfair" test of cookbook.

	MMPI Curve Type			
Validities	Code 123'	Code 27'	Code 13'	Code 87'
Cookbook	.63	.64	.36	.70
Rule-of-thumb (2 readers)..........	.37, .49	.29, .42	.30, .30	.50, .55

Mean of 4 cookbook "validities," through $z_r = .60$
Mean of 8 rule-of-thumb validities, through $z_r = .41$
Cookbook's superiority in validly predicted variance = 19%

How does the rule-of-thumb method show up in competition with the cookbook? Here we run into the problem of differences in clinical skill, so Halbower had each MMPI profile read blind by more than one clinician. The task was to interpret the profile by doing a Q-sort. From two to five clinicians thus "read" each of the eight individual profiles, and the resulting 25 sorts were Q-correlated with the appropriate therapist criterion sorts. These validity coefficients run from .29 to .63 with a median of .46. The clinicians were all Minnesota-trained, and they varied in their experience with MMPI from less than a year (first year VA trainees) through all training levels to Ph.D. staff psychologists with six years' experience. The more experienced clinicians had probably seen over two thousand MMPI profiles in relation to varying amounts of other clinical data, including intensive psychotherapy. Yet not one of the 25 rule-of-thumb readings was as valid as the cookbook reading. Of the 25 comparisons which can be made between the validity of a single clinician's rule-of-thumb reading and that of the corresponding cookbook reading of the same patient's profile, 18 are significant in favor of the cookbook at the .01 level of confidence and 4 at the .05 level. The remaining 3 are also in favor of the cookbook but not significantly so.

Confining our attention to the more appropriate outpatient population, for (and upon) which the cookbook was developed, the mean r (estimated through z-transformation) is .78 for the cookbook method, as contrasted with a mean (for 17 rule-of-thumb descriptions) of only .48, a difference of 30 points of correlation, which in this region amounts to a difference of 38 per cent in the validly predicted variance. The cookbook seems to be superior to the rule-of-thumb, not merely in the sense of statistical significance but by an amount which is of very practical importance. It is also remarkable that even when the cookbook recipes are applied to patients from a quite different kind of population, their validity still excels that of rule-of-thumb MMPI readers who are in daily clinical contact with that other population. The improvement in valid variance in the hospital sample averages 19 per cent (see item 6 in the Summary above).

A shrewd critic may be thinking, "Perhaps this is because all kinds of psychiatric patients are more or less alike, and the cookbook has simply taken advantage of this rather trivial fact." In answer to this objection, let me say first that to the extent the cookbook's superiority did arise from its actuarially determined tendency to "follow the base-rates," that would be a perfectly sound application of the inverse probability considerations I at first advanced. For example, most psychiatric patients are in some degree depressed. Let us suppose the mean Q-sort placement given by therapists to the item "depressed" is 7. "Hysteroid" patients, who characteristically exhibit the so-called "conversion V" on their MMPI profiles (Halbower's cookbook code 13'), are less depressed than most neurotics. The clinician, seeing such a conversion valley on the Multiphasic, takes this relation into account by attributing "lack of depression" to the patient. But maybe he over-interprets, giving undue weight to the psychometric finding and under-stressing the base-rate. So his rule-of-thumb placement is far down at the non-depressed and, say at position 3. The cookbook, on the other hand, "knows" (actuarially) that the mean Q-placement for the item "depressed" is at 5 in patients with such profiles—lower than the over-all mean 7 but not displaced as much in the conversion subgroup as the clinician thinks. What I am saying is that if patients are so homogeneous with respect to a certain characteristic that the psychometrics ought not to influence greatly our attribution or placement in defiance of the over-all actuarial trend, then the clinician's tendency to be unduly influenced is a source of erroneous clinical decisions and a valid argument in favor of the cookbook.

However, if this were the chief explanation of Halbower's findings, the obvious conclusion would be merely that MMPI was not differentiating, since any test-induced departure from a description of the "average patient" would tend to be more wrong than right. Our original question would then be rephrased, "What is the comparative efficiency of the cookbook and the rule-of-thumb methods when each is applied to psychometric information having some degree of intrinsic validity?" Time permits me only brief mention of the several lines of evidence in Halbower's study which eliminate the Barnum effect as an explanation. First of all, Halbower had selected his 154 items from a much larger initial Q-pool by a preliminary study of therapist sortings on a heterogeneous sample of patients in which items were eliminated if they showed low interpatient dispersal. Secondly, study of the placements given an item over the four cookbook recipes reveals little similarity (e.g., only two items recur in the top quartile of all four recipes; 60 per cent of the items occur in the top quartile of only one recipe). Thirdly, several additional correlational findings combine to show that the cookbook was not succeeding merely by describing an "average patient" four times over. For example, the clinicians' Q-descriptions of their conceptions of the "average patient" gave very low validity for three of the four codes, and a "mean average patient" description constructed by pooling these clinicians' stereotypes was not much better. (See the table below.) For Code 123 (interestingly enough, the commonest code among therapy cases in this clinic) the pooled stereotype was actually more valid than rule-of-thumb Multiphasic readings. (This is Bayes' Theorem with a vengeance!) Nevertheless, I am happy to report that this "average patient" description was still inferior to the Multiphasic cookbook (significant at the .001 level).

Validities of Four Clinicians' Descriptions of "Average Patient," of the Mean of These Stereotypes, and of the Cookbook Recipe (Outpatient Cases Only)

Code Type	Validities of "Average Patient," Descriptions by 4 Clinicians	Validity of Mean of These Four "Average Patient" Stereotypes	Validity of Cookbook Recipe
Code 123'	.63 to .69	.74	.88
Code 27'	−.03 to .20	.09	.69
Code 13'	.25 to .37	.32	.84
Code 87'	.25 to .35	.31	.68

In the little time remaining, let me ruminate about the implications of this study, supposing it should prove to be essentially generalizable to other populations and to other psychometric instruments. From a theoretical standpoint, the trend is hardly surprising. It amounts to the obvious fact that the human is an inefficient recording and computing device. The cookbook method has an advantage over the rule-of-thumb method because it (a) samples more representatively, (b) records and stores information better, and (c) computes statistical weights which are closer to the optimal. We can perhaps learn more by putting the theoretical question negatively: When should we expect the cookbook to be inferior to the brain? The answer to this question presumably lies in the highly technical field of computing-machine theory, which I am not competent to discuss. As I understand it, the use of these machines requires that certain rules of data-combination be fed initially into the machine, followed by the insertion of suitably selected and coded information. Putting it crudely, the machine can "remember" and can "think routinely," but it cannot "spontaneously notice what is relevant" nor can it "think" in the more high-powered, creative sense (e.g., it cannot invent theories). To be sure, noticing what is relevant must involve the exemplification of some rule, perhaps of a very complex form. But it is a truism of behavior science that organisms can *exemplify* rules without *formulating* them.

To take a non-controversial example outside the clinical field, no one today knows how to state fully the rules of "similarity" or "stimulus equivalence" for patterned visual perception or verbal generalization; but of course we all exemplify daily these undiscovered rules. This suggests that so long as psychology cannot give a complete, explicit, quantitative account of the "dimensions of relevance" in behavior connections, the cookbook will not completely duplicate the clinician (11). The clinician here acts as an inefficient computer, but that is better than a computer with certain major rules completely left out (because we can't build them in until we have learned how to formulate them). The use of the therapist's own unconscious in perceiving verbal and imaginal relations during dream interpretation is, I think, the clearest example of this. But I believe the exemplification of currently unformulable rules is a widespread phenomenon in most clinical inference. However, you will note that these considerations apply chiefly (if not wholly) to matters of *content*, in which a rich, highly varied, hard-to-classify content (such as free associations) is the input information. The problem of "stimulus equivalence" or "noticing the relevant" does not arise when the input data are in the form of preclassified responses, such as a Multiphasic profile or a Rorschach psychogram. I have elsewhere (10, pp. 110–11) suggested that even in the case of such prequantified patterns there arises the possibility of causal-theory-mediated idiographic extrapolations into regions of the profile space in which we lack adequate statistical experience; but I am now inclined to view that suggestion as a mistake. The underlying theory must itself involve some hypothesized function, however crudely quantified. Otherwise how is the alleged "extrapolation" possible? I can think of no reason why the estimation of the parameters in this underlying theoretical function should constitute an exception to the cookbook's superiority. If I am right in this, my "extrapolation" argument applies strictly only when a clinician literally *invents new theoretical relations or variables* in thinking about the individual patient. In spite of some clinicians' claims along this line, I must say I think it very rarely happens in daily clinical practice.

Furthermore, even when it does happen, Bayes' Rule still applies. The *joint* probability of the theory's correctness, and of the attribute's presence (granting the theory but remembering nuisance variables) must be high enough to satisfy the inequalities I have presented; otherwise use of the theory will not pay off.

What are the pragmatic implications of the preceding analysis? Putting it bluntly, it suggests that for a rather wide range of clinical problems involving personality description from tests, the clinical interpreter is a costly middleman who might better be eliminated. An initial outlay of research time could result in a cookbook whose recipes would encompass the great majority of psychometric configurations seen in daily work. I am fully aware that the prospect of a "clinical clerk" simply looking up Rorschach pattern number 73 J 10-5 or Multiphasic curve "Halbower Verzeichnis 626" seems very odd and even dangerous. I reassure myself by recalling that the number of phenotypic and genotypic attributes is, after all, finite; and that the number which are ordinarily found attributed or denied even in an extensive sample of psychological reports on patients is actually very limited. A best estimate of a Q-sort placement is surely more informative than a crude "yes-or-no" decision of low objective confidence. I honestly cannot see, in the case of a *determinate trait domain* and a *specified clinical population*, that there is a serious intellectual problem underlying one's uneasiness. I invite you to consider the possibility that the emotional block we all experience in connection with the cookbook approach could be dissolved simply by trying it out until our daily successes finally get us accustomed to the idea.

Admittedly this would take some of the "fun" out of psychodiagnostic activity. But I suspect that most of the clinicians who put a high value on this kind of fun would have even more fun doing intensive psychotherapy. The great personnel needs today, and for the next generation or more, are for psychotherapists and researchers. (If you don't believe much in the efficacy of therapy, this is all the more reason for research.) If all the thousands of clinical hours currently being expended in concocting clever and flowery personality sketches from test data could be devoted instead to scientific investigation (assuming we are still selecting and training clinicians to be scientists), it would probably mean a marked improvement in our net social contribution. If a reasonably good cookbook could help bring about this result, the achieve-

P. E. Meehl

ment would repay tenfold the expensive and tedious effort required in its construction.

REFERENCES

1. Cronbach, L. J., and P. E. Meehl. "Construct Validity in Psychological Tests," *Psychological Bulletin*, 52:281–302 (1955).
2. Daily, C. A. "The Practical Utility of the Clinical Report," *Journal of Consulting Psychology*, 17:297–302 (1953).
3. Davenport, Beverly F. "The Semantic Validity of TAT Interpretations," *Journal of Consulting Psychology*, 16:171–75 (1952).
4. Halbower, C. C. "A Comparison of Actuarial Versus Clinical Prediction to Classes Discriminated by MMPI." Unpublished Ph.D. thesis, University of Minnesota, 1955.
5. Hathaway, S. R. "A Coding System for MMPI Profiles," *Journal of Consulting Psychology*, 11:334–37 (1947).
6. Holsopple, J. Q., and J. G. Phelan. "The Skills of Clinicians in Analysis of Projective Tests," *Journal of Clinical Psychology*, 10:307–20 (1954).
7. Kostlan, A. "A Method for the Empirical Study of Psychodiagnosis," *Journal of Consulting Psychology*, 18:83–88 (1954).
8. Little, K. B., and E. S. Shneidman. "The Validity of MMPI Interpretations," *Journal of Consulting Psychology*, 18:425–28 (1954).
9. Little, K. B., and E. S. Shneidman. "The Validity of Thematic Projective Technique Interpretations," *Journal of Personality*, 23:285–94 (1955).
10. Meehl, P. E. *Clinical Versus Statistical Prediction.* Minneapolis: Univ. of Minn. Pr., 1954.
11. Meehl, P. E. " 'Comment' on McArthur, C. Analyzing the Clinical Process," *Journal of Counseling Psychology*, 1:203–8 (1954).
12. Meehl, P. E., and A. Rosen. "Antecedent Probability and the Efficiency of Psychometric Signs, Patterns, or Cutting Scores," *Psychological Bulletin*, 52:194–216 (1955).
13. Paterson, D. G. "Character Reading at Sight of Mr. X According to the System of Mr. P. T. Barnum." Unpublished paper; mimeographed copies obtainable from the author, Department of Psychology, University of Minnesota, Minneapolis.
14. Rosen, A. "Detection of Suicidal Patients: An Example of Some Limitations in the Prediction of Infrequent Events," *Journal of Consulting Psychology*, 18:397–403 (1954).
15. Skinner, B. F. *The Behavior of Organisms.* New York: Appleton-Century-Crofts, 1938.

On the Logic of General Behavior
Systems Theory

SCIENCE, or at least programmatic science, can degenerate into naive and low-grade speculative philosophy by overextending itself in various ways. One typical motive for such overextension is the aim of synthesizing several existing disciplines; another, closely related, is that of extending the concepts and techniques of physics to areas where these concepts have no present application. In this paper, I shall explore an unusually clear instance of such metaphysical overextension: the "scientific" thesis of General Behavior Systems Theory.* Professor Miller's paper, which functions as a general introduction to the symposium, sets forth starkly the major tenets of general systems theory, in its search for an "embracing theory" of behavior. On two subsequent occasions Miller has returned to this theme, so it is especially appropriate to consider his views.†

What exactly are the central theses of general systems theory? According to Miller, this theory "finds formal identities between various physical systems, the cell, the organ, the individual, the small group or species,

* The first published version of this theory is a symposium by members of the Committee on Behavioral Sciences, University of Chicago (1). The publication is undated, but it consists of papers read at a meeting of the American Psychological Association, in September, 1953. Of the five contributions to this symposium, only one, that of Professor James G. Miller, is extensively considered here. (Parenthetical page references are to this publication.)

† The first of these occasions was at another symposium: the Joint Session of the Southern Society for Philosophy and Psychology, at Atlanta, April 17, 1954. My paper is a revised version of some comments contributed at the same Joint Session. The second occasion is Miller's "Toward a General Theory for the Behavioral Sciences," (2). This paper appeared too late to be considered here in detail. In it Miller tries, I think unsuccessfully, to meet criticisms of the kind here offered. Those interested in the question of the impact of methodological criticism on the procedures of scientific theorists, should consider this most recent paper of Miller's in the light of the criticisms offered here.

and the society" (p. 5). These identities "offer promise not only of coordinating the theories of scholars but also of confirming their conclusions empirically, employing the dimensions and units of the natural sciences" (p. 6). Behavior is conceived as energy exchange within a system or between systems. "Every system has its environment, and all living systems are open systems with inputs and outputs, and tend to maintain steady states" (Ibid.). Living systems "are also ordinarily in equilibrium with the environment" (Ibid.).* Inputs and outputs may be either "coded" or "uncoded," and inputs can force a system beyond its range of stability, thus creating stresses and strains which "may or may not be capable of being reduced, depending upon the equilibratory resources of the system" (Ibid.). In individual psychology "reduction of strains is called drive satisfaction" (Ibid.). "The total of the strains within the individual resulting from his genetic input and variations in the input from his environment is often referred to as his values" (p. 7).

Miller recognizes that this "empty shell of general systems theory resounds hollowly without specific illustrations of how it can be applied" (p. 7). And he goes on to present "a few anecdotal examples of its usefulness" (Ibid.). I shall consider several of these examples, raising questions about their usefulness and especially about their significance. But first we must look briefly at the notions of "formal identity," and of "system."

I

The most serious conceptual problems in general systems theory concern the employment of analogies. Miller at first employed the expression "formal identity" to refer to what are generally known as analogies, reserving the word analogy as a term of abuse for "metaphysical or artistic statements that two or more phenomena elicit similar feelings in the observer" (p. 3). Those who recognize the kinship between Miller's organic theories of groups and societies, and the metaphysical theory of the state as advanced by Hegel and Bosanquet, will note the irony in this. In any event, Miller has now lost his faith in the efficacy of this verbal maneuver, and has adopted the sound practice of calling analogies what they are.

* The usefulness of the concept of dynamic equilibrium in the social sciences is investigated in the same symposium by David Eastman, another member of the Chicago Committee. He argues very reasonably that there is little present evidence for the utility of this concept in social science, and that there are many obstacles in the way of its employment there.

The questions which need to be raised about the analogies in which general systems theory is interested are mostly of the "So what?" variety. They take the form of "granting that you have shown that there is some analogy, what follows?" A closely related question concerns disanalogy— a subject which is almost completely neglected by general systems theory.* Yet surely such neglect is dangerous, for if there is anything that is clear about analogies, it is that things or systems are analogous in some respect or respects, not in all.

The sort of analogies which particularly interest general systems theory, in its search for an "embracing theory" of behavior, are what might be called structural analogies. This, of course, is connected with their concentration on systems. A system, whatever else it may be, is certainly the sort of thing that has a structure, and the kinds of analogies general systems theory is interested in are those which relate two systems because of a similarity of structure. The notion of formal identity is, I suppose, suggested by the fact that when two systems exhibit such a similarity of structure, then a sufficiently general description can be seen to apply to both. As an example, compare a chessboard and a well-planned, mixed, dinner party. The dinner party will be such that between any two men there will be a woman, and vice versa. The chessboard will be such that between any two black squares there will be a white square, and vice versa. Now it is obvious that one could construct a sufficiently general statement in terms of "two kinds of things" and the spatial relations between them, to cover both cases. The fact that the sense of "between" is different in the two cases—one roughly a linear and the other a two-dimensional sense—is, of course, part of the disanalogy in this case. If one is tempted to say "All right, so they're structurally analogous, so what?" my answer is "So, nothing!" But I welcome the question, for while I was concerned simply to illustrate the employment of the concept of structural analogy, this kind of question will certainly be in point in dealing with many of Miller's analogies.

I turn now to an examination of the central concept of general systems theory, the concept of "system" itself. There are strong philosophical reasons for deploring the kind of employment which is given here to the concept of system. About systems Professor Miller says that "A

* But cf. Miller's most recent paper (2).

system is a bounded region of space-time, in which component parts are associated in functional relationships" (p. 6). This already is pretty sweeping, for goodness only knows where some sort of functional relationship between two items may not turn up. And the notion of a *bounded* region is itself a good deal less definite and specific than it sounds, as is clear when it is realized that such logically heterogeneous items as an organism, a cell, a jury, a society, and a biological species (salmon) are all to be regarded as systems, and hence presumably as thus *bounded*. The idea of system can be seen as further generalized and extended through the following considerations. First, there is the rather sweeping claim that "Every system has subsystems" (p. 6). Taking this together with "Every system has its environment" (Ibid.), we are indeed confronted with limitless vistas of systems. One is unable to think of anything, or of any combination of things, which could not be regarded as a system. And, of course, a concept that applies to everything is logically empty.

What characteristics are there which any object or group of objects could have, such that they would fail to form some kind of system? In my view, general systems theory not only does not, but further could not, answer this question. And it is partly for this reason that I believe that general systems theory is not in fact science at all, but rather naive and speculative philosophy. Miller approves of so formulating scientific statements that they can be empirically confirmed (pp. 5–6). This is a laudable, and a scientific, ideal. But has he tried to apply this criterion to his own statements about systems? What would it be like to disprove the statement that every system has subsystems? If general systems theory can answer this question, the answer should certainly be provided. For such an answer would have to include a criterion for recognizing something which is not a system; and possession of such a criterion would help immeasurably in clarifying the central concept of system. An important part of the significance of any concept is given by contrast, by knowing the kinds of things to which it does *not* apply. And the trouble with the concept of system here, as I see it, is that this contrast is absent. Here, rather, the situation seems to be that statements such as "I am a system," "The membership committee is a system," "The economy of the United States is a system," "The species, salmon, is a system"—that these statements, in the language of general systems theory, couldn't even be false.

II

I turn now to construct a possible defense against my charge of the emptiness of the central concept of "system." This defense, though not explicitly offered by general systems theorists, seems to me to be one that they very likely would offer, *if* they paid more attention to logical and conceptual problems.

Suppose, then, that the general systems theorist answers my charge of emptiness in some such vein as this:

We grant your contention that the notion of "system" is an extremely vague and virtually empty one; to say that something is a system is really to say no more than that it is the locus of a set of structural relations. And, of course, it is a consequence of this that some of the statements we make about systems are, as you suggest, non-empirical, are such that they couldn't be false. But we maintain that, while it is true that for general systems theory everything is a system, this statement is to be understood as like a statement which a physicist might make to the effect that all physical objects have mass. Such a statement too is non-empirical, and could not be false. It rather records the physicist's decision to treat his subject matter in a unified way, and this determination is to be justified, though not of course *verified* in the usual sense of that term, by noting the tremendous fruitfulness which this approach has in the actual practice of physics. That is, this determination or decision can be justified pragmatically. And so with "system." Our determination to treat everything as a system justifies itself by its great fruitfulness in the practice of the behavioral sciences.

I have several comments on this hypothetical defense. First, notice that it rests, appropriately enough, on an alleged analogy between the behavioral sciences and physics. (This is doubly appropriate in that (a) it is an analogy, and (b) the analogue here, physics, is quite apparently the model of science at its best, to which general systems theory is attempting to assimilate the behavior sciences.)

Again, the justification here is explicitly claimed to be "pragmatic" in both cases. This could raise general problems about the worth, adequacy or acceptability of pragmatic justifications. But I propose to dodge such questions, offering only two general remarks under this head. (1) Something very much like this justification strikes me as the only one either possible or necessary for the universal application within physics of the concept of mass. And (2) that where the notion of "practice" itself is so watered down as to cover all the heterogeneous activities of the physicist—from theorizing and calculation through experiment and measurement—the reference to practice and the pragmatic is just as well omitted. The stress on practice suggests, what is false, that one is here distinguishing between, e.g., practice and theory, or that one is insisting on utilitarian consequences.

But in order to challenge this justification as applied to general systems theory, one need not offer a general criticism of so-called pragmatic justification. One can, and I propose to, challenge this justification by rebutting the contention that it has been shown to be fruitful to apply the notion of system thus universally. The particular analogies between systems which are offered need to be critically examined. Other analogies of similar merit and closeness should be suggested for purposes of comparison. And the general fruitfulness of analogies should be briefly discussed.

As to the last, the general usefulness of analogies, especially as suggesting plausible hypotheses for subsequent testing, is explained in most beginning logic books. But surely, one feels, general systems theory is doing, or at least is trying to do, something more than this. (And in any event the logic books, or at least the good ones, warn us also to consider and notice the negative analogies, the *disanalogies*, in each case.) Now I am convinced that general systems theory is trying to do something more, but just exactly *what* more it is extraordinarily difficult to discover. And the basic reason for the difficulty is that, after drawing our attention to some positive analogy, these theorists in general simply fail to say anything about what the analogy is supposed to prove or suggest, while nevertheless managing to convey the impression that something pretty momentous has been proved or suggested. Let me offer an example taken from Miller's previously mentioned "anecdotal examples of its usefulness."

From the field of botany we find a remarkable study in systems theory in the slime mold, mentioned by Ralph Gerard (another member of the Chicago committee). Under conditions of adequate water and food supply a colony of this plant is made up of quite independent individuals, each with its own inputs, outputs, equilibratory mechanisms and ability to reproduce. Under more stressful conditions, when the environment is less favorable, however, these individuals flow together to form what is essentially a single multicellular organism, with specialization of function or distribution of labor. Some become central cells, others peripheral cells which always flow toward the center, wherever it may be; some cells reproduce, and others cannot—a remarkable model of how humans band together under stress from a common enemy, as did the Londoners for example, during the fire raids of World War II (pp. 8–9).

At this point I must stress that my above quotation is everything, literally everything, that Miller has to say about this alleged example of the usefulness of general systems theory; nor does Professor Gerard say anything more about its usefulness, though he does go into more detail as to the actual behavior of the slime mold. Well, so what? What are we to conclude from all this? That Londoners are a form of slime mold? That myxamoebae are a sort of city dweller? Or, perhaps, that during the battle of London some citizens, due to their new and more specialized activities, became sterile, while others devoted themselves exclusively to reproductive activities? One finds it difficult to believe that these are the conclusions he is expected to draw, but, if not these, what others? And, if no conclusions, why all the fuss, why bother with the analogy at all?

Or look at the matter in this way. Consider an army, in the days when soldiers used to live off the land. Under stressful conditions, say in winter time when food tended to be inadequate, their behavior was in obvious ways directly the reverse of that of the slime mold. Instead of becoming more centralized, and with their members more specialized, they rather broke up into small units, operating in considerable independence, and ranged far and wide in search of food. Now what does this prove? Does it follow that there is *any important respect* in which Londoners are like slime mold, whereas such an army is unlike it? I don't think so. If one wanted to say anything on the basis of these bits of information, surely it would be rather that the Londoners, the myxamoebae, and the soldiers in our foraging army all displayed reasonably successful adaptive behavior when confronted with changes in their environment.

To guard against the impression that I have selected an isolated and bizarre instance of an analogy from general systems theory, let me cite some others which presumably support the usefulness of these theorists' approach. In the same section in which "examples of its usefulness" are presented, we encounter the following:

". . . generalization can be made from one level of analysis to another. Quantitative similarities may be discovered between the characteristics of an input of impulses into the axon of a neuron; an input of words to a jury; and an input of raw materials into the economy of an isolated community" (p. 7).

Indeed, such similarities almost certainly can be discovered, if we can make sense of the notion of "input" in all these cases, and if in addition, as Miller suggests, we select our units and dimensions with such an end in view. But so what? What conceivable difference could such a similarity make?

Again, we are invited to compare (1) the reaction of various cells to the invasion of the lung by tubercle bacilli, in which "certain cells are destroyed, but others come in from the surrounding areas and eventually wall off or destroy the bacilli" (p. 9); with (2) ". . . various isolating or 'walling off' mechanisms of defense recognized in the field of psychodynamics" (Ibid.). These two cases are said to be similar. But is there any important similarity here? Is this any more than verbal magic, employing the words "defense," "walling off," etc. in both cases, and letting this language convince us that there is an important resemblance between the two states of affairs described? But this is not all. We are next urged to compare both (1) and (2) with (3): the way "a committee may at first retreat from a position it formerly held under the attack of a dominant new addition to their membership, but will eventually return to a stable generally acceptable compromise" (Ibid.). And what here? Does the new member kill off a few of the old? Are new resources added to the committee from the outside to cope with the invader? Who knows? We are not told. Finally, in the pursuit of yet further enlightenment, all of these cases are to be usefully compared with the behavior of the Allies in the Battle of the Bulge. Miller remarks of this series of examples that "All this may sound like imaginative analogy" (using the word "analogy" in his abusive sense). But "we believe that it is more. It is the postulation of formal identities between many sorts of response to attack, which can be quantitatively demonstrated if the proper dimensions are used" (Ibid.).

But exactly what is it that one is being urged to believe, and what reasons can be offered in support of that belief? The question of factual justification for our beliefs, and hence for a particular employment of concepts in the formulation of those beliefs, is a vast and difficult one. Still, something may be said on this question, and must be said if I am to make clear the sense in which I feel that these so-called theories are lacking in empirical foundation.

Let me consider an example of my own devising. First, we have a scientist, A, who with considerable ingenuity devises a means of expressing the rate of frost formation on the coils of a refrigerator as a function of the number of times the refrigerator door is opened. Next, we have another scientist, B, who with similar ingenuity succeeds in representing the rate of carbon deposit on the cylinder head of an automobile engine as a function of the number of times the car is started. Finally, we have a general systems theorist, C, who notices that the mathematical function is the same in both cases. Now, the mathematical function, when interpreted for A's case, or for B's case, can indeed be regarded as a statement about the behavior of refrigerators or automobiles, and as such it can certainly be based on a solid foundation of empirical fact. But what of C? Well, immediately the problem arises as to exactly what C means to imply or thinks he has proved or suggested by drawing our attention to the formal identity here. He seems to be very excited about his discovery; he seems to feel that this is something much more than merely an odd coincidence. But what more? Well, first, it proves that both refrigerators and automobiles are systems, but we have already noticed the strikingly empty character of this assertion. Does it further prove that a refrigerator is a kind of automobile, or vice versa? One just doesn't know. The bare possibility of functional or structural analogies is cited as proving or suggesting that, e.g., a committee is a sort of an organism, or that a jury is rather like the economy of an isolated community.

The truth of the matter seems to be that the only grounding in empirical data which the general systems theorist offers is the data which have already been cited by A and B in support of their special theories. These data, together with the fact that the same function fits both cases, will prove or substantiate only the two special theories and the believe-it-or-not coincidence that the same function really does fit both cases. If the general systems theorist would *be* more than a mere collector of such coincidences, then he must *do* more than make impressive gestures in the direction of various analogies. This last remark requires a qualification. The general systems theorist is seldom, perhaps never, *only* such a theorist. It is much more likely, in any actual case, that A, B, and C in our example will all be the same person. This seems to be pretty clearly so for Professor Anatol Rappaport, the mathematical biologist on the Chicago committee. He has developed equations to describe the spread of neural impulses, the spread of rumors, and the spread of epidemics, and has demonstrated great ingenuity in so doing. And he too has found that "models of all these phenomena look mathematically very much alike" (p. 19). I do not see, however, that it detracts from his genuine achievements to point out that this similarity of mathematical models is, for all he tells us, a sheer coincidence.

But the basic point should now be clear. Either we are to conclude something from the analogies, or we are not. If the latter, then it is difficult to see why the analogy needs to be noticed at all. And if the former, we want to know: (1) What are we to conclude? (2) How extensive is the analogy, and what in each particular case is the disanalogy, together with its bearing, if any, on the conclusion? And (3) is there, or could there logically be, any independent evidence for the conclusion?

Under what sorts of circumstances could these conditions be met? Perhaps they are impossible conditions. I think not! It might well have been that when biologists first began to hit on the concept of homology, they actually proceeded in some such fashion. A biologist might have noticed that a certain fin on a fish stands in relation to the rest of the fish, in a way similar to the relation between, say, the leg of an animal and the rest of that animal. And then, from reflection on several such cases, together with what was already known or guessed about the role of inheritance in determining the characteristics of organisms, he may have concluded from his analogy that certain fish and certain animals must have had common specific ancestors. This would be (1) above—what we are to conclude; and note that it is not merely a repetition of the analogy. The disanalogy (2) in this case would include that legs can be walked on while fins cannot; while (3), the possibility of independent confirmation, would be present in the possibility of discovering missing links, and of thus filling out the phylogenetic story.

III

While the major conceptual difficulties specific to Miller's version of general systems theory lie in these questions about the interpretation of analogies, other problems of a more general character are worth noticing. Like many other would-be new departures in social science, general systems theory interests itself in "information theory," with its crucial concept of "communication." "Communication" is a fashionable word nowadays. What I want to notice about the word is that its employment to cover all cases of people talking to each other may be seriously misleading, and that this use may involve an implicit commitment to a theory of mind.

The theory is, roughly, that everyone always has complete access to his own thoughts, that these are always transparently clear to him, and that he always knows exactly what he means when he speaks; but that because of a queer sort of barrier other people are often, or even always, liable to misunderstand him and to fail to grasp clearly what he means. The theory would also usually add that A never has direct, but at best only inferential and indirect, access to the thoughts of B. Now this is a theory that many contemporary psychologists and philosophers are concerned to reject. But notice the extent to which the very general use of the word "communication," for all sorts of talk other than soliloquy, tends to reinforce this picture. Look to the antecedents of this use of the word. Think of its uses in, e.g., geography, where the transportation and communications of a country are discussed. Remember the sense of "communication" in which it has been respectively true of the telegraph, the undersea cable, the telephone, and radio—that each was a new form of communication. Notice that in all these earlier, and perhaps outside academic circles still standard, uses of the word "communication," there really is some obstacle to overcome, usually distance. Jones is in his office, and his wife is at home, and if she were right there with him, he could tell her that he would be a bit late for dinner. There would be no difficulty about telling her this. But she's not there; there is a difficulty; even if he yells, she won't hear him. So he uses a medium of communication, the telephone, with which he overcomes the difficulty.

The basis for my conceptual query about "communication" should now be getting clear. If he and his wife are sitting in the same room, and she wants to know what time it is, and he looks at his watch and tells her, he certainly does not have any difficulty about telling her. But, in the newly fashionable extended use of the word "communication," this latter transaction too is described as communication. He wants to let her know what time it is, so he has to get word to her, there, across the room, so he casts about for some means of doing this and finally he hits on it: "I know, I'll utter the words, 'half past six.'" Thus described, it is clear that there's something curious going on here. And the employment of the word "communication" to cover such cases fits in only too well with the theory of mind sketched above. If his wife were only here (i.e., "in" his mind), he could tell her with no difficulty. But, alas, his mind is private, there is a barrier to be overcome, and a medium of communication, namely language, is employed to surmount that barrier.

Another conceptual muddle can easily arise over the notion of "environment," in a context of systems and subsystems. We often speak of someone's *social environment*, and, from this, the move to saying that the society in which he lives is his *environment* is natural and perhaps proper. But such moves can lead to odd results if we now start to specify the relation between the individual and the society, especially if that specification be in terms of the notions of "part" or "member." And general systems theory is peculiarly liable to do this with its treatment of both individuals and the groups to which they belong as "systems." For example, Miller at one time * proposed that we so use the word "environment" that where any system at level n has a component, a subsystem, at level $n - 1$, there the level n system is said to be the *environment* of the level $n - 1$ system. Now this is a strange use of "environment." Consider, e.g., Ted Williams and the Boston Red Sox. In any sense in which it is true that a person is a subsystem in a group, then I take it that a baseball player is a subsystem in his team. But, of course, Williams is a member of that team. So Williams is a member of his environment? But is this even an intelligible, much less a true, thing to say? Do we have any clear idea at all what would be meant by saying that Williams either is, or is not, a member of his environment? And, similarly, with Jones' heart and Jones. (Levels $n - 1$ and n, respectively.) His heart is a part of him. Is it also a part of its environment? The truth would seem to be that, as the term "environment" is usually used, we *distinguish between* an organism and its environment, in a way which logically precludes that an organism should be spoken of as a part of, or as a member of, its environment.

At this point, let me interject a remark about the role of philosophi-

* In his paper read at Atlanta.

cal analysis, vis-à-vis psychology or any other science. I take it that there is a legitimate activity called conceptual or linguistic analysis, and that it can proceed very much as in my last two examples, to locate and, at least partially, to clarify conceptual problems. But in an important sense it cannot solve them. A general systems theorist might reply that his use of "environment" is indeed different from the conventional one, but that his use is preferable. Now it seems to me that, qua philosopher, I cannot decide such an issue. Nor does it seem to me that the general systems theorist is in any better case. Any changes of concepts, or alteration of the logical powers of words, have ramifications throughout the set—or system—of concepts in which they function. In actual on-going scientific research, the logical powers of words are constantly undergoing changes. But the test of the adequacy of any set or system of concepts is the adequacy of the body of scientific laws which is formulated in terms of those concepts. And, of course, the latter is tested, at least in part, by the usual scientific procedures of observation, experiment, prediction, and the like. This last reflection is yet another reason for my feeling that in an important sense general systems theory is not science at all. For the experiments and the data which it mentions never seem to be such that they would enable us to decide either for or against the terminological legislation which it explicitly proposes, or implicitly requires. And, hence, in appraising these terminological recommendations, one is driven to fall back on logical analysis, of the kind I have been employing.

There are many other conceptual problems in general systems theory which would need to be investigated in any complete analysis. The notion of coding is a very general notion. You might very well be doing a bit of coding if you say "ouch," on instructions from the dentist, when he hurts you; as well as if you devise and employ a new notation for describing a chess game. The notions of "input" and "output" might well repay attention. They, too, are employed with a tremendous generality, as witness the "input of words to a jury," already cited. And, of course, the idea of "equilibrium," and the related notions of "homeostasis" and "negative feedback" would also have to be treated. Here, the appropriate question to ask would be like those we raised concerning "system." Could there, logically, be a non-homeostatic system? Are these terms used in such a way that one could describe what a non-homeostatic system would be like? My own impression is that general systems theory uses "system" and "homeostatic" in such a way that a non-homeostatic system would be a contradiction in terms. And, if so, the general systems theorist may be doing no more, when he announces that all systems may be rewardingly treated as homeostatic, than I should be if I announced that all uncles may be regarded as males.

But my final specimen from Miller's terminological recommendations involves that delightful pair of terms "adience" and "abience" which he attributes to E. B. Holt, and whose adoption he recommends. He mentions them specifically in connection with his stress on the desirability of physicalizing the language and the procedures of behavior theory. They, like the grams-seconds-centimeters approach, are to do great things for psychology. He says,

Admittedly the dimensions of behavior are highly complex, and to translate them into physical dimensions will frequently be extremely involved, but we believe that a beginning can now be made. For example, take the terms 'adience' and 'abience' of E. B. Holt. He used these terms to represent something like affiliation or love and dislike or hate. Adience may be measured as motion through space over time towards a goal, and abience as motion away. The psychological conception of ambivalence may be equated to the behavior of an ambivalent organism that oscillates back and forth, toward and away from a goal, with motions describable in space-time dimensions (p. 8).

This is indeed Empedocles turned upside down. The ancients, too, had hold of an analogy when they described various changes and motions, e.g., the falling of an unsupported body, on the model of purposive behavior and striving. And physics began to make progress at exactly that point at which these conceptions of natural teleology were abandoned for physical objects qua physical. So now we are to resurrect this confusion, but from the opposite end, and assimilate to the motions of physical objects the behavior of goal-oriented, loving and hating, affiliating and disliking, organisms. Here indeed the analogy is very thin. Does one find himself invariably experiencing a rapid upsurge of "something like affiliation or love" as he drives rapidly to the hotel to meet a stranger he has corresponded with; and perhaps a slower building-up of this feeling as he drives slowly to meet someone else? And, when he leaves home in the morning, does something like dislike or hate for his wife well up in him, becoming more intense as he gets farther away? May we then go on to use the sad fate of Buridan's ass, who starved to death at a point equidistant between two bales of hay, as not merely an amusing instance of conflict of desires, but as a veritable paradigm of such conflict?

Let us grant the obvious fact that physics is a wonderful science, and that both the precision of its conceptual structures and its power to predict and control far exceed those of the behavior sciences. Let us grant too that human beings are physical objects, that, e.g., when they tumble off tall buildings, they fall to the ground with an acceleration of 32ft/sec². Still it does not follow from all this that the way to solve conceptual problems in psychology is to abandon psychology altogether in favor of the physics of organisms. If the physicalizing of psychology can solve these problems, then there aren't really any problems at all, and there is nothing we want to say or explain about the behavior of organisms which we do not also want to say or explain about the behavior of stones and electromagnetic fields. But this is obviously false, so we would need to complicate and alter the structure of physical concepts sufficiently to enable physics to cope with the kind of subject matter which we all know psychology must deal with, and which we do all of us manage to talk about in daily life. And this, of course, is where "adience" and "abience" fail us. We know that we can much more adequately describe and explain the behavior of organisms in terms of our everyday language, than can Miller in terms of "adience" and "abience."

A final word on physics. Perhaps those behavior theorists who are so attracted by physics as a model science should look not only at its internal conceptual structure, but also at the logical relations between the language of physics and the ways in which non-scientists talk about physical phenomena. And perhaps it would be even more instructive to compare these two at a time when physics was groping its way, very much as psychology is today. There are such relations, plenty of them. They are not neat and tidy equivalences of meaning; these occur only within systems of concepts, whereas the relations I am talking about transcend such systems. It seems certain that the intelligibility and the adequacy of the physics of macro-objects of the kind we see and touch rests in part on the adequacy with which such everyday concepts as weight, speed, force, resistance, etc. find their counterparts in physics without too great distortion.

And, of course, some of my criticism of general systems theory has rested on a comparable conviction for psychology. If, in the adience and abience of Jones, the physical object, we cannot recognize even a caricature of Jones, the lover and hater, then we cannot be sold a science of love and hate in which these concepts are replaced by the directional acceleration of Jones' body.

REFERENCES

1. *Chicago Behavioral Sciences Publications*, No. 1. *Profits and Problems of Homeostatic Models in the Behavioral Sciences*. Chicago: Univ. of Chicago Pr.
2. Miller, James G. "Toward a General Theory for the Behavioral Sciences," *The American Psychologist*, 10:513–31 (1955).

—————— P. E. MEEHL and WILFRID SELLARS ——————

The Concept of Emergence

SOMEWHAT over a quarter of a century ago, Professor Stephen Pepper published a paper on "Emergence" (1) which was (and still is) symptomatic of a certain way of thinking on this topic. The paper had the virtues of brevity and clarity, and, which is more important, it went to the heart of the matter. The fact that the crucial step in its argument is a simple *non sequitur* by no means detracts from its diagnostic value as a document in the controversy over emergence.

Before we examine Professor Pepper's argument, two introductory remarks are in order.

1. Our aim is not to defend an emergentist picture of the world, but rather to criticize an argument which, if successful, would make this picture indefensible. As we see it, the question whether the world is to be conceived along emergentist lines is a scientific question which cannot be settled on a priori grounds.

2. The question "Does the world contain emergents?" requires to be answered in terms of a scientific account of observable phenomena, and although with reference to a given scientific picture of the world the question is a *logical* one which concerns the formal structure of this picture, taken absolutely, the question shares the inductive character, and hence corrigibility in principle, of the scientific enterprise. Indeed, since science presents us today not with one integrated interpretation of the totality of observable phenomena, but rather with a large number of partially integrated theories of more limited scope, the question inevitably takes on a *speculative* character, and becomes an attempt to anticipate the logical structure of a theoretical framework which is still in gestation. This speculative dimension must, of course, be distinguished from the previously noted corrigibility (in principle) of any answer to the question "Are there emergents?"

239

Professor Pepper writes,

Emergence signifies a kind of change. There seem to be three important kinds of change considered possible in modern metaphysical discussion. First, there is chance occurrence, the assertion of a cosmic irregularity, an occurrence about which no law could be stated. Second, there is what we may call a "shift," a change in which one characteristic replaces another, the sort of change traditionally described as invariable succession and when more refined described as a functional relation. Thirdly, there is emergence, which is a cumulative change, a change in which certain characteristics supervene upon other characteristics, these characteristics being adequate to explain the occurrence on their level. The important points here are first, that in discussing emergence we are not discussing the possibility of cosmic chance. The emergent evolutionists admit a thoroughgoing regularity in nature. And secondly, we are not discussing the legitimacy of shifts. These also are admitted. The issue is whether in addition to shifts there are emergent changes.

The theory of emergence involves three propositions: (1) that there are levels of existence defined in terms of degrees of integration; (2) that there are marks which distinguish these levels from one another over and above the degrees of integration; (3) that it is impossible to deduce the marks of a higher level from those of a lower level, and perhaps also (though this is not clear) impossible to deduce marks of a lower level from those of a higher. The first proposition, that there are degrees of integration in nature, is not controversial. The specific issue arises from the second and third propositions. The second states that there is cumulative change, the third that such change is not predictable.

What I wish to show is that each of these propositions is subject to a dilemma: (1) either the alleged emergent change is not cumulative or it is epiphenomenal; (2) either the alleged emergent change is predictable like any physical change, or it is epiphenomenal. I assume that a theory of wholesale epiphenomenalism is metaphysically unsatisfactory. I feel the more justified in making this assumption because I have been led to understand that the theory of emergent evolution has been largely developed as a corrective of mechanistic theories with their attendant psycho-physical dualisms and epiphenomenalisms. (p. 241)

The distinctions drawn in the first of these paragraphs provides the basic framework of Pepper's argument. Pointing out, quite correctly, that indeterminism is neither essential to, nor characteristic of, theories of emergent evolution, Pepper draws a distinction between two possible types of regularity: (a) "shifts"—that is to say regularities of the kind "traditionally described as invariable succession"; (b) regularities "in which certain characteristics supervene upon other characteristics." Notice, however, that to his description of the second kind of regularity he adds the phrase "these [latter] characteristics being adequate to explain the occurrences on their level." By adding this phrase, Pepper implies that there could be no such thing as a regularity in which certain characteristics supervene upon other characteristics but in which the lower level characteristics were not adequate to explain the occurrences on their level. In other words, he implies that "supervening" or emergent characteristics are, merely by virtue of being such, unnecessary to the explanation of occurrences at the lower level—that is to say, of occurrences insofar as they exemplify nonemergent characteristics. And, indeed, he implies that this is such a well-known and generally accepted fact that its use requires no justification in this day and age. We are not surprised, then, to find him claiming, without further ado, in the fifth paragraph, that "a theory of emergent qualities is palpably a theory of epiphenomena" (p. 242).

Now the claim that emergent qualities are ("palpably") epiphenomenal can scarcely be just the claim that emergent qualities have necessary-and-sufficient conditions. "Epiphenomenal" carries, and is intended by Pepper to carry, the connotation "making no difference." Obviously "having a necessary-and-sufficient condition" is not identical in sense with "making no difference." Yet the idea that emergent qualities must be epiphenomenal is clearly tied up with the idea that a certain context specified in terms of lower level characteristics is the necessary-and-sufficient condition for the appearance of the emergent quality. A glance at the conventional diagram will show what is going on.

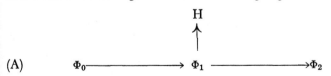

(A)

This diagram is designed to be a representation of the following propositions: (1) Φ_0 is a sufficient condition of Φ_1; (2) Φ_1 is a sufficient condition of Φ_2; (3) Φ_1 is also the necessary and sufficient condition of H. But while this is all that the diagram is *intended* to represent, it strongly suggests that H is, in the proper sense of the term, an epiphenomenon. That this suggestion is unwarranted, that the information summed up in the diagram leaves open the question as to whether H is an epiphenomenon, will be established at a later stage in our argument. For the moment we shall limit ourselves to some reflection on the phrase "making no difference."

It is obvious that if H is to "make a difference" there must be a difference between situations in which it is present and situations in which it is not. That there is one such difference is clear; H-situations differ from non-H-situations in that the former are also Φ_1 situations and the latter not. But this difference, far from being a difference that would keep H from being epiphenomenal, is at least part of what is meant by calling H an epiphenomenon. And, indeed, if there were no other difference between H-situations and non-H-situations, H would be epiphenomenal. But what other difference could there be? Clearly it is a mistake to look for this new difference in the form of another characteristic that is present when H is present and absent when H is absent. There remains only the possibility that H-situations are governed by different laws than non-H-situations. And this not in the trivial sense that H-situations conform to the law "H if and only if Φ_1," whereas non-H-situations do not (save vacuously), but in the important sense that the lower level characteristics themselves exhibit a different lawfulness in H-situations. In other words, for emergent qualities to make a difference which removes them from the category of the epiphenomenal, in any significant sense of this term, there must be "emergent laws." We hasten to add that the last few remarks are informal in character, and are intended to be hints and signposts of what is coming, rather than definitive clarifications.

II

Pepper's "first dilemma," designed to prove that "either the alleged emergent change is not cumulative or it is epiphenomenal" begins with a distinction between those theories of emergence according to which what emerges are *qualities* and those according to which what emerges are *laws*. He points out that in Alexander's system it is new qualities which emerge; but he expresses the conviction that "most emergent evolutionists have theories of emergent laws" (p. 242). As we have already noted, he claims that "a theory of emergent qualities is palpably a theory of epiphenomena." On the other hand "it is not so obvious that a theory of emergent laws must also be such—or else cease to be a theory of emergence" (p. 242). But though he finds the latter claim "not so obvious," it is, as he sees it, equally true, and it is to the task of showing it to be true that he now turns.

Before we take up his argument, some remarks on his classification of theories of emergence are in order. Once again we find fewer alternatives presented than are abstractly possible. Postponing (with Pepper) the question as to what could be meant by "emergent law," the dichotomy "emergent quality"—"emergent law" yields a trichotomy of emergentist theories: (a) theories of emergent qualities without emergent laws; (b) theories of emergent qualities with emergent laws; (c) theories of emergent laws without emergent qualities. Now we have already suggested that of these three only the first is "palpably" committed to epiphenomenalism (unless, that is, a theory of emergent qualities is "epiphenomenalistic" merely by virtue of the fact that it recognizes that emergent qualities have necessary-and-sufficient conditions). We now notice that to make this first alternative consistent with determinism (which is not in question in this paper) we must either refuse to call the regularities between emergent qualities and the contexts in which they emerge "laws," or, calling them "laws," we must deny that they are "emergent." Pepper, in effect, by drawing his distinction between "shifts" and "superveniencies" takes the former alternative. In these terms, the regularities in diagram (A) between Φ_0 and Φ_1, and between Φ_1 and Φ_2 would be shifts, whereas that between Φ_1 and H would be a regularity of supervenience. And in these terms, the three alternatives above become (a') theories of emergent qualities without emergent shifts; (b') theories of emergent qualities with emergent shifts; (c') theories of emergent shifts without emergent qualities. But from the standpoint of one whose concern is with the question "Does emergence involve epiphenomenalism?" and who is convinced that emergent qualities must as such be epiphenomenal, this trichotomy reduces to this dichotomy: theories without emergent shifts—theories with emergent shifts. And from this standpoint, and in these terms, the issue would be "Do emergent shifts involve epiphenomenalism?"

But this is not how Pepper sets up his problem. In his first formulation, as we have seen, he makes use of the general notion of law, and sees his purpose as that of showing that "a theory of emergent laws . . . must be [a theory of epiphenomena] or else cease to be a theory of emergence." Then, after drawing a distinction between *laws* and the *regularities* they describe, he reformulates his task as that of showing that "all natural regularities are shifts." At first sight this is puzzling indeed, for as the term "shift" was introduced, it amounts to the task of showing that no natural regularities are regularities in which "certain characteristics supervene upon other characteristics." And since the understood context is "under pain of epiphenomenalism," this amounts, in turn, to the task of showing that supervening *characteristics* must be epiphenomena. But at first sight this is only verbally different from the task of showing that emergent qualities are epiphenomena—and this, for Pepper, is no task, since the *demonstrandum* is "palpably" true.

Now the key to the resolution of this difficulty is the philosophical virtuosity of the term "characteristic." Often used in the sense of *property*, frequently used to cover both *properties* and *relations*, it is here being used in so broad a sense that even *regularities* become characteristics. Pepper, indeed, is thinking of an emergent law as a *supervening regularity*—as, so to speak, a regularity which rides piggy-back on a lower level regularity. It is little wonder that, approaching it with this mental set, he finds the notion of an emergent law absurd. As he sees it, the emergentist who speaks of emergent laws is able to swallow this absurdity because he mistakes a "whole hierarchy of different laws"—each of which, according to Pepper, describes "the same natural regularities"—for a "ladder of cosmic regularities." Pepper does not develop this point. However, in terms of contemporary controversy, the initial mistake of the emergentist, according to Pepper, is to be so fascinated by the difference between one framework of concepts and laws (e.g., biology) and the proximate lower level framework of concepts and laws (e.g., organic chemistry) that he finds it difficult to believe that the one could be reducible to the other. What is not clear is whether Pepper believes that the denial (in principle) of reducibility involves the absurdities he finds in the notion of emergent laws.

III

Be this as it may, the fact remains that Pepper does find the emergentist view absurd, and offers an argument to prove it. He seeks, as we have seen, to show that "all natural regularities are shifts." Now this thesis is equivalent to "there are no emergent (supervening) regularities" only if "shifts" is being used in such a way that it connotes absence of supervenience. Given this connotation, Pepper's formulation of his task is equivalent to our formulation at the end of the preceding section, namely, "Do emergent shifts involve epiphenomenalism?" Indeed, in the terminology of that section, it becomes "Is the notion of an emergent shift absurd?" Here is his argument:

Let us suppose a shift at level B is described as a function of four variables q, r, s, and t. Let us then suppose that r and s constitute an integration giving rise to level C at which level a new cosmic regularity emerges that can be described as a function of four variables r, s, a, and b. r and s must necessarily be variables in this emergent law even though they are variables of level B, because they constitute part of the conditions under which the emergent law is possible. Theoretically, to be sure, the emergent law may be thought of either as a function of new variables or as a new function of C-level variables. But actually only the former is possible. For if the new law were not f_1 (q,r,s,t), but were f_2 (q,r,s,t), then, of course, it would never be $f_1(q,r,s,t)$, unless the event were a chance occurrence in which case no regularity could be described anyway. The point is, either f_1 adequately describes the interrelationships of (q,r,s,t) or f_2 does; or if neither adequately describes the interrelationships there is some f_3 that does, but there cannot be two adequate descriptions of the same interrelationships among the same variables.

An emergent law must, therefore, involve the emergence of new variables. But these new variables either have some functional relationship with the rest of the lower level variables or they haven't. If they haven't, they are sheer epiphenomena, and the view resolves itself into a theory of qualitative emergence. If they have, they have to be included among the total set of variables described by the lower level functional relation; they have to drop down and take their places among the lower level variables as elements in a lower level shift.

Such being the case, our dilemma is established so far as concerns cumulative change—either there is no such thing or it is epiphenomenal . . . (pp. 242–43)

Before embarking upon a more general discussion, we shall examine the argument in Pepper's form. It can be restated as follows:

1. If a function f_1 (q,r,s,t) "adequately describes the interrelationships" among four variables q, r, s and t, then no other function f_2, nonequivalent to f_1, of these variables can do so. "There cannot be two adequate descriptions of the same interrelationships among the same variables."

2. If f_2 "adequately describes the interrelationships" among these

variables *after* the 'integration' (and putative emergence) then, since sheer difference of time has no material consequence, f_2 must also be the adequate description of these interrelationships before the integration. Consequently f_1 could only be the adequate description of these interrelationships before the integration if it were equivalent to f_2, which, *ex hypothesi*, it is not.

3. Hence, if f_2 "adequately describes the interrelationships" after the integration, f_1 cannot adequately describe the relationships which obtain before the integration. "The point is, either f_1 adequately describes the interrelationships of (q,r,s,t) or f_2 does; or if neither adequately describes the interrelationships, there is some f_3 which does . . ."

But surely this is too strong—a veritable *ignoratio elenchi*. What the emergentist says is that there is a region in the fourspace $qrst$ within which f_1 $(q,r,s,t) = 0$ holds. This region is the "lower level of integration"—e.g., physicochemical processes which are not occurring in protoplasm. On the other hand, there is another region—the "emergent" region—in which f_2 $(q,r,s,t) = 0$ holds, $f_1 \neq f_2$. And a claim of this kind is mathematically unexceptionable, since it amounts to no more than the claim that a function may graduate the empirical data in restricted regions but break down when extrapolated. Such a "breakdown" does not mean, however, that the fit attained in either the subregion fitted by f_1 or that fitted by f_2 is a "chance occurrence." The fit may be excellent, and the demarcation of the regions precise (or, if gradual, thoroughly lawful) so that the "chance occurrence" interpretation is as definitely excludable as it ever can be by inductive methods. It should be noted that phenomena in describing which scientists speak of "laws of composition" belong to this category.

But while the notion of different regions in the fourspace $qrst$ exhibiting different functional relationships is mathematically unexceptionable, is it emergence? Here the first thing to note is that the notion, as such, involves no "supervenience." For (a) no emergent variables have been introduced; f_1 and f_2 being functions of the same four variables; and (b) it is not being claimed that there are 'piggy-back' regularities. When a situation exhibits a constellation of values of q,r,s, and t falling within region$_1$ of the fourspace, it is not exhibiting a constellation falling within region$_2$, and vice versa. When a situation conforms to f_2, it is not conforming to f_1, and vice versa. Thus, to the extent that 'emergence' connotes the simultaneous presence in a single situation of two or more levels, the notion we have been analyzing is not, as such, a matter of emergence. This, however, is not to say that there is no philosophical use of "emergence"—a use, that is, to connote something of philosophical interest—according to which cases of this kind are cases of emergence. Thus, the mere fact that the highly complex organic compounds which are found in protoplasm made their appearance late in the history of the universe would not be a fact of emergence in any philosophically interesting sense. But if we add to this the notion that protoplasm exhibits a constellation of physicochemical variables which belongs in a region of the n-space defined by those variables that conform to a different function than do the regions to which belong constellations exhibited by less complex physicochemical situations, then the use of the term "emergence" seems not inappropriate. And, indeed, many philosophers who have made use of the concept of *levels of integration* or *levels of causality* seem to have had something like the above in mind.

But it is reasonably clear that most emergentist philosophers have had something more in mind. They have spoken of the emergence of *properties*. And while there is a usage of "property" (in the sense of *dispositional* property) in which to mention a property of an object is to mention a functional correlation exhibited by that object—so that to say, for example, that protoplasm has an emergent property would be just another way of saying what was said above in terms of different functions holding for different regions in the n-space of physicochemical variables—not all the 'properties' that have been said to 'emerge' can be given this interpretation. Thus, the qualia of feeling and sensation have been said to emerge. It must be confessed, however, that emergentists have tended to lump into one category of "emergent properties" items which require radically different treatment, e.g., *sense qualities, life, purpose, value, thought*.

IV

We are now in a position to make a more penetrating analysis of Pepper's claim that theories of emergent qualities are committed to epiphenomenalism. If determinism is assumed, so that these qualities are themselves lawfully related to the lower level variables, then it must be granted that descriptive laws predicting the course of the latter can, in principle, always be formulated in terms of them alone. For suppose the emergents to be a and b, depending for their appearance upon, say, appropriate values of q,r,s and t, so that, for example,

$$a = g(q,r)$$
$$b = h(s,t)$$

then the function which adequately describes the interrelationships of the inclusive set of variables (q,r,s,t,a,b), call it $E(q,r,s,t,a,b)$, can be written without a and b, for it can be written as $E[q,r,s,t,g(q,r),h(s,t)]$ or $f_3(q,r,s,t)$.

Now Pepper at this point develops an argument which can be represented as follows:

1. Unless $f_3(q,r,s,t)$ is equivalent to $f_1(q,r,s,t)$, they cannot both hold (and, of course, Pepper is quite right if both f_3 and f_1 are intended to cover the entire fourspace determined by these variables).

2. But for f_3 to be equivalent to f_1, is for a and b to be epiphenomenal. (Again Pepper is quite right on the same condition we have pointed out in our comment on 1.)

3. Thus, if f_3 holds, and a and b are not epiphenomenal, then f_1 cannot hold. In other words, if f_3 holds and a and b are not epiphenomenal, then f_3 must hold both 'before' and 'after' the appearance of a and b.

4. But $f_3(q,r,s,t)$ is just another way of writing $E(q,r,s,t,a,b)$. Therefore, both 'before' and 'after' integration the phenomena in question are adequately described by the function $E(q,r,s,t,a,b)$.

5. Thus, the supposed emergents a and b "have to be included among the total set of variables described by the lower level functional relation; they have to drop down and take their place among the lower level variables as elements in a lower level shift" (pp. 242–43).

However, once we drop, as we have seen we must, the assumption that f_3 and f_1 are intended by the emergentist to hold for the same regions in qrst-space (f_3 presumably holds for all regions, f_1 only for the "lower level of integration"), the argument falls apart. For while the emergentist must indeed admit that if f_3 and f_1 are equivalent, then a and b make no difference, it is open to him to say that the difference made by a and b is just the fact that f_1(qrst), which holds in regions of qrst-space which are unaccompanied by a and b, is not equivalent to the function which holds of these variables for regions in which they are accompanied by a and/or b.

V

A survey of the literature makes it clear that 'sense quality,' 'sensa,' 'raw feels,' '(sensory) consciousness'—the terms are almost as numerous as the authors—are among the more confidently backed candidates for the role of emergent. And it may be helpful to conclude our examination of emergence on the more concrete note of a discussion of certain logical aspects of this particular claim. In doing so, however, we shall avoid, as far as possible, those labyrinthine issues concerning the sense, if any, in which sense qualities, supposing them to be emergent, can appropriately be said to be 'in' the brain. It should, however, be pointed out that this problem concerns the structure of a (future) *scientific* account of sensory consciousness, and it must be carefully distinguished from the problem of analyzing ordinary language to determine the relation of talk about seeing colors, feeling pain, having an itch, etc., to talk about the body and bodily behavior. Science has the task of *creating* a way of talking about the sensory activities of the central nervous system, not that of analyzing antecedent ordinary language about sense experience. After all, we were talking about seeing colors and itching long before there was such a notion as that of the C.N.S., and long before it was realized that the brain had anything to do with these matters. Our present concern is with a possible logical feature (namely emergence) of the coming scientific account of what goes on "in Jones" when common sense correctly says that Jones is seeing green or has a toothache, etc.

Now, to suppose that "raw feels" as we shall call them, will be found to be emergent—though not epiphenomenal—in this future scientific account, is to suppose that raw feels (or, better, raw feel dimensions) are the a's and b's in the *generalized* function

$$E(q,r,s,t,a,b,) = f_3(q,r,s,t)$$

where

$$a = g(q,r)$$
$$b = h(s,t)$$

That is, raw feels depend upon the variables q,r,s,t which also characterize pre-emergent situations. But raw feels do not occur in the presence of matter generally; only matter as it is in the living brain. The function $f_1(q,r,s,t)$ which fits the behavior of matter everywhere else, breaks down when applied to brains. This, as we have seen, is the sense in which raw feels "make a difference."

But how will the scientist be led to introduce raw feels into his picture of the world? Will he, indeed should he, not be content with noting that one region of qrst-space conforms to f_1 whereas another region (roughly brains) conforms to f_2? Or, to put it differently, constructing the function $E[q,r,s,t,g(q,r),h(s,t)]$ which combines these into one function holding for the entire space, what would lead him, as scientist, to speak of the part-functions g and h as correlating values of the lower level variables $q,r,s,$ and t with values of raw-feel variables? Now one answer would be that, after all, we experience raw feels, and it is the business of science to fit them into its world picture. And even in the present primitive state of psychophysiology we can confirm certain crude functional dependencies both of the (psychophysical) kind g and h, and of the (physicopsychical kind $f_3(q,r,s,t,g,h)$.

But the controversy over Behaviorism has made us sensitive about the scientific standing of 'sensations,' 'images,' and 'raw feels' generally. Thus, it is often thought that the only concept of 'seeing green' that belongs in a scientifically constructed psychology is one that is defined in terms of molar behavior. And it is obvious that at best such concepts would designate *correlates* of raw feels, and not the latter themselves. But how could we legitimately introduce raw feels or other emergent qualities into the "psychology of the other one?" Here we have to distinguish between "descriptive" and "theoretical" aims. While it is true that prior to the examination of living brains, the function f_1 was quite adequate, and though afterwards we saw that f_2 was required for the case of brains, this does not force us to introduce the new variables a and b. For, as we have seen, a and b are eliminable from the descriptive laws. Nevertheless, the introduction of these new variables might be 'forced' upon us by theoretical necessities (insofar as we are ever forced to make theoretical sense by the postulation of hypothetical entities). For example, a brain consists of matter of special kinds in certain arrangements. Complex hydrocarbon molecules, potassium ions, free iron, and electromagnetic fields exhibit certain "exceptionless" regularities (outside of brains) which correspond to Pepper's f_1. Many arrangements turn out to be such that we can deduce their properties, including the ways in which the components will behave *in situ*, from the f_1 functions. But for living brains this turns out not to be the case.

The flow of electrons at the synaptic interface "breaks the laws." But it is not lawless, since the more general function f_3 takes care of it. However, we were able to *derive* f_1 from other laws, those of the micro-theory, involving only variables q,r,s,t. When we have succeeded in working up a theory which will enable us to derive f_3, the theoretical primitives include other terms than those which were sufficient for an explanation of pre-emergent phenomena. These other terms—a_1, a_2, a_3, etc.—are the items to which the variables a and b pertain; and while we can write a and b as functions (g and h) of q, r, s, and t, it should not be supposed that the a's have thereby been shown to be analyzable into the entities for which q, r, s, and t in turn suffice as descriptive functors. If this seems odd, one should remember that whenever a theory is "correct" it means that we have succeeded (among other things) in formulating a lawful relation between a value, x, appertaining to the theoretical entity and a value, y, taken on by the observed. Hence, in the present case we can write an equation explicitly relating these values,

$$x = f(y)$$

But the fact that we can write this equation obviously does not mean that the entity to which the value x appertains is being equated with the situation to which the value y appertains, any more than the discovery of a functional relation between a person's height and weight would require us to suppose that somehow a person's height is the same thing as his weight.

Now an argument offered by Pepper in the closing section of his paper hinges partly on a failure to make this last distinction.

It is a natural ideal of science to derive all laws from a certain limited number of primitive laws or principles—not necessarily from one single law—and so to convert science into a mathematics. If it could be assumed that there are no chance occurrences such a system of laws should be obtainable, though it might look very different from the traditional mechanics. The assumption of science appears to be that such a system is obtainable. I do not know what else the dissatisfaction of science with inconsistencies could mean.

Now, there seems to be no intention on the part of emergent evolutionists to deny that such a system is possible or to assert that there are chance occurrences. If that is so, they seem to be faced with the following dilemma: either the emergent laws they are arguing for are ineffectual and epiphenomenal, or they are effectual and capable of being absorbed into the physical system. But apparently they want their laws to be both effectual and at the same time no part of the physical system . . . (pp. 243–44)

First a terminological point. Among the various meanings of the word *physical* let us distinguish the following for present purposes:

Physical₁: an event or entity is physical₁ if it belongs in the space-time network.

Physical₂: an event or entity is physical₂ if it is definable in terms of theoretical primitives adequate to describe completely the actual states though not necessarily the potentialities of the universe before the appearance of life.

Now, an emergentist account (of the kind we have been constructing) of raw feels denies that the latter are physical₂. But this in no way involves the denial that they are physical₁. And indeed this emergentist account definitely gives them a physical₁ status. And if the equations

$$a = g(q,r)$$
$$b = h(s,t)$$

permit the elimination of a and b from the descriptive function relating the physical₂ variables q,r,s, and t, this fact, as we have just seen, by no means involves that the emergent entities with which the variables a and b are associated must also be physical₂.

Whether or not there are any emergents in the sense we have sought to clarify is an empirical question. Our only aim has been to show that Pepper's "formal" demonstration of the impossibility of non-epiphenomenal emergents is invalid.

REFERENCE

1. Pepper, Stephen C. "Emergence," *Journal of Philosophy*, 23:241–45 (1926).

Empiricism and the Philosophy of Mind

I. An Ambiguity in Sense-Datum Theories

I PRESUME that no philosopher who has attacked the philosophical idea of givenness or, to use the Hegelian term, immediacy, has intended to deny that there is a difference between *inferring* that something is the case and, for example, *seeing* it to be the case. If the term "given" referred merely to what is observed as being observed, or, perhaps, to a proper subset of the things we are said to determine by observation, the existence of "data" would be as noncontroversial as the existence of philosophical perplexities. But, of course, this just isn't so. The phrase "the given" as a piece of professional—epistemological—shoptalk carries a substantial theoretical commitment, and one can deny that there are "data" or that anything is, in this sense, "given" without flying in the face of reason.

Many things have been said to be "given": sense contents, material objects, universals, propositions, real connections, first principles, even givenness itself. And there is, indeed, a certain way of construing the situations which philosophers analyze in these terms which can be said to be the framework of givenness. This framework has been a common feature of most of the major systems of philosophy, including, to use a Kantian turn of phrase, both "dogmatic rationalism" and "skeptical empiricism." It has, indeed, been so pervasive that few, if any, philosophers have been altogether free of it; certainly not Kant, and, I would argue, not even Hegel, that great foe of "immediacy." Often what is attacked under its name are only specific varieties of "given." Intuited first principles and synthetic necessary connections

NOTE: This paper was first presented as the University of London Special Lectures on Philosophy for 1955–56, delivered on March 1, 8, and 15, 1956, under the title "The Myth of the Given: Three Lectures on Empiricism and the Philosophy of Mind."

were the first to come under attack. And many who today attack "the whole idea of givenness"—and they are an increasing number—are really only attacking sense data. For they transfer to other items, say physical objects or relations of appearing, the characteristic features of the "given." If, however, I begin my argument with an attack on sense datum theories, it is only as a first step in a general critique of the entire framework of givenness.

2. Sense-datum theories characteristically distinguish between an act of awareness and, for example, the color patch which is its object. The act is usually called *sensing*. Classical exponents of the theory have often characterized these acts as "phenomenologically simple" and "not further analyzable." But other sense-datum theorists—some of them with an equal claim to be considered "classical exponents"— have held that sensing is analyzable. And if some philosophers seem to have thought that if sensing is analyzable, then it can't be an act, this has by no means been the general opinion. There are, indeed, deeper roots for the doubt that sensing (if there is such a thing) is an act, roots which can be traced to one of two lines of thought tangled together in classical sense-datum theory. For the moment, however, I shall simply assume that however complex (or simple) the fact that x is sensed may be, it has the form, whatever exactly it may be, by virtue of which for x to be sensed is for it to be the object of an act.

Being a sense datum, or sensum, is a relational property of the item that is sensed. To refer to an item which is sensed in a way which does not entail that it *is* sensed, it is necessary to use some other locution. *Sensibile* has the disadvantage that it implies that sensed items could exist without being sensed, and this is a matter of controversy among sense-datum theorists. *Sense content* is, perhaps, as neutral a term as any.

There appear to be varieties of sensing, referred to by some as *visual sensing*, *tactual sensing*, etc., and by others as *directly seeing*, *directly hearing*, etc. But it is not clear whether these are species of sensing in any full-blooded sense, or whether "x is visually sensed" amounts to no more than "x is a color patch which is sensed," "x is directly heard" than "x is a sound which is sensed" and so on. In the latter case, being a *visual sensing* or a *direct hearing* would be a relational property of an act of sensing, just as being a sense datum is a relational property of a sense content.

254

3. Now if we bear in mind that the point of the epistemological category of the given is, presumably, to explicate the idea that empirical knowledge rests on a 'foundation' of non-inferential knowledge of matter of fact, we may well experience a feeling of surprise on noting that according to sense-datum theorists, it is *particulars* that are sensed. For what is *known*, even in non-inferential knowledge, is *facts* rather than particulars, items of the form *something's being thus-and-so* or *something's standing in a certain relation to something else*. It would seem, then, that the sensing of sense contents *cannot* constitute knowledge, inferential or non-inferential; and if so, we may well ask, what light does the concept of a sense datum throw on the 'foundations of empirical knowledge?' The sense-datum theorist, it would seem, must choose between saying:

(a) It is *particulars* which are sensed. Sensing is not knowing. The existence of sense-data does not *logically* imply the existence of knowledge.

or

(b) Sensing *is* a form of knowing. It is *facts* rather than *particulars* which are sensed.

On alternative (a) the fact that a sense content was sensed would be a *non-epistemic* fact about the sense content. Yet it would be hasty to conclude that this alternative precludes any logical connection between the sensing of sense contents and the possession of non-inferential knowledge. For even if the sensing of sense contents did not logically imply the existence of non-inferential knowledge, the converse might well be true. Thus, the non-inferential knowledge of particular matter of fact might logically imply the existence of sense data (for example, *seeing that a certain physical object is red* might logically imply *sensing a red sense content*) even though the sensing of a red sense content were not itself a cognitive fact and did not imply the possession of non-inferential knowledge.

On the second alternative, (b), the sensing of sense contents would logically imply the existence of non-inferential knowledge for the simple reason that it would *be* this knowledge. But, once again, it would be facts rather than particulars which are sensed.

4. Now it might seem that when confronted by this choice, the sense-datum theorist seeks to have his cake and eat it. For he characteristically insists *both* that sensing is a knowing *and* that it is particu-

lars which are sensed. Yet his position is by no means as hopeless as this formulation suggests. For the 'having' and the 'eating' can be combined without logical nonsense provided that he uses the word *know* and, correspondingly, the word *given* in two senses. He must say something like the following:

The non-inferential knowing on which our world picture rests is the knowing that certain items, e.g. red sense contents, are of a certain character, e.g. red. When such a fact is non-inferentially known about a sense content, I will say that the sense content is sensed *as being*, e.g., red. I will then say that a sense content is *sensed* (full stop) if it is *sensed as being* of a certain character, e.g. red. Finally, I will say of a sense content that it is *known* if it is sensed (full stop), to emphasize that sensing is a *cognitive* or *epistemic* fact.

Notice that, given these stipulations, it is logically necessary that if a sense content be *sensed*, it be *sensed as being* of a certain character, and that if it be *sensed as being* of a certain character, the *fact that it is of this character* be *non-inferentially known*. Notice also that the being sensed of a sense content would be *knowledge* only in a stipulated sense of *know*. To say of a *sense content*—a color patch, for example—that it was 'known' would be to say that *some fact about it* was non-inferentially known, e.g. that it was red. This *stipulated* use of *know* would, however, receive aid and comfort from the fact that there is, in ordinary usage, a sense of *know* in which it is followed by a noun or descriptive phrase which refers to a particular, thus

> Do you know John?
> Do you know the President?

Because these questions are equivalent to "Are you acquainted with John?" and "Are you acquainted with the President?" the phrase "knowledge by acquaintance" recommends itself as a useful metaphor for this stipulated sense of *know* and, like other useful metaphors, has congealed into a technical term.

5. We have seen that the fact that a sense content is a *datum* (if, indeed, there are such facts) will logically imply that someone has non-inferential knowledge only if to say that a sense content is given is contextually defined in terms of non-inferential knowledge of a fact about this sense content. If this is not clearly realized or held in mind, sense-datum theorists may come to think of the givenness of sense contents as the *basic* or *primitive* concept of the sense-datum frame-

work, and thus sever the logical connection between sense data and non-inferential knowledge to which the classical form of the theory is committed. This brings us face to face with the fact that in spite of the above considerations, many if not most sense-datum theorists *have* thought of the givenness of sense contents as the basic notion of the sense-datum framework. What, then, of the logical connection in the direction *sensing sense contents → having non-inferential knowledge?* Clearly it is severed by those who think of sensing as a unique and unanalyzable act. Those, on the other hand, who conceive of sensing as an *analyzable* fact, while they have prima facie severed this connection (by taking the sensing of sense contents to be the basic concept of the sense-datum framework) will nevertheless, in a sense, have maintained it, if the result they get by analyzing *x is a red sense datum* turns out to be the same as the result they get when they analyze *x is non-inferentially known to be red.* The entailment which was thrown out the front door would have sneaked in by the back.

It is interesting to note, in this connection, that those who, in the classical period of sense-datum theories, say from Moore's "Refutation of Idealism" until about 1938, analyzed or sketched an analysis of sensing, did so in *non-epistemic* terms. Typically it was held that for a sense content to be sensed is for it to be an element in a certain kind of relational array of sense contents, where the relations which constitute the array are such relations as spatiotemporal juxtaposition (or overlapping), constant conjunction, mnemic causation—even real connection and belonging to a self. There is, however, one class of terms which is conspicuous by its absence, namely *cognitive* terms. For these, like the 'sensing' which was under analysis, were taken to belong to a higher level of complexity.

Now the idea that epistemic facts can be analyzed without remainder—even "in principle"—into non-epistemic facts, whether phenomenal or behavioral, public or private, with no matter how lavish a sprinkling of subjunctives and hypotheticals is, I believe, a radical mistake—a mistake of a piece with the so-called "naturalistic fallacy" in ethics. I shall not, however, press this point for the moment, though it will be a central theme in a later stage of my argument. What I do want to stress is that whether classical sense-datum philosophers have conceived of the givenness of sense contents as analyzable in non-epistemic terms, or as constituted by acts which are somehow both irreducible and knowings, they have without exception taken them to be fundamental in another sense.

6. For they have taken givenness to be a fact which presupposes no learning, no forming of associations, no setting up of stimulus-response connections. In short, they have tended to equate *sensing sense contents* with *being conscious*, as a person who has been hit on the head is *not* conscious whereas a new born babe, alive and kicking, *is* conscious. They would admit, of course, that the ability to know that a person, namely oneself, is *now*, at a certain time, feeling a pain, *is* acquired and does presuppose a (complicated) process of concept formation. But, they would insist, to suppose that the simple ability to *feel* a pain or *see* a *color*, in short, to sense sense contents, is *acquired* and involves a process of concept formation, would be very odd indeed.

But if a sense-datum philosopher takes the ability to sense sense contents to be unacquired, he is clearly precluded from offering an analysis of *x senses a sense content* which presupposes acquired abilities. It follows that he could analyze *x senses red sense content s* as *x non-inferentially knows that s is red* only if he is prepared to admit that the ability to have such non-inferential knowledge as that, for example, a red sense content is red, is itself unacquired. And this brings us face to face with the fact that most empirically minded philosophers are strongly inclined to think that all classificatory consciousness, all knowledge *that something is thus-and-so*, or, in logicians' jargon, all subsumption of particulars under universals, involves learning, concept formation, even the use of symbols. It is clear from the above analysis, therefore, that *classical* sense-datum theories—I emphasize the adjective, for there are other, 'heterodox,' sense-datum theories to be taken into account—are confronted by an inconsistent triad made up of the following three propositions:

A. X *senses red sense content s* entails *x non-inferentially knows that s is red.*

B. The ability to sense sense contents is unacquired.

C. The ability to know facts of the form *x is ϕ* is acquired.

A and B together entail not-C; B and C entail not-A; A and C entail not-B.

Once the classical sense-datum theorist faces up to the fact that A, B, and C do form an inconsistent triad, which of them will he choose to abandon?

1) He can abandon A, in which case the sensing of sense contents becomes a noncognitive fact—a noncognitive fact, to be sure which may be a necessary condition, even a *logically* necessary condition, of non-inferential knowledge, but a fact, nevertheless, which cannot *constitute* this knowledge.

2) He can abandon B, in which case he must pay the price of cutting off the concept of a sense datum from its connection with our ordinary talk about sensations, feelings, afterimages, tickles and itches, etc., which are usually thought by sense-datum theorists to be its common sense counterparts.

3) But to abandon C is to do violence to the predominantly nominalistic proclivities of the empiricist tradition.

7. It certainly begins to look as though the classical concept of a sense datum were a mongrel resulting from a crossbreeding of two ideas:

(1) The idea that there are certain inner episodes—e.g. sensations of red or of C♯ which can occur to human beings (and brutes) without any prior process of learning or concept formation; and without which it would *in some sense* be impossible to see, for example, that the facing surface of a physical object is red and triangular, or *hear* that a certain physical sound is C♯.

(2) The idea that there are certain inner episodes which are the non-inferential knowings that certain items are, for example, red or C♯; and that these episodes are the necessary conditions of empirical knowledge as providing the evidence for all other empirical propositions.

And I think that once we are on the lookout for them, it is quite easy to see how these two ideas came to be blended together in traditional epistemology. The *first* idea clearly arises in the attempt to explain the facts of sense perception in scientific style. How does it happen that people can have the experience which they describe by saying "It is as though I were seeing a red and triangular physical object" when either there is no physical object there at all, or, if there is, it is neither red nor triangular? The explanation, roughly, posits that in every case in which a person has an experience of this kind, whether veridical or not, he has what is called a 'sensation' or 'impression' 'of a red triangle.' The core idea is that the proximate cause of such a sensation is *only for the most part* brought about by the presence in the neighborhood of the perceiver of a red and triangular physical object; and that while a baby, say, can have the 'sensation of a red triangle' without either *seeing* or *seeming to see that the facing side of a physical object is red and triangular*, there usually looks, to adults, to be a physical object with a red and triangular facing surface, when they are caused to have a 'sensation of a red triangle'; while *without* such a sensation, no such experience can be had.

I shall have a great deal more to say about this kind of 'explanation' of perceptual situations in the course of my argument. What I want to emphasize for the moment, however, is that, as far as the above formulation goes, there is no reason to suppose that having the sensation of a red triangle is a *cognitive* or *epistemic* fact. There is, of course, a temptation to assimilate "having a sensation of a red triangle" to "thinking of a celestial city" and to attribute to the former the epistemic character, the 'intentionality' of the latter. But this temptation *could* be resisted, and it *could* be held that having a sensation of a red triangle is a fact *sui generis*, neither epistemic nor physical, having its own logical grammar. Unfortunately, the idea that there are such things as sensations of red triangles—in itself, as we shall see, quite legitimate, though not without its puzzles—seems to fit the requirements of another, and less fortunate, line of thought so well that it has almost invariably been distorted to give the latter a reinforcement without which it would long ago have collapsed. This unfortunate, but familiar, line of thought runs as follows:

The seeing that the facing surface of a physical object is red and triangular is a *veridical* member of a class of experiences—let us call them 'ostensible seeings'—some of the members of which are non-veridical; and there is no inspectible hallmark which guarantees that any such experience is veridical. To suppose that the non-inferential knowledge on which our world picture rests consists of such ostensible seeings, hearings, etc., as *happen* to be veridical is to place empirical knowledge on too precarious a footing—indeed, to open the door to skepticism by making a mockery of the word *knowledge* in the phrase "empirical knowledge."

Now it is, of course, possible to delimit subclasses of ostensible seeings, hearings, etc., which are progressively less precarious, i.e. more reliable, by specifying the circumstances in which they occur, and the vigilance of the perceiver. But the possibility that any given ostensible seeing, hearing, etc., is non-veridical can never be entirely eliminated. Therefore, given that the foundation of empirical knowledge cannot consist of the veridical members of a class not all the members of which are veridical, and from which the non-veridical members cannot be weeded out by 'inspection,' this foundation cannot consist of such items as *seeing that the facing surface of a physical object is red and triangular.*

Thus baldly put, scarcely anyone would accept this conclusion. Rather they would take the contrapositive of the argument, and reason that *since* the foundation of empirical knowledge *is* the non-inferential knowledge of such facts, it *does* consist of members of a class which contains non-veridical members. But before it is thus baldly put, it gets tangled up with the first line of thought. The idea springs to mind that *sensations of red triangles* have exactly the virtues which *ostensible seeings of red triangular physical surfaces* lack. To begin with, the grammatical similarity of 'sensation of a red triangle' to "thought of a celestial city" is interpreted to mean, or, better, gives rise to the presupposition, that *sensations* belong in the same general pigeonhole as *thoughts*—in short, are cognitive facts. *Then*, it is noticed that sensations are *ex hypothesi* far more intimately related to mental processes than external physical objects. It would seem easier to "get at" a red triangle of which we are having a sensation, than to "get at" a red and triangular physical surface. But, above all, it is the fact that it *doesn't make sense* to speak of unveridical sensations which strikes these philosophers, though for it to strike them as it does, they must overlook the fact that if it makes sense to speak of an experience as *veridical* it must correspondingly make sense to speak of it as *unveridical*. Let me emphasize that not *all* sense-datum theorists—even of the classical type—have been guilty of *all* these confusions; nor are these *all* the confusions of which sense-datum theorists have been guilty. I shall have more to say on this topic later. But the confusions I have mentioned are central to the tradition, and will serve my present purpose. For the upshot of blending all these ingredients together is the idea that a sensation of a red triangle is the very paradigm of empirical knowledge. And I think that it can readily be seen that this idea leads straight to the orthodox type of sense-datum theory and accounts for the perplexities which arise when one tries to think it through.

II. Another Language?

8. I shall now examine briefly a heterodox suggestion by, for example, Ayer (1)(2) to the effect that discourse about sense data is, so to speak,

Wilfrid Sellars

another language, a language contrived by the epistemologist, for situations which the plain man describes by means of such locutions as "Now the book looks green to me" and "There seems to be a red and triangular object over there." The core of this suggestion is the idea that the vocabulary of sense data embodies no increase in the content of descriptive discourse, as over and against the plain man's language of physical objects in Space and Time, and the properties they have and appear to have. For it holds that sentences of the form

X presents S with a ϕ sense datum

are simply *stipulated* to have the same force as sentences of the form

X looks ϕ to S.

Thus "The tomato presents S with a bulgy red sense-datum" would be the contrived counterpart of "The tomato looks red and bulgy to S" and would mean exactly what the latter means for the simple reason that it was stipulated to do so.

As an aid to explicating this suggestion, I am going to make use of a certain picture. I am going to start with the idea of a code, and I am going to enrich this notion until the codes I am talking about are no longer mere codes. Whether one wants to call these "enriched codes" codes at all is a matter which I shall not attempt to decide.

Now a code, in the sense in which I shall use the term, is a system of symbols each of which represents a complete sentence. Thus, as we initially view the situation, there are two characteristic features of a code: (1) Each code symbol is a unit; the parts of a code symbol are not themselves code symbols. (2) Such logical relations as obtain among code symbols are completely parasitical; they derive entirely from logical relations among the sentences they represent. Indeed, to speak about logical relations among code symbols is a way of talking which is introduced in terms of the logical relations among the sentences they represent. Thus, if "○" stands for "Everybody on board is sick" and "△" for "Somebody on board is sick," then "△" would follow from "○" in the sense that the sentence represented by "△" follows from the sentence represented by "○".

Let me begin to modify this austere conception of a code. There is no reason why a code symbol might not have parts which, without becoming full-fledged symbols on their own, do play a role in the system. Thus they might play the role of *mnemonic devices* serving to put us in mind of features of the sentences represented by the symbols

262

of which they are parts. For example, the code symbol for "Someone on board is sick" might contain the letter S to remind us of the word "sick," and, perhaps, the reversed letter E to remind those of us who have a background in logic of the word "someone." Thus, the flag for "Someone on board is sick" might be 'ƎS.' Now the suggestion at which I am obviously driving is that someone might introduce so-called sense-datum sentences as code symbols or "flags," and introduce the vocables and printables they contain to serve the role of reminding us of certain features of the sentences in ordinary perceptual discourse which the flags as wholes represent. In particular, the role of the vocable or printable "sense datum" would be that of indicating that the symbolized sentence contains the context ". . . looks . . .," the vocable or printable "red" that the correlated sentence contains the context ". . . looks red . . ." and so on.

9. Now to take this conception of sense datum 'sentences' seriously is, of course, to take seriously the idea that there are no independent logical relations between sense-datum 'sentences.' It *looks* as though there were such independent logical relations, for these 'sentences' look like *sentences*, and they have as proper parts vocables or printables which function *in ordinary usage* as *logical words*. Certainly if sense-datum talk is a code, it is a code which is easily mistaken for a language proper. Let me illustrate. At first sight it certainly seems that

A. The tomato presents S with a red sense datum

entails both

B. There are red sense data

and

C. The tomato presents S with a sense datum which has some specific shade of red.

This, however, on the kind of view I am considering, would be a mistake. (B) would follow—even in the inverted commas sense of 'follows' appropriate to code symbols—from (A) only because (B) is the flag for (β), "Something looks red to somebody," which *does* follow from (α), "The tomato looks red to Jones" which is represented in the code by (A). And (C) would 'follow' from (A), in spite of appearances, only if (C) were the flag for a *sentence* which *follows* from (α).

I shall have more to say about this example in a moment. The point to be stressed now is that to carry out this view consistently one must deny to such vocables and printables as "quality," "is," "red," "color," "crimson," "determinable," "determinate," "all," "some," "exists," etc., etc., *as they occur in sense-datum talk*, the full-blooded status of their counterparts in ordinary usage. They are rather *clues* which serve to remind us which sense-datum 'flag' it would be proper to fly along with which other sense-datum 'flags.' Thus, the vocables which make up the two 'flags'

(D) All sense-data are red

and

(E) Some sense data are not red

remind us of the genuine logical incompatibility between, for example,

(F) All elephants are grey

and

(G) Some elephants are not grey,

and serve, therefore, as a clue to the impropriety of flying these two 'flags' together. For the sentences they symbolize are, presumably,

(δ) Everything looks red to everybody

and

(ε) There is a color other than red which something looks to somebody to have,

and these are incompatible.

But one would have to be cautious in using these clues. Thus, from the fact that it is proper to infer

(H) Some elephants have a determinate shade of pink

from

(I) Some elephants are pink

it would clearly be a mistake to infer that the right to fly

(K) Some sense data are pink

carries with it the right to fly

(L) Some sense data have a determinate shade of pink.

9. But if sense-datum sentences are really sense-datum 'sentences'—i.e. code flags—it follows, of course, that sense-datum talk neither clarifies nor explains facts of the form *x looks φ to S* or *x is φ*. That it would appear to do so would be because it would take an almost superhuman effort to keep from taking the vocables and printables which occur in the code (and let me now add to our earlier list the vocable "directly known") to be *words* which, if homonyms of words in ordinary usage, have their ordinary sense, and which, if invented, have a meaning specified by their relation to the others. One would be constantly tempted,

that is, to treat sense-datum flags as though they were sentences in a theory, and sense-datum talk as a *language* which gets its use by coordinating sense-datum sentences with sentences in ordinary perception talk, as *molecule talk gets its use by coordinating sentences about populations of molecules with talk about the pressure of gases on the walls of their containers*. After all,

x looks red to S $\cdot \equiv \cdot$ there is a class of red sense data which
belong to x, and are sensed by S

has at least a superficial resemblance to

g exerts pressure on w $\cdot \equiv \cdot$ there is a class of molecules which
make up g, and which are bouncing
off w,

a resemblance which becomes even more striking once it is granted that the former is not an *analysis* of x looks red to S in terms of sense data.

There is, therefore, reason to believe that it is the fact that both codes and theories are contrived systems which are under the control of the language with which they are coordinated, which has given aid and comfort to the idea that sense-datum talk is "another language" for ordinary discourse about perception. Yet although the logical relations between sentences in a theoretical language are, in an important sense, under the control of logical relations between sentences in the observation language, nevertheless, within the framework of this control, the theoretical language has an *autonomy* which contradicts the very idea of a code. If this essential difference between theories and codes is overlooked, one may be tempted to try to eat his cake and have it. By thinking of sense-datum talk as *merely another language*, one draws on the fact that codes have no surplus value. By thinking of sense-datum talk as *illuminating* the "language of appearing," one draws on the fact that theoretical languages, though *contrived*, and depending for their meaningfulness on a coordination with the language of observation, have an explanatory function. Unfortunately, these two characteristics are incompatible; for it is just because theories have "surplus value" that they can provide explanations.

No one, of course, who thinks—as, for example, does Ayer—of the existence of sense data as entailing the existence of "direct knowledge," would wish to say that sense data are theoretical entities. It could scarcely be a theoretical fact that I am directly knowing that a certain sense content is red. On the other hand, the idea that sense *contents* are theoretical entities is not *obviously* absurd—so absurd as to preclude the above interpretation of the plausibility of the "another-language" approach. For even those who introduce the expression "sense content" by means of the context ". . . is directly known to be . . ." may fail to keep this fact in mind when putting this expression to use—for example, by developing the idea that physical objects and persons alike are patterns of sense contents. In such a specific context, it is possible to forget that sense *contents*, thus introduced, are essentially sense *data* and not merely items which exemplify sense qualities. Indeed, one may even lapse into thinking of the *sensing* of sense contents, the givenness of sense *data*, as *non-epistemic* facts.

I think it fair to say that those who offer the "another-language" interpretation of sense data find the illumination it provides to consist primarily in the fact that in the language of sense data, physical objects are patterns of sense contents, so that, viewed in this framework, there is no "iron curtain" between the knowing mind and the physical world. It is to elaborating plausible (if schematic) translations of physical-object statements into statements about sense contents, rather than to spelling out the force of such sentences as "Sense content *s* is directly known to be red," that the greater part of their philosophical ingenuity has been directed.

However this may be, one thing can be said with confidence. If the language of sense data *were* merely a code, a notational device, then the cash value of any philosophical clarification it might provide must lie in its ability to illuminate logical relations *within* ordinary discourse about physical objects and our perception of them. Thus, the fact (if it were a fact) that a code can be constructed for ordinary perception talk which 'speaks' of a "relation of identity" between the components ("sense data") of "minds" and of "things," would presumably have as its cash value the insight that ordinary discourse about physical objects and perceivers could (in principle) be constructed from sentences of the form "There looks to be a physical object with a red and triangular facing surface over there" (the counterpart in ordinary language of the basic expressions of the code). In more traditional terms, the clarification would consist in making manifest the fact that persons and things are alike logical constructions out of *lookings* or *appearings* (*not* appearances!). But any claim to this effect soon runs into insuperable difficulties which become apparent once the role of "looks" or "appears" is understood. And it is to an examination of this role that I now turn.

III. The Logic of 'Looks'

10. Before turning aside to examine the suggestion that the language of sense data is "another language" for the situations described by the so-called "language of appearing," I had concluded that classical sense-datum theories, when pressed, reveal themselves to be the result of a mismating of two ideas: (1) The idea that there are certain "inner episodes," e.g. the sensation of a red triangle or of a C♯ sound, which occur to human beings and brutes without any prior process of learning or concept formation, and without which it would—in some sense—be impossible to see, for example, that the facing surface of a physical object is red and triangular, or hear that a certain physical sound is C♯; (2) The idea that there are certain "inner episodes" which are the non-inferential knowings that, for example, a certain item is red and triangular, or, in the case of sounds, C♯, which inner episodes are the necessary conditions of empirical knowledge as providing the evidence for all other empirical propositions. If this diagnosis is correct, a reasonable next step would be to examine these two ideas and determine how that which survives criticism in each is properly to be combined with the other. Clearly we would have to come to grips with the idea of *inner episodes*, for this is common to both.

Many who attack the idea of the given seem to have thought that the central mistake embedded in this idea is exactly the idea that there are inner episodes, whether thoughts or so-called "immediate experiences," to which each of us has privileged access. I shall argue that this is just not so, and that the Myth of the Given can be dispelled without resorting to the crude verificationisms or operationalisms characteristic of the more dogmatic forms of recent empiricism. Then there are those who, while they do not reject the idea of inner episodes, find the Myth of the Given to consist in the idea that knowledge of these episodes furnishes *premises* on which empirical knowledge rests as on a foundation. But while this idea has, indeed, been the most widespread form of the Myth, it is far from constituting its essence. Everything hinges on *why* these philosophers reject it. If, for example, it is on the ground that the learning of a language is a *public* process which proceeds in a domain of *public* objects and is governed by *public* sanctions, so that private episodes—with the exception of a mysterious nod in their direction—must needs escape the net of rational discourse, then, while these philosophers are immune to the form of the myth which has flowered in sense-datum theories, they have no defense against the myth in the form of the givenness of such facts as that *physical object x looks red to person S at time t*, or that *there looks to person S at time t to be a red physical object over there*. It will be useful to pursue the Myth in this direction for a while before more general issues are raised.

11. Philosophers have found it easy to suppose that such a sentence as "The tomato looks red to Jones" says that a certain triadic relation, *looking* or *appearing*, obtains among a physical object, a person, and a quality.* "A looks φ to S" is assimilated to "x gives y to z"—or, better, since giving is, strictly speaking, an action rather than a relation—to "x is between y and z," and taken to be a case of the general form "R(x,y,z)." Having supposed this, they turn without further ado to the question, "Is this relation analyzable?" Sense-datum theorists have, on the whole, answered "Yes," and claimed that facts of the form *x looks red to X* are to be analyzed in terms of sense data. Some of them, without necessarily rejecting this claim, have argued that facts of this kind are, at the very least, to be *explained* in terms of sense data. Thus, when Broad (4) writes "If, in fact, nothing elliptical is before my mind, it is very hard to understand why the penny should seem *elliptical* rather than of any other shape (p. 240)," he is appealing to sense-data as a means of *explaining* facts of this form. The difference, of course, is that whereas if *x looks φ to S* is correctly *analyzed* in terms of sense data, then no one could believe that x looks φ to S without believing that S has sense data, the same need not be true if *x looks φ to S* is explained in terms of sense data, for, in the case of some types of explanation, at least, one can believe a fact without believing its explanation.

On the other hand, those philosophers who reject sense-datum theories in favor of so-called theories of appearing have characteristically held that facts of the form *x looks φ to S* are ultimate and irreducible, and that sense data are needed neither for their analysis nor for their explanation. If asked, "Doesn't the statement 'x looks red to S' have as part of its meaning the idea that s stands in some relation to something that *is* red?" their answer is in the negative, and, I believe, rightly so.

---

* A useful discussion of views of this type is to be found in (9) and (13).

12. I shall begin my examination of "X looks red to S at t" with the simple but fundamental point that the sense of "red" in which things look red is, on the face of it, the same as that in which things are red. When one glimpses an object and decides that it looks red (to me, now, from here) and wonders whether it really is red, one is surely wondering whether the color—red—which it looks to have is the one it really does have. This point can be obscured by such verbal manipulations as hyphenating the words "looks" and "red" and claiming that it is the insoluble unity "looks-red" and not just "looks" which is the relation. Insofar as this dodge is based on insight, it is insight into the fact that looks is not a relation between a person, a thing, and a quality. Unfortunately, as we shall see, the reason for this fact is one which gives no comfort at all to the idea that it is looks-red rather than looks which is the relation.

I have, in effect, been claiming that being red is logically prior, is a logically simpler notion, than looking red; the function "x is red" to "x looks red to y." In short, that it just won't do to say that x is red is analyzable in terms of x looks red to y. But what, then, are we to make of the necessary truth—and it is, of course, a necessary truth—that

$$x \text{ is red} \cdot \equiv \cdot x \text{ would look red to standard observers in standard}$$
conditions?

There is certainly some sense to the idea that this is at least the schema for a definition of physical redness in terms of looking red. One begins to see the plausibility of the gambit that looking-red is an insoluble unity, for the minute one gives "red" (on the right-hand side) an independent status, it becomes what it obviously is, namely "red" as a predicate of physical objects, and the supposed definition becomes an obvious circle.

13. The way out of this troubling situation has two parts. The second is to show how "x is red" can be necessarily equivalent to "x would look red to standard observers in standard situations" without this being a definition of "x is red" in terms of "x looks red." But the first, and logically prior, step is to show that "x looks red to S" does not assert either an unanalyzable triadic relation to obtain between x, red, and S, or an unanalyzable dyadic relation to obtain between x and S. Not, however, because it asserts an analyzable relation to obtain, but because looks is not a relation at all. Or, to put the matter in a familiar way, one can say that looks is a relation if he likes, for the

sentences in which this word appears show some grammatical analogies to sentences built around words which we should not hesitate to classify as relation words; but once one has become aware of certain other features which make them very unlike ordinary relation sentences, he will be less inclined to view his task as that of *finding the answer* to the question "Is looks a relation?"

14. To bring out the essential features of the use of "looks," I shall engage in a little historical fiction. A young man, whom I shall call John, works in a necktie shop. He has learned the use of color words in the usual way, with this exception. I shall suppose that he has never looked at an object in other than standard conditions. As he examines his stock every evening before closing up shop, he says "This is red," "That is green," "This is purple," etc., and such of his linguistic peers as happen to be present nod their heads approvingly.

Let us suppose, now, that at this point in the story, electric lighting is invented. His friends and neighbors rapidly adopt this new means of illumination, and wrestle with the problems it presents. John, however, is the last to succumb. Just after it has been installed in his shop, one of his neighbors, Jim, comes in to buy a necktie.

"Here is a handsome green one," says John.

"But it *isn't* green," says Jim, and takes John outside.

"Well," says John, "it was green in there, but now it is blue."

"No," says Jim, "you know that neckties don't change their color merely as a result of being taken from place to place."

"But perhaps electricity changes their color and they change back again in daylight?"

"That would be a queer kind of change, wouldn't it?" says Jim.

"I suppose so," says bewildered John. "But we *saw* that it was green *in there.*"

"No, we didn't see that it was green in there, because it wasn't green, and you can't see what isn't so!"

"Well, this is a pretty pickle," says John. "*I just don't know what to say.*"

The next time John picks up this tie in his shop and someone asks what color it is, his first impulse is to say "It is green." He suppresses this impulse, and, remembering what happened before, comes out with "It is blue." He doesn't see that it is blue, nor would he say that he sees it to be blue. What does he see? Let us ask him.

"I don't know *what* to say. If I didn't know that the tie is blue—and the alternative to granting this is odd indeed—I would swear that I was seeing a green tie and seeing that it is green. It is *as though* I were seeing the necktie to be green."

If we bear in mind that such sentences as "This is green" have both a *fact-stating* and a *reporting* use, we can put the point I have just been making by saying that once John learns to stifle the *report* "This necktie is green" when looking at it in the shop, there is no other *report* about color and the necktie which he knows how to make. To be sure, he now says "This necktie is blue." But he is not making a *reporting* use of this sentence. He uses it as the conclusion of an inference.

15. We return to the shop after an interval, and we find that when John is asked "What is the color of this necktie?" he makes such statements as "It looks green, but take it outside and see." It occurs to us that perhaps in learning to say "This tie *looks* green" when in the shop, he has learned to make a new kind of report. Thus, it might seem as though his linguistic peers have helped him to notice a new kind of *objective* fact, one which, though a relational fact involving a perceiver, is as logically independent of the beliefs, the conceptual framework of the perceiver, as the fact that the necktie is blue; but a *minimal* fact, one which it is safer to report because one is less likely to be mistaken. Such a minimal fact would be the fact that the necktie looks green to John on a certain occasion, and it would be properly reported by using the sentence "This necktie *looks* green." It is this type of account, of course, which I have already rejected.

But what is the alternative? If, that is, we are not going to adopt the sense-datum analysis. Let me begin by noting that there certainly seems to be something to the idea that the sentence "This looks green to me now" has a reporting role. Indeed, it would seem to be essentially a report. But if so, *what* does it report, if not a minimal objective fact, and if what it reports is not to be analyzed in terms of sense data?

16. Let me next call attention to the fact that the experience of having something look green to one at a certain time is, insofar as it is an experience, obviously very much like that of seeing something to be green, insofar as the latter is an experience. But the latter, of course, is not *just* an experience. And this is the heart of the matter. For to say that a certain experience is a *seeing that* something is the case, is to do more than describe the experience. It is to characterize it as, so

to speak, making an assertion or claim, and—which is the point I wish to stress—to *endorse* that claim. As a matter of fact, as we shall see, it is much more easy to see that the statement "Jones sees that the tree is green" ascribes a propositional claim to Jones' experience and endorses it, than to specify how the statement *describes* Jones' experience.

I realize that by speaking of experiences as containing propositional claims, I may seem to be knocking at closed doors. I ask the reader to bear with me, however, as the justification of this way of talking is one of my major aims. If I am permitted to issue this verbal currency now, I hope to put it on the gold standard before concluding the argument.

16. It is clear that the experience of seeing that something is green is not *merely* the occurrence of the propositional claim 'this is green'— not even if we add, as we must, that this claim is, so to speak, evoked or wrung from the perceiver by the object perceived. Here Nature— to turn Kant's simile (which he uses in another context) on its head—puts us to the question. The something more is clearly what philosophers have in mind when they speak of "visual impressions" or "immediate visual experiences." What exactly is the logical status of these "impressions" or "immediate experiences" is a problem which will be with us for the remainder of this argument. For the moment it is the propositional claim which concerns us.

I pointed out above that when we use the word "see" as in "S sees that the tree is green" we are not only ascribing a claim to the experience, but endorsing it. It is this endorsement which Ryle has in mind when he refers to *seeing that something is thus and so* as an *achievement*, and to "sees" as an *achievement word*. I prefer to call it a "so it is" or "just so" word, for the root idea is that of *truth*. To characterize S's experience as a *seeing* is, in a suitably broad sense—which I shall be concerned to explicate—to apply the semantical concept of truth to that experience.

Now the suggestion I wish to make is, in its simplest terms, that the statement "X looks green to Jones" differs from "Jones sees that x is green" in that whereas the latter both ascribes a propositional claim to Jones' experience *and endorses it*, the former ascribes the claim but does not endorse it. This is the essential difference between the two, for it is clear that two experiences may be identical *as experiences*, and yet one be properly referred to as a *seeing* that something is green, and the other merely as a case of something's *looking* green. Of course, if I say "X merely *looks* green to S" I am not only failing to endorse the claim, I am rejecting it.

Thus, when I say "X looks green to me now" I am *reporting* the fact that my experience is, so to speak, intrinsically, as an experience, indistinguishable from a veridical one of seeing that x is green. Involved in the report is the ascription to my experience of the claim 'x is green'; and the fact that I make this report rather than the simple report "X is green" indicates that certain considerations have operated to raise, so to speak in a higher court, the question 'to endorse or not to endorse.' I may have reason to think that x may not after all be green.

If I make at one time the report "X looks to be green"—which is not only a report, but the withholding of an endorsement—I may later, when the original reasons for withholding endorsement have been rebutted, endorse the original claim by saying "I saw that it was green, though at the time I was only sure that it looked green." Notice that I will only say "I see that x is green" (as opposed to "X is green") when the question "to endorse or not to endorse" has come up. "I see that x is green" belongs, so to speak, on the same level as "X looks green" and "X merely *looks* green."

17. There are many interesting and subtle questions about the dialectics of "looks talk," into which I do not have the space to enter. Fortunately, the above distinctions suffice for our present purposes. Let us suppose, then, that to say that "X looks green to S at t" is, in effect, to say that S has that kind of experience which, if one were prepared to endorse the propositional claim it involves, one would characterize as *seeing x to be green at t*. Thus, when our friend John learns to use the sentence "This necktie looks green to me" he learns a way of reporting an experience of the kind which, as far as any categories I have yet permitted him to have are concerned, he can only characterize by saying that as an experience it does not differ from seeing something to be green, and that evidence for the proposition 'This necktie is green' is *ipso facto* evidence for the proposition that the experience in question is *seeing that the necktie is green*.

Now one of the chief merits of this account is that it permits a parallel treatment of 'qualitative' and 'existential' seeming or looking. Thus, when I say "The tree looks bent" I am endorsing that part of the claim involved in my experience which concerns the existence of the tree, but withholding endorsement from the rest. On the other hand, when I say "There looks to be a bent tree over there" I am refusing to endorse any but the most general aspect of the claim, namely, that there is an 'over there' as opposed to a 'here.' Another merit of the account is that it explains how a necktie, for example, can look red to S at t, without looking scarlet or crimson or any other determinate shade of red. In short it explains how things can have a *merely generic* look, a fact which would be puzzling indeed if looking red were a *natural* as opposed to *epistemic* fact about objects. The core of the explanation, of course, is that the propositional claim involved in such an experience may be, for example, either the more determinable claim 'This is red' or the more determinate claim 'This is crimson.' The complete story is more complicated, and requires some account of the role in these experiences of the 'impressions' or 'immediate experiences' the logical status of which remains to be determined. But even in the absence of these additional details, we can note the resemblance between the fact that x can look red to S, without it being true of some specific shade of red that x looks to S to be of that shade, and the fact that S can believe that Cleopatra's Needle is tall, without its being true of some determinate number of feet that S believes it to be that number of feet tall.

18. The point I wish to stress at this time, however, is that the concept of *looking green*, the ability to recognize that something *looks green*, presupposes the concept of *being green*, and that the latter concept involves the ability to tell what colors objects have by looking at them—which, in turn, involves knowing in what circumstances to place an object if one wishes to ascertain its color by looking at it. Let me develop this latter point. As our friend John becomes more and more sophisticated about his own and other people's visual experiences, he learns under what conditions it is as though one were seeing a necktie to be of one color when in fact it is of another. Suppose someone asks him "Why does this tie look green to me?" John may very well reply "Because it is blue, and blue objects look green in this kind of light." And if someone asks this question when looking at the necktie in plain daylight, John may very well reply "Because the tie *is* green"—to which he may add "We are in plain daylight, *and in daylight things look what they are*." We thus see that

$$x \text{ is red} \cdot \equiv \cdot x \text{ looks red to standard observers in standard conditions}$$

is a necessary truth *not* because the right-hand side is the definition of "x is red," but because "standard conditions" means conditions in which things look what they are. And, of course, which conditions are standard for a given mode of perception is, at the common-sense level, specified by a list of conditions which exhibit the vagueness and open texture characteristic of ordinary discourse.

19. I have arrived at a stage in my argument which is, at least prima facie, out of step with the basic presuppositions of logical atomism. Thus, as long as *looking green* is taken to be the notion to which *being green* is reducible, it could be claimed with considerable plausibility that fundamental concepts pertaining to observable fact have that logical independence of one another which is characteristic of the empiricist tradition. Indeed, at first sight the situation is *quite* disquieting, for if the ability to recognize that x looks green presupposes the concept of *being green*, and if this in turn involves knowing in what circumstances to view an object to ascertain its color, then, since one can scarcely determine what the circumstances are without noticing that certain objects have certain perceptible characteristics—including colors—it would seem that one couldn't form the concept of *being green*, and, by parity of reasoning, of the other colors, unless he already had them.

Now, it just won't do to reply that to have the concept of green, to know what it is for something to be green, it is sufficient to respond, when one is *in point of fact* in standard conditions, to green objects with the vocable "This is green." Not only must the conditions be of a sort that is appropriate for determining the color of an object by looking, the subject must *know* that conditions of this sort are appropriate. And while this does not imply that one must have concepts before one has them, it does imply that one can have the concept of green only by having a whole battery of concepts of which it is one element. It implies that while the process of acquiring the concept of green may—indeed does—involve a long history of acquiring *piecemeal* habits of response to various objects in various circumstances, there is an important sense in which one has no concept pertaining to the observable properties of physical objects in Space and Time unless one has them all—and, indeed, as we shall see, a great deal more besides.

20. Now, I think it is clear what a logical atomist, supposing that he found any merit at all in the above argument, would say. He would

say that I am overlooking the fact that the logical space of physical objects in Space and Time rests on the logical space of sense contents, and he would argue that it is concepts pertaining to sense contents which have the logical independence of one another which is characteristic of traditional empiricism. "After all," he would point out, "concepts pertaining to theoretical entities—molecules, for example—have the mutual dependence you have, perhaps rightly, ascribed to concepts pertaining to *physical* fact. But," he would continue, "theoretical concepts have empirical content because they rest on—are coordinated with—a more fundamental logical space. Until you have disposed, therefore, of the idea that there is a more fundamental logical space than that of physical objects in Space and Time, or shown that it too is fraught with coherence, your incipient *Meditations Hegeliènnes* are premature."

And we can imagine a sense-datum theorist to interject the following complaint: "You have begun to write as though you had shown not only that *physical redness* is not to be analyzed in terms of *looking red*—which I will grant—but also that physical redness is not to be analyzed at all, and, in particular, not to be analyzed in terms of the redness of red sense contents. Again, you have begun to write as though you had shown not only that observing that x *looks* red is not more basic than observing that x *is* red, but also that there is *no* form of visual noticing more basic than seeing that x is red, such as the sensing of a red sense content. I grant," he continues, "that the tendency of sense-datum theorists has been to claim that the *redness* of physical objects is to be analyzed in terms of *looking red*, and *then* to claim that *looking red* is itself to be analyzed in terms of *red sense contents*, and that you may have undercut this line of analysis. But what is to prevent the sense-datum theorist from taking the line that the properties of physical objects are *directly* analyzable into the qualities and phenomenal relations of sense contents?"

Very well. But once again we must ask, How does the sense-datum theorist come by the framework of sense contents? and How is he going to convince us that there are such things? For even if *looking red* doesn't enter into the analysis of physical redness, it is by asking us to reflect on the experience of having something look red to us that he hopes to make this framework convincing. And it therefore becomes relevant to note that my analysis of x *looks red to S at t* has not, at least as far as I have pushed it to date, revealed any such items as sense-contents. And it may be relevant to suggest that once we see clearly that physical redness is not to be given a dispositional analysis in terms of *looking red*, the idea that it is to be given any kind of dispositional analysis loses a large measure of its plausibility. In any event, the next move must be to press further the above account of qualitative and existential looking.

IV. Explaining Looks

21. I have already noted that sense-datum theorists are impressed by the question "How can a physical object look red to S, unless something in that situation *is* red and S is taking account of it? If S isn't experiencing something red, how does it happen that the physical object looks red, rather than green or streaky?" There is, I propose to show, *something* to this line of thought, though the story turns out to be a complicated one. And if, in the course of telling the story, I shall be led to make statements which resemble *some* of the things sense-datum theorists have said, this story will amount to a sense-datum theory only in a sense which robs this phrase of an entire dimension of its traditional epistemological force, a dimension which is characteristic of even such heterodox forms of sense-datum theory as the "another language" approach.

Let me begin by formulating the question: "Is the fact that an object looks to S to be red and triangular, or that there looks to S to be a red and triangular object over there, to be explained in terms of the idea that Jones has a sensation—or impression, or immediate experience—of a red triangle? One point can be made right away, namely that if these expressions are so understood that, say, the immediate experience of a red triangle implies the existence of something—not a physical object—which is red and triangular, and if the redness which this item has is the same as the redness which the physical object *looks* to have, then the suggestion runs up against the objection that the redness physical objects *look* to have is the same as the redness physical objects actually *do* have, so that items which *ex hypothesi* are not physical objects, and which radically, even categorially, differ from physical objects, would have the same redness as physical objects. And while this is, perhaps, not entirely out of the question, it certainly provides food for thought. Yet when it is claimed that "obviously" physical objects can't *look* red to one unless one is experiencing something that *is* red, is it not presumed that the redness which the *something* has is the redness which the physical object *looks to have?*

Now there are those who would say that the question "Is the fact that an object looks red and triangular to S to be explained—as opposed to notationally reformulated—in terms of the idea that S has an impression of a red triangle?" simply doesn't arise, on the ground that there are perfectly sound explanations of qualitative and existential lookings which make no reference to 'immediate experiences' or other dubious entities. Thus, it is pointed out, it is perfectly proper to answer the question "Why does this object look red?" by saying "Because it is an orange object looked at in such and such circumstances." The explanation is, in principle, a good one, and is typical of the answers we make to such questions in everyday life. But because these explanations are good, it by no means follows that explanations of other kinds might not be equally good, and, perhaps, more searching.

22. On the face of it there are at least two ways in which additional, but equally legitimate explanations *might* be forthcoming for such a fact as that x *looks* red. The first of these is suggested by a simple analogy. Might it not be the case that just as there are two kinds of good explanation of the fact that this balloon has expanded, (a) in terms of the Boyle-Charles laws which relate the empirical concepts of volume, pressure, and temperature pertaining to gases, and (b) in terms of the kinetic theory of gases; so there are two ways of explaining the fact that this object looks red to S: (a) in terms of empirical generalizations relating the colors of objects, the circumstances in which they are seen, and the colors they look to have, and (b) in terms of a theory of perception in which 'immediate experiences' play a role analogous to that of the molecules of the kinetic theory.

Now there is such an air of paradox to the idea that 'immediate experiences' are mere theoretical entities—entities, that is, which are postulated, along with certain fundamental principles concerning them, to explain uniformities pertaining to sense perception, as molecules, along with the principles of molecular motion, are postulated to explain the experimentally determined regularities pertaining to gases—that I am going to lay it aside until a more propitious context of thought may make it seem relevant. Certainly, those who have thought that qualitative and existential lookings are to be explained in terms of 'immediate experiences' thought of the latter as the most untheoretical of entities, indeed, as *the* observables *par excellence.*

Let us therefore turn to a second way in which, at least prima facie, there might be an additional, but equally legitimate explanation of existential and qualitative lookings. According to this second account, when we consider items of this kind, we find that they contain as components items which are properly referred to as, for example, 'the immediate experience of a red triangle.' Let us begin our exploration of this suggestion by taking another look at our account of existential and qualitative lookings. It will be remembered that our account of qualitative looking ran, in rough and ready terms, as follows:

'x looks red to S' has the sense of 'S has an experience which involves in a unique way the idea *that x is red* and involves it in such a way that if this idea were true, the experience would correctly be characterized as a seeing that x is red.'

Thus, our account implies that the three situations

(a) Seeing that x, over there, is red

(b) Its looking to one that x, over there, is red

(c) Its looking to one as though there were a red object over there

differ primarily in that (a) is so formulated as to involve an endorsement of the idea that x, over there, is red, whereas in (b) this idea is only partially endorsed, and in (c) not at all. Let us refer to the idea *that x, over there, is red* as the *common propositional content* of these three situations. (This is, of course, not strictly correct, since the propositional content of (c) is *existential*, rather than about a presupposedly designated object x, but it will serve my purpose. Furthermore, the common propositional content of these three experiences is much more complex and determinate than is indicated by the sentence we use to describe our experience to others, and which I am using to represent it. Nevertheless it is clear that, subject to the first of these qualifications, the propositional content of these three experiences *could* be identical.)

The propositional content of these three experiences is, of course, but a part of that to which we are logically committed by characterizing them as situations of these three kinds. Of the remainder, as we have seen, part is a matter of the extent to which this propositional content is endorsed. It is the residue with which we are now concerned. Let us call this residue the *descriptive content.* I can then point out that it is implied by my account that not only the *propositional content*, but also the *descriptive content* of these three experiences may be identical. I shall suppose this to be the case, though that there must be some factual difference in the *total* situations is obvious.

Now, and this is the decisive point, in characterizing these three experiences as, respectively, a *seeing that x, over there, is red*, its *looking to one as though x, over there, were red*, and *its looking to one as though there were a red object over there*, we do not specify this common *descriptive* content save *indirectly*, by implying that *if the common propositional content were true, then all these three situations would be cases of seeing that x, over there, is red*. Both existential and qualitative lookings are experiences that would be *seeings* if their propositional contents were true.

Thus, the very nature of "looks talk" is such as to raise questions to which it gives no answer: What is the *intrinsic* character of the common descriptive content of these three experiences? and How are they able to have it in spite of the fact that whereas in the case of (a) the perceiver must be in the presence of a red object over there, in (b) the object over there need not be red, while in (c) there need be no object over there at all?

23. Now it is clear that if we were required to give a more direct characterization of the common descriptive content of these experiences, we would begin by trying to do so in terms of the quality red. Yet, as I have already pointed out, we can scarcely say that this descriptive content is itself something red unless we can pry the term "red" loose from its prima-facie tie with the category of physical objects. And there is a line of thought which has been one of the standard gambits of perceptual epistemology and which seems to promise exactly this. If successful, it would convince us that redness—in the most basic sense of this term—is a characteristic of items of the sort we have been calling sense contents. It runs as follows:

While it would, indeed, be a howler to say that we don't see chairs, tables, etc., but only their facing surfaces, nevertheless, although we see a table, say, and although the table has a back as well as a front, we do not see the back of the table as we see its front. Again, although we see the table, and although the table has an 'inside,' we do not see the inside of the table as we see its facing outside. Seeing an object entails seeing its facing surface. If we are seeing that an object is red, this entails seeing that its facing surface is red. A red surface is a two-dimensional red expanse—two-dimensional in that though it may be bulgy, and in *this* sense three-dimensional, it has no *thickness*. As far as the analysis of perceptual consciousness is concerned, a red physical object is one that has a red expanse as its surface.

Now a red expanse is not a physical object, nor does the existence of a red expanse entail the existence of a physical object to which it belongs. (Indeed, there are "wild" expanses which do not belong to any physical object.) The "descriptive content"—as you put it—which is common to the three experiences (a), (b) and (c) above, is exactly this sort of thing, a bulgy red expanse.

Spelled out thus baldly, the fallacy is, or should be, obvious; it is a simple equivocation on the phrase "having a red surface." We start out by thinking of the familiar fact that a physical object may be of one color "on the surface" and of another color "inside." We may express this by saying that, for example, the 'surface' of the object is red, but its 'inside' green. But in saying this we are *not* saying that there is a 'surface' in the sense of a bulgy two-dimensional particular, a red 'expanse' which is a component particular in a complex particular which also includes green particulars. The notion of two-dimensional bulgy (or flat) particulars is a product of philosophical (and mathematical) sophistication which can be *related to* our ordinary conceptual framework, but does not belong in an *analysis* of it. I think that in its place it has an important contribution to make. (See below, Section 61, (5), pp. 325–26.) But this place is in the logical space of an ideal *scientific* picture of the world and not in the logical space of ordinary discourse. It has nothing to do with the logical grammar of our ordinary color words. It is just a mistake to suppose that as the word "red" is actually used, it is ever surfaces in the sense of two-dimensional particulars which are red. The only particular involved when a physical object is "red on the outside, but green inside" is the physical object itself, located in a certain region of Space and enduring over a stretch of Time. The fundamental grammar of the attribute red is *physical object x is red at place p and at time t*. Certainly, when we say of an object that it is red, we commit ourselves to no more than that it is red "at the surface." And sometimes it is red at the surface by having what we would not hesitate to call a "part" which is red through and through—thus, a red table which is red by virtue of a layer of red paint. But the red paint is not itself red by virtue of a

component—a 'surface' or 'expanse'; a particular with no thickness—
which is red. There may, let me repeat, turn out to be some place in
the total philosophical picture for the statement that there "really
are" such particulars, and that they are elements in perceptual experience. But this place is not to be found by an analysis of ordinary
perceptual discourse, any more than Minkowski four-dimensional Space-
Time worms are an *analysis* of what we mean when we speak of physical objects in Space and Time.

V. Impressions and Ideas: a Logical Point

24. Let me return to beating the neighboring bushes. Notice that
the common descriptive component of the three experiences I am
considering is itself often referred to (by philosophers, at least) as an
experience—as, for example, an *immediate experience*. Here caution is
necessary. The notorious "ing-ed" ambiguity of "experience" must be
kept in mind. For although *seeing that x, over there, is red* is an experiencing—indeed, a paradigm case of experiencing—it does not follow
that the descriptive content of this experiencing is itself an experiencing.
Furthermore, because the fact that *x, over there, looks to Jones to be
red* would be a *seeing*, on Jones' part, *that x, over there, is red*, if its
propositional content were true, and because if it were a seeing, it
would be an experiencing, we must beware of concluding that the fact
that *x, over there, looks red to Jones* is itself an experiencing. Certainly,
the fact that something looks red to me can itself be *experienced*. But
it is not itself an experiencing.

All this is not to say that the common descriptive core may not
turn out to be an experien*cing,* though the chances that this is so
appear less with each step in my argument. On the other hand, I can
say that it is a component in states of affairs which are experienced,
and it does not seem unreasonable to say that it is itself experienced.
But what kind of experience (in the sense of experien*ced*) *is* it? If
my argument to date is sound, I cannot say that it is a *red* experience,
that is, a red experienced item. I could, of course, introduce a new
use of "red" according to which to say of an 'immediate experience'
that it was red, would be the stipulated equivalent of characterizing it
as that which could be the common descriptive component of a *seeing*
that something is red, and the corresponding qualitative and existential
lookings. This would give us a *predicate* by which to describe and report

the experience, but we should, of course, be only verbally better off than if we could only refer to this kind of experience as *the kind which could be the common descriptive component of a seeing* and a qualitative or existential *looking*. And this makes it clear that one way of putting what we are after is by saying that we want to have a *name* for this kind of experience which is truly a *name*, and not just shorthand for a definite description. Does ordinary usage have a *name* for this kind of experience?

I shall return to this quest in a moment. In the meantime it is important to clear the way of a traditional obstacle to understanding the status of such things as *sensations of red triangles*. Thus, suppose I were to say that while the experience I am examining is not a red experience, it is an experience *of red*. I could expect the immediate challenge: "Is 'sensation of a red triangle' any better off than 'red and triangular experience'? Does not the existence of a sensation of a red triangle entail the existence of a red and triangular item, and hence, *always on the assumption that red is a property of physical objects*, of a red and triangular physical object? Must you not, therefore abandon this assumption, and return to the framework of sense contents which you have so far refused to do?"

One way out of dilemma would be to assimilate "Jones has a sensation of a red triangle" to "Jones believes in a divine Huntress." For the truth of the latter does not, of course, entail the existence of a divine Huntress. Now, I think that most contemporary philosophers are clear that it is possible to attribute to the context

    . . . sensation of . . .

the *logical* property of being such that "There is a sensation of a red triangle" does not entail "There is a red triangle" without assimilating the context ". . . sensation of . . ." to the context ". . . believes in . . ." in any closer way. For while mentalistic verbs characteristically provide nonextensional contexts (when they are not "achievement" or "endorsing" words), not all nonextensional contexts are mentalistic. Thus, as far as the purely *logical* point is concerned, there is no reason why "Jones has a sensation of a red triangle" should be assimilated to "Jones believes in a divine Huntress" rather than to "It is possible that the moon is made of green cheese" or to any of the other nonextensional contexts familiar to logicians. Indeed there is no reason why it should be assimilated to any of these. ". . . sensation of . . ." or ". . . impression of . . ." could be a context which, though sharing with these others the logical property of nonextensionality, was otherwise in a class by itself.

25. Yet there is no doubt but that *historically* the contexts ". . . sensation of . . ." and ". . . impression of . . ." were assimilated to such mentalistic contexts as ". . . believes . . .," ". . . desires . . .," ". . . chooses . . .," in short to contexts which are either themselves 'propositional attitudes' or involve propositional attitudes in their analysis. This assimilation took the form of classifying sensations with *ideas* or *thoughts*. Thus Descartes uses the word "thought" to cover not only *judgments, inferences, desires, volitions,* and (occurrent) *ideas of abstract qualities,* but also *sensations, feelings,* and *images.* Locke, in the same spirit, uses the term "idea" with similar scope. The apparatus of Conceptualism, which had its genesis in the controversy over universals, was given a correspondingly wide application. Just as objects and situations were said to have 'objective being' in our *thoughts,* when we think of them, or judge them to obtain—as contrasted with the 'subjective' or 'formal being' which they have in the world—so, when we have a sensation of a red triangle, the red triangle was supposed to have 'objective being' in our sensation.

In elaborating, for a moment, this conceptualistic interpretation of sensation, let me refer to that which has 'objective being' in a *thought* or *idea* as its *content* or *immanent object.* Then I can say that the fundamental difference between occurrent *abstract ideas* and *sensations,* for both Locke and Descartes, lay in the *specificity* and, above all, the *complexity* of the content of the latter. (Indeed, both Descartes and Locke assimilated the contrast between the simple and the complex in ideas to that between the generic and the specific.) Descartes thinks of sensations as confused thoughts of their external cause; Spinoza of sensations and images as confused thoughts of bodily states, and still more confused thoughts of the external causes of these bodily states. And it is interesting to note that the conceptualistic thesis that abstract entities have only *esse intentionale* (their esse is *concipi*) is extended by Descartes and, with less awareness of what he is doing, Locke, to include the thesis that colors, sounds, etc., exist "only in the mind" (their *esse* is *percipi*) and by Berkeley to cover all perceptible qualities.

Now, I think we would all agree, today, that this assimilation of sensations to thoughts is a mistake. It is sufficient to note that if "sensation of a red triangle" had the sense of "episode of the kind which is the common descriptive component of those experiences which *would be* cases of seeing that the facing surface of a physical object is red and triangular if an object *were* presenting a red and triangular facing surface" then it would have the nonextensionality the noticing of which led to this mistaken assimilation. But while we have indeed escaped from this blind alley, it is small consolation. For we are no further along in the search for a 'direct' or 'intrinsic' characterization of 'immediate experience.'

VI. Impressions and Ideas: an Historical Point

26. There are those who will say that although I have spoken of exploring blind alleys, it is really I who am blind. For, they will say, if that which we wish to characterize intrinsically is an *experience*, then there can be no puzzle about knowing *what kind* of experience it is, though there may be a problem about how this knowledge is to be communicated to others. And, indeed, it is tempting to suppose that if we *should* happen, at a certain stage of our intellectual development, to be able to classify an experience *only* as *of the kind which* could be common to a *seeing* and corresponding qualitative and existential *lookings*, all we would have to do to acquire a 'direct designation' for this kind of experience would be to pitch in, 'examine' it, locate the kind which it exemplifies and which satisfies the above description, name it—say "ϕ"—and, in full possession of the concept of ϕ, classify such experiences, from now on, as ϕ experiences.

At this point, it is clear, the concept—or, as I have put it, the myth—of the given is being invoked to explain the possibility of a direct account of immediate experience. The myth insists that what I have been treating as one problem really subdivides into two, one of which is really no problem at all, while the other may have no solution. These problems are, respectively

(1) How do we become aware of an immediate experience as of one sort, and of a simultaneous immediate experience as of another sort?

(2) How can I know that the labels I attach to the sorts to which my immediate experiences belong, are attached by you to the same sorts? May not the sort I call "red" be the sort you call "green"—and so on systematically throughout the spectrum?

We shall find that the second question, to be a philosophical perplexity, presupposes a certain answer to the first question—indeed the answer given by the myth. And it is to this first question that I now turn. Actually there are various forms taken by the myth of the given in this connection, depending on other philosophical commitments. But they all have in common the idea that the awareness of certain sorts—and by "sorts" I have in mind, in the first instance, determinate sense repeatables—is a primordial, non-problematic feature of 'immediate experience.' In the context of conceptualism, as we have seen, this idea took the form of treating sensations as though they were absolutely specific, and infinitely complicated, *thoughts*. And it is essential to an understanding of the empiricist tradition to realize that whereas the contemporary problem of universals primarily concerns the status of repeatable *determinate* features of particular situations, and the contemporary problem of abstract ideas is at least as much the problem of what it is to be aware of determinate repeatables as of what it is to be aware of determinable repeatables, Locke, Berkeley and, for that matter, Hume saw the problem of abstract ideas as the problem of what it is to be aware of *determinable* repeatables.* Thus, an examination of Locke's *Essay* makes it clear that he is thinking of a sensation of white as the sort of thing that can become an abstract idea (occurrent) of White—a thought of White "in the Understanding"—merely by virtue of being separated from the context of other sensations (and images) which accompany it on a particular occasion. In other words, for Locke an abstract (occurrent) idea of the determinate repeatable Whiteness is nothing more than an isolated *image of white*, which, in turn, differs from a *sensation of white* only (to use a modern turn of phrase) by being "centrally aroused."

In short, for Locke, the problem of how we come to be aware of *determinate* sense repeatables is no problem at all. Merely by virtue of having sensations and images we have this awareness. *His* problem of abstract ideas is the problem of how we come to be able to think of generic properties. And, as is clear from the *Essay*, he approaches *this* problem in terms of what might be called an "adjunctive theory of specification," that is, the view that (if we represent the idea of a determinable as *the idea of being A*) the idea of a determinate form of A can be represented as *the idea of being A and B*. It is, of course,

* For a systematic elaboration and defence of the following interpretation of Locke, Berkeley, and Hume, the reader should consult (11).

notorious that this won't account for the relation of *the idea of being red* to *the idea of being crimson*. By thinking of *conjunction* as the fundamental logical relation involved in building up complex ideas from simple ones, and as the principle of the difference between determinable and determinate ideas, Locke precluded himself from giving even a plausible account of the relation between ideas of determinables and ideas of determinates. It is interesting to speculate what turn his thought might have taken had he admitted *disjunctive* as well as *conjunctive* complex ideas, *the idea of being A or B* alongside *the idea of being A and B*.

27. But my purpose here is not to develop a commentary on the shortcomings of Locke's treatment of abstract ideas, but to emphasize that something which is a problem for us was not a problem for him. And it is therefore important to note that the same is true of Berkeley. His problem was not, as it is often construed, "How do we go from the awareness of *particulars* to ideas of *repeatables?*" but rather "Granted that in immediate experience we are aware of absolutely *specific* sense qualities, how do we come to be conscious of genera pertaining to them, and in what does this consciousness consist?" (This is not the only dimension of "abstraction" that concerned him, but it is the one that is central to our purpose.) And, contrary to the usual interpretation, the essential difference between his account and Locke's consists in the fact that whereas Locke was on the whole * committed to the view that there can be an idea which is *of the genus* without being *of*

---

* I say that Locke was "on the whole" committed to the view that there can be an idea which is *of the genus* without being *of any of its species*, because while he saw that it couldn't be *of any one of the species* to the exclusion of the others, and saw no way of avoiding this except by making it *of none of the species*, he was greatly puzzled by this, for he saw that in some sense the idea *of the genus* must be *of all the species*. We have already noted that if he had admitted disjunction as a principle of compounding ideas, he could have said that the idea *of the genus* is the idea *of the disjunction of all its species*, that the idea of *being triangular* is the idea of *being scalene or isosceles*. As it was, he thought that to be *of all the species* it would have to be the idea of *being scalene and isosceles*, which is, of course, the idea of an impossibility.

It is interesting to note that if Berkeley had faced up to the implications of the criterion we shall find him to have adopted, this disjunctive conception of the generic idea is the one he would have been led to adopt. For since *being G*—where 'G' stands for a generic character—entails *being S_1 or S_2 or S_3 . . . . . or S_n,*—where 'S_1' stands for a specific character falling under G—Berkeley should have taken as the unit of ideas concerning triangles, the idea of the genus Triangle as differentiated into the set of specific forms of triangularity. But, needless to say, if Berkeley *had* taken this step, he could not have thought of a sensation of crimson as a determinate *thought*.

any of its species, Berkeley insists that we can have an idea of a genus only by having an idea of the genus as, to borrow a useful Scotist term, 'contracted' into one of its species.

Roughly, Berkeley's contention is that if *being A* entails *being B*, then there can be no such thing as an idea which is of *A* without being of *B*. He infers that since *being triangular* entails *having some determinately triangular shape*, there cannot be an idea which is *of triangle* without being *of some determinately triangular shape*. We can be aware of generic triangularity only by having an idea which is of triangularity as 'contracted' into one of the specific forms of triangularity. Any of the latter will do; they are all "of the same sort."

28. Now, a careful study of the *Treatise* makes it clear that Hume is in the same boat as Berkeley and Locke, sharing with them the presupposition that we have an unacquired ability to be aware of determinate repeatables. It is often said that whereas he begins the *Treatise* by characterizing 'ideas' in terms which do not distinguish between *images* and *thoughts*, he corrects this deficiency in Book I, Part I, Section vii. What these students of Hume tend to overlook is that what Hume does in this later section is give an account *not* of what it is to think of *repeatables* whether determinable or determinate, but of what it is to think of *determinables*, thus of color as contrasted with particular shades of color. And his account of the consciousness of determinables takes for granted that we have a primordial ability to take account of *determinate* repeatables. Thus, his later account is simply built on, and in no sense a revision of, the account of ideas with which he opens the *Treatise*.

How, then, does he differ from Berkeley and Locke? The latter two had supposed that there must be such a thing as an *occurrent* thought of a determinable, however much they differed in their account of such thoughts. Hume, on the other hand, assuming that there are occurrent thoughts of *determinate* repeatables, *denies* that there are occurrent thoughts of *determinables*. I shall spare the reader the familiar details of Hume's attempt to give a constructive account of our consciousness of determinables, nor shall I criticize it. For my point is that however much Locke, Berkeley, and Hume differ on the problem of abstract ideas, they all take for granted that the human mind has an innate ability to be aware of certain determinate sorts—indeed, *that we are aware of them simply by virtue of having sensations and images.*

29. Now, it takes but a small twist of Hume's position to get a radically different view. For suppose that instead of characterizing the initial elements of experience as impressions of, e.g. red, Hume had characterized them as red particulars (and I would be the last to deny that not only Hume, but perhaps Berkeley and Locke as well, often treat impressions or ideas of red as though they were red particulars) then Hume's view, expanded to take into account determinates as well as determinables, would become the view that all consciousness of sorts or repeatables rests on an association of words (e.g. "red") with classes of resembling particulars.

It clearly makes all the difference in the world how this association is conceived. For if the formation of the association involves not only the occurrence of resembling particulars, but also the occurrence of the awareness *that they are resembling particulars*, then the givenness of determinate kinds or repeatables, say crimson, is merely being replaced by the givenness of *facts* of the form x resembles y, and we are back with an unacquired ability to be aware of repeatables, in this case the repeatable *resemblance*. Even more obviously, if the formation of the association involves not only the occurrence of red particulars, but the awareness *that they are red*, then the conceptualistic form of the myth has merely been replaced by a realistic version, as in the classical sense-datum theory.

If, however, the association is not mediated by the awareness of facts either of the form x resembles y, or of the form x is ϕ, then we have a view of the general type which I will call *psychological nominalism*, according to which *all* awareness of sorts, resemblances, facts, etc., in short, all awareness of abstract entities—indeed, all awareness even of particulars—is a linguistic affair. According to it, not even the awareness of such sorts, resemblances, and facts as pertain to so-called immediate experience is presupposed by the process of acquiring the use of a language.

Two remarks are immediately relevant: (1) Although the form of psychological nominalism which one gets by modifying Hume's view along the above lines has the essential merit that it avoids the mistake of supposing that there are pure episodes of being aware of sensory repeatables or sensory facts, and is committed to the view that any event which can be referred to in these terms must be, to use Ryle's expression, a mongrel categorical-hypothetical, in particular, a verbal episode as *being the manifestation* of associative connections of the word-object and word-word types, it nevertheless is impossibly crude and inadequate as an account of the simplest concept. (2) Once sensations and images have been purged of epistemic aboutness, the primary reason for supposing that the fundamental associative tie between language and the world must be between words and 'immediate experiences' has disappeared, and the way is clear to recognizing that basic word-world associations hold, for example, between "red" and red *physical objects*, rather than between "red" and a supposed class of private red particulars.

The second remark, it should be emphasized, does not imply that private sensations or impressions may not be essential to the formation of these associative connections. For one can certainly admit that the tie between "red" and red physical objects—which tie makes it possible for "red" to mean the quality red—is *causally* mediated by sensations of red without being committed to the mistaken idea that it is "really" sensations of red, rather than red physical objects, which are the primary denotation of the word "red."

VII. The Logic of 'Means'

30. There is a source of the Myth of the Given to which even philosophers who are suspicious of the whole idea of *inner episodes* can fall prey. This is the fact that when we picture a child—or a carrier of slabs—learning his first language, we, of course, locate the language learner in a structured logical space in which we are at home. Thus, we conceive of him as a person (or, at least, a potential person) in a world of physical objects, colored, producing sounds, existing in Space and Time. But though it is we who are familiar with this logical space, we run the danger, if we are not careful, of picturing the language learner as having *ab initio* some degree of awareness—"pre-analytic," limited and fragmentary though it may be—of this same logical space. We picture his state as though it were rather like our own when placed in a strange forest on a dark night. In other words, unless we are careful, we can easily take for granted that the process of teaching a child to use a language is that of teaching it to discriminate elements within a logical space of particulars, universals, facts, etc., of which it is already undiscriminatingly aware, and to associate these discriminated elements with verbal symbols. And this mistake is in principle the same whether

the logical space of which the child is supposed to have this undiscriminating awareness is conceived by us to be that of physical objects or of private sense contents.

The real test of a theory of language lies not in its account of what has been called (by H. H. Price) "thinking in absence," but in its account of "thinking in presence"—that is to say, its account of those occasions on which the fundamental connection of language with non-linguistic fact is exhibited. And many theories which look like psychological nominalism when one views their account of thinking in absence, turn out to be quite "Augustinian" when the scalpel is turned to their account of thinking in presence.

31. Now, the friendly use I have been making of the phrase "psychological nominalism" may suggest that I am about to *equate* concepts with words, and thinking, in so far as it is episodic, with verbal episodes. I must now hasten to say that I shall do nothing of the sort, or, at least, that if I *do do something* of the sort, the view I shall shortly be developing is only in a relatively Pickwickian sense an equation of thinking with the use of language. I wish to emphasize, therefore, that as I am using the term, the primary connotation of "psychological nominalism" is the denial that there is any awareness of logical space prior to, or independent of, the acquisition of a language.

However, although I shall later be distinguishing between *thoughts* and their *verbal expression*, there is a point of fundamental importance which is best made before more subtle distinctions are drawn. To begin with, it is perfectly clear that the word "red" would not be a *predicate* if it didn't have the logical syntax characteristic of predicates. Nor would it be the predicate it is, unless, in certain frames of mind, at least, we tended to respond to red objects in standard circumstances with something having the force of "This is red." And once we have abandoned the idea that learning to use the word "red" involves antecedent episodes of the *awareness of redness*—not to be confused, of course, with *sensations of red*—there is a temptation to suppose that the word "red" means the quality red by virtue of these two facts: briefly, the fact that it has the *syntax* of a predicate, and the fact that it is a *response* (in certain circumstances) to red objects.

But this account of the meaningfulness of "red," which Price has correctly stigmatized as the "thermometer view," would have little plausibility if it were not reinforced by another line of thought which takes its point of departure from the superficial resemblance of

(In German) "rot" means red

to such relational statements as

Cowley adjoins Oxford.

For once one assimilates the form

". . ." means - - -

to the form   x R y

and thus takes it for granted that meaning is a relation between a word and a nonverbal entity, it is tempting to suppose that the relation in question is that of association.

The truth of the matter, of course, is that statements of the form "'. . .' means - - -" are not relational statements, and that while it is indeed the case that the word "rot" could not mean the quality red unless it were associated with red things, it would be misleading to say that the semantical statement " 'Rot' means red" says of "rot" that it associated with red things. For this would suggest that the semantical statement is, so to speak, definitional shorthand for a longer statement about the associative connections of "rot," which is not the case. The rubric "'. . .' means - - -" is a linguistic device for conveying the information that a *mentioned* word, in this case "rot," plays the same role in a certain linguistic economy, in this case the linguistic economy of German-speaking peoples, as does the word "red," which is not mentioned but used—used in a unique way; *exhibited*, so to speak—and which occurs "on the right-hand side" of the semantical statement.

We see, therefore, how the two statements

"Und" means and

and

"Rot" means red

can tell us quite different things about "und" and "rot," for the first conveys the information that "und" plays the purely formal role of a certain logical connective, the second that "rot" plays in German the role of the observation word "red"—in spite of the fact that means has the same sense in each statement, and without having to say that the first says of "und" that it stands in "the meaning relation" to Conjunction, or the second that "rot" stands in "the meaning relation" to Redness.*

* For an analysis of the problem of abstract entities built on this interpretation of semantical statements, see (20).

292

These considerations make it clear that nothing whatever can be inferred about the complexity of the role played by the word "red" or about the exact way in which the word "red" is related to red things, from the truth of the semantical statement " 'red' means the quality red." And no consideration arising from the 'Fido'-Fido aspect of the grammar of "means" precludes one from claiming that the role of the word "red" by virtue of which it can correctly be said to have the meaning it does is a complicated one indeed, and that one cannot understand the meaning of the word "red"—"know what redness is"—unless one has a great deal of knowledge which classical empiricism would have held to have a purely contingent relationship with the possession of fundamental empirical concepts.

VIII. Does Empirical Knowledge Have a Foundation?

32. One of the forms taken by the Myth of the Given is the idea that there is, indeed *must be*, a structure of particular matter of fact such that (a) each fact can not only be noninferentially known to be the case, but presupposes no other knowledge either of particular matter of fact, or of general truths; and (b) such that the noninferential knowledge of facts belonging to this structure constitutes the ultimate court of appeals for all factual claims—particular and general—about the world. It is important to note that I characterized the knowledge of fact belonging to this stratum as not only noninferential, but as presupposing no knowledge of other matter of fact, whether particular or general. It might be thought that this is a redundancy, that knowledge (not belief or conviction, but knowledge) which logically presupposes knowledge of other facts *must* be inferential. This, however, as I hope to show, is itself an episode in the Myth.

Now, the idea of such a privileged stratum of fact is a familiar one, though not without its difficulties. Knowledge pertaining to this level is *noninferential*, yet it is, after all, *knowledge*. It is ultimate, yet it has *authority*. The attempt to make a consistent picture of these two requirements has traditionally taken the following form:

Statements pertaining to this level, in order to 'express knowledge' must not only be made, but, so to speak, must be worthy of being made, *credible*, that is, in the sense of worthy of credence. Furthermore, and this is a crucial point, they must be made in a way which *involves* this credibility. For where there is no connection between the making of a statement and its authority, the assertion may express *conviction*, but it can scarcely be said to express knowledge.

The authority—the credibility—of statements pertaining to this level cannot exhaustively consist in the fact that they are supported by *other* statements, for in that case all *knowledge* pertaining to this level would have to be inferential, which not only contradicts the hypothesis, but flies in the face of good sense. The conclusion seems inevitable that if some statements pertaining to this level are to express *noninferential* knowledge, they must have a credibility which is not a matter of being supported by other statements. Now there does seem to be a class of statements which fill at least part of this bill, namely such statements as would be said to *report observations*, thus, "This is red." These statements, candidly made, have authority. Yet they are not expressions of inference. How, then, is this authority to be understood?

Clearly, the argument continues, it springs from the fact that they are made in just the circumstances in which they are made, as is indicated by the fact that they characteristically, though not necessarily or without exception, involve those so-called token-reflexive expressions which, in addition to the tenses of verbs, serve to connect the circumstances in which a statement is made with its sense. (At this point it will be helpful to begin putting the line of thought I am developing in terms of the *fact-stating* and *observation-reporting* roles of certain sentences.) Roughly, two verbal performances which are tokens of a non-token-reflexive sentence can occur in widely different circumstances and yet make the same statement; whereas two tokens of a token-reflexive sentence can make the same statement only if they are uttered in the same circumstances (according to a relevant criterion of sameness). And two tokens of a sentence, whether it contains a token-reflexive expression—over and above a tensed verb—or not, can make the same *report* only if, made in all candor, they express the *presence*—in *some* sense of "presence"—of the state of affairs that is being reported; if, that is, they stand in that relation to the state of affairs, whatever the relation may be, by virtue of which they can be said to formulate observations of it.

It would appear, then, that there are two ways in which a sentence token can have credibility: (1) The authority may accrue to it, so to speak, from above, that is, as being a token of a sentence type all the tokens of which, in a certain use, have credibility, e.g. "$2 + 2 = 4$." In this case, let us say that token credibility is inherited from type authority. (2) The credibility may accrue to it from the fact that it came to exist in a certain way in a certain set of circumstances, e.g. "This is red." Here token credibility is not derived from type credibility.

Now, the credibility of some sentence types appears to be *intrinsic*—at least in the limited sense that it is *not* derived from other sentences, type or token. This is, or seems to be, the case with certain sentences used to make analytic statements. The credibility of *some* sentence types accrues to them by virtue of their logical relations to other sentence types, thus by virtue of the fact that they are logical consequences of more basic sentences. It would seem obvious, however, that the credibility of empirical sentence types cannot be traced without remainder to the credibility of other sentence types. And since no empirical sentence type appears to have *intrinsic* credibility, this means that credibility must accrue to *some* empirical sentence types by virtue of their logical relations to certain sentence tokens, and, indeed, to sentence tokens the authority of which is not derived, in its turn, from the authority of sentence types.

The picture we get is that of their being two *ultimate* modes of credibility: (1) The intrinsic credibility of analytic sentences, which accrues to tokens as being tokens of such a type; (2) the credibility of such tokens as "express observations," a credibility which flows from tokens to types.

33. Let us explore this picture, which is common to all traditional empiricisms, a bit further. How is the authority of such sentence tokens as "express observational knowledge" to be understood? It has been tempting to suppose that in spite of the obvious differences which exist between "observation reports" and "analytic statements," there is an essential similarity between the ways in which they come by their authority. Thus, it has been claimed, not without plausibility, that whereas *ordinary* empirical statements can be *correctly* made without being *true*, observation reports resemble analytic statements in that being correctly made is a sufficient as well as necessary condition of their truth. And it has been inferred from this—somewhat hastily, I believe—that "correctly making" the report "This is green" is a matter of "following the rules for the use of 'this,' 'is' and 'green.' "

Three comments are immediately necessary:

(1) First a brief remark about the term "report." In ordinary usage a report is a report made *by* someone *to* someone. To make a report is to *do* something. In the literature of epistemology, however, the word "report" or "*Konstatierung*" has acquired a technical use in which a sentence token can play a reporting role (a) without being an *overt* verbal performance, and (b) without having the character of being "by someone to someone"—even oneself. There is, of course, such a thing as "talking to oneself"—*in foro interno*—but, as I shall be emphasizing

in the closing stages of my argument, it is important not to suppose that all "covert" verbal episodes are of this kind.

(2) My second comment is that while we shall not assume that because 'reports' *in the ordinary sense* are actions, 'reports' in the sense of *Konstatierungen* are also actions, the line of thought we are considering treats them as such. In other words, it interprets the correctness of *Konstatierungen* as analogous to the rightness of actions. Let me emphasize, however, that not all *ought* is *ought to do*, nor all correctness the correctness of *actions*.

(3) My third comment is that if the expression "following a rule" is taken seriously, and is not weakened beyond all recognition into the bare notion of exhibiting a uniformity—in which case the lightning, thunder sequence would "follow a rule"—then it is the knowledge or belief that the circumstances are of a certain kind, and not the mere fact that they *are* of this kind, which contributes to bringing about the action.

34. In the light of these remarks it is clear that if observation reports are construed as *actions*, if their correctness is interpreted as the correctness of an *action*, and if the authority of an observation report is construed as the fact that making it is "following a rule" in the proper sense of this phrase, then we are face to face with givenness in its most straightforward form. For these stipulations commit one to the idea that the authority of *Konstatierungen* rests on nonverbal episodes of awareness—awareness *that* something is the case, e.g. *that this is green*—which nonverbal episodes have an intrinsic authority (they are, so to speak 'self-authenticating') which the *verbal* performances (the *Konstatierungen*) properly performed "express." One is committed to a stratum of authoritative nonverbal episodes ("awarenesses") the authority of which accrues to a superstructure of *verbal actions*, provided that the expressions occurring in these actions are properly used. These self-authenticating episodes would constitute the tortoise on which stands the elephant on which rests the edifice of empirical knowledge. The essence of the view is the same whether these intrinsically authoritative episodes are such items as the awareness that a certain sense content is green or such items as the awareness that a certain physical object looks to someone to be green.

35. But what is the alternative? We might begin by trying something like the following: An overt or covert token of "This is green"

in the presence of a green item is a *Konstatierung* and expresses observational knowledge if and only if it is a manifestation of a tendency to produce overt or covert tokens of "This is green"—given a certain set— if and only if a green object is being looked at in standard conditions. Clearly on this interpretation the occurrence of such tokens of "This is green" would be "following a rule" only in the sense that they are instances of a uniformity, a uniformity differing from the lightning-thunder case in that it is an acquired causal characteristic of the language user. Clearly the above suggestion, which corresponds to the "thermometer view" criticized by Professor Price, and which we have already rejected, won't do as it stands. Let us see, however, if it can't be revised to fit the criteria I have been using for "expressing observational knowledge."

The first hurdle to be jumped concerns the *authority* which, as I have emphasized, a sentence token must have in order that it may be said to express knowledge. Clearly, on this account the only thing that can remotely be supposed to constitute such authority is the fact that one can infer the presence of a green object from the fact that someone makes this report. As we have already noticed, the correctness of a report does not have to be construed as the rightness of an *action*. A report can be correct as being an instance of a general mode of behavior which, in a given linguistic community, it is reasonable to sanction and support.

The second hurdle is, however, the decisive one. For we have seen that to be the expression of knowledge, a report must not only *have* authority, this authority must *in some sense be recognized* by the person whose report it is. And this is a steep hurdle indeed. For if the authority of the report "This is green" lies in the fact that the existence of green items appropriately related to the perceiver can be inferred from the occurrence of such reports, it follows that only a person who is able to draw this inference, and therefore who has not only the concept green, but also the concept of uttering "This is green"—indeed, the concept of certain conditions of perception, those which would correctly be called 'standard conditions'—could be in a position to token "This is green" in recognition of its authority. In other words, for a *Konstatierung* "This is green" to "express observational knowledge," not only must it be a *symptom* or *sign* of the presence of a green object in standard conditions, but the perceiver must know that tokens of

"This is green" are symptoms of the presence of green objects in conditions which are standard for visual perception.

36. Now it might be thought that there is something obviously absurd in the idea that before a token uttered by, say, Jones could be the expression of observational knowledge, Jones would have to know that overt verbal episodes of this kind are reliable indicators of the existence, suitably related to the speaker, of green objects. I do not think that it is. Indeed, I think that something very like it is true. The point I wish to make now, however, is that if it *is* true, then it follows, as a matter of simple logic, that one couldn't have observational knowledge of any fact unless one knew many other things as well. And let me emphasize that the point is not taken care of by distinguishing between *knowing how* and *knowing that*, and admitting that observational knowledge requires a lot of "know how." For the point is specifically that observational knowledge of any particular fact, e.g. that this is green, presupposes that one knows general facts of the form X *is a reliable symptom of* Y. And to admit this requires an abandonment of the traditional empiricist idea that observational knowledge "stands on its own feet." Indeed, the suggestion would be anathema to traditional empiricists for the obvious reason that by making observational knowledge *presuppose* knowledge of general facts of the form X *is a reliable symptom of* Y, it runs counter to the idea that we come to know general facts of this form only *after* we have come to know by observation a number of particular facts which support the hypothesis that X is a symptom of Y.

And it might be thought that there is an obvious regress in the view we are examining. Does it not tell us that observational knowledge at time t presupposes knowledge of the form X *is a reliable symptom of* Y, which presupposes *prior* observational knowledge, which presupposes *other* knowledge of the form X *is a reliable symptom of* Y, which presupposes still other, and *prior*, observational knowledge, and so on? This charge, however, rests on too simple, indeed a radically mistaken, conception of what one is saying of Jones when one says that he *knows* that p. It is not just that the objection supposes that knowing is an *episode*; for clearly there are episodes which we can correctly characterize as knowings, in particular, *observings*. The essential point is that in characterizing an episode or a state as that of *knowing*, we are not giving an empirical description of that episode or state; we are placing it in the logical space of reasons, of justifying and being able to justify what one says.

37. Thus, all that the view I am defending requires is that no tokening by S now of "This is green" is to count as "expressing observational knowledge" unless it is also correct to say of S that he now knows the appropriate fact of the form X *is a reliable symptom of* Y, namely that (and again I oversimplify) utterances of "This is green" are reliable indicators of the presence of green objects in standard conditions of perception. And while the correctness of this statement about Jones requires that Jones could now cite prior particular facts as evidence for the idea that these utterances are reliable indicators, it requires only that it is correct to say that Jones now knows, thus remembers, that these particular facts *did* obtain. It does not require that it be correct to say that at the time these facts did obtain he *then knew* them to obtain. And the regress disappears.

Thus, while Jones' ability to give inductive reasons *today* is built on a long history of acquiring and manifesting verbal habits in perceptual situations, and, in particular, the occurrence of verbal episodes, e.g. "This is green," which is superficially like those which are later properly said to express observational knowledge, it does not require that any episode in this prior time be characterizeable as expressing knowledge. (At this point, the reader should reread Section 19 above.)

38. The idea that observation "strictly and properly so-called" is constituted by certain self-authenticating nonverbal episodes, the authority of which is transmitted to verbal and quasi-verbal performances when these performances are made "in conformity with the semantical rules of the language," is, of course, the heart of the Myth of the Given. For the *given*, in epistemological tradition, is what is *taken* by these self-authenticating episodes. These 'takings' are, so to speak, the unmoved movers of empirical knowledge, the 'knowings in presence' which are presupposed by all other knowledge, both the knowledge of general truths and the knowledge 'in absence' of other particular matters of fact. Such is the framework in which traditional empiricism makes its characteristic claim that the perceptually given is the foundation of empirical knowledge.

Let me make it clear, however, that if I reject this framework, it is not because I should deny that observings are *inner* episodes, nor that *strictly speaking* they are *nonverbal* episodes. It will be my contention.

however, that the sense in which they are nonverbal—which is also the sense in which thought episodes are nonverbal—is one which gives no aid or comfort to epistemological givenness. In the concluding sections of this paper, I shall attempt to explicate the logic of inner episodes, and show that we can distinguish between observations and thoughts, on the one hand, and their verbal expression on the other, without making the mistakes of traditional dualism. I shall also attempt to explicate the logical status of *impressions* or *immediate experiences*, and thus bring to a successful conclusion the quest with which my argument began.

One final remark before I begin this task. If I reject the framework of traditional empiricism, it is not because I want to say that empirical knowledge has *no* foundation. For to put it this way is to suggest that it is really "empirical knowledge so-called," and to put it in a box with rumors and hoaxes. There is clearly *some* point to the picture of human knowledge as resting on a level of propositions—observation reports—which do not rest on other propositions in the same way as other propositions rest on them. On the other hand, I do wish to insist that the metaphor of "foundation" is misleading in that it keeps us from seeing that if there is a logical dimension in which other empirical propositions rest on observation reports, there is another logical dimension in which the latter rest on the former.

Above all, the picture is misleading because of its static character. One seems forced to choose between the picture of an elephant which rests on a tortoise (What supports the tortoise?) and the picture of a great Hegelian serpent of knowledge with its tail in its mouth (Where does it begin?). Neither will do. For empirical knowledge, like its sophisticated extension, science, is rational, not because it has a *foundation* but because it is a self-correcting enterprise which can put *any* claim in jeopardy, though not *all* at once.

IX. Science and Ordinary Usage

39. There are many strange and exotic specimens in the gardens of philosophy: Epistemology, Ontology, Cosmology, to name but a few. And clearly there is much good sense—not only rhyme but reason—to these labels. It is not my purpose, however, to animadvert on the botanizing of philosophies and things philosophical, other than to call attention to a recent addition to the list of philosophical flora and fauna,

the Philosophy of Science. Nor shall I attempt to locate this new specialty in a classificatory system. The point I wish to make, however, can be introduced by calling to mind the fact that classificatory schemes, however theoretical their purpose, have practical consequences: nominal causes, so to speak, have real effects. As long as there was no such subject as 'philosophy of science,' all students of philosophy felt obligated to keep at least one eye part of the time on both the methodological and the substantive aspects of the scientific enterprise. And if the result was often a confusion of the task of philosophy with the task of science, and almost equally often a projection of the framework of the latest scientific speculations into the common-sense picture of the world (witness the almost unquestioned assumption, today, that the common-sense world of physical objects in Space and Time must be analyzable into spatially and temporally, or even spatiotemporally, related events), at least it had the merit of ensuring that reflection on the nature and implications of scientific discourse was an integral and vital part of philosophical thinking generally. But now that philosophy of science has nominal as well as real existence, there has arisen the temptation to leave it to the specialists, and to confuse the sound idea that philosophy is not science with the mistaken idea that philosophy is independent of science.

40. As long as discourse was viewed as a map, subdivided into a side-by-side of sub-maps, each representing a sub-region in a side-by-side of regions making up the total subject matter of discourse, and as long as the task of the philosopher was conceived to be the piecemeal one of analysis in the sense of definition—the task, so to speak, of "making little ones out of big ones"—one could view with equanimity the existence of philosophical specialists—specialists in formal and mathematical logic, in perception, in moral philosophy, etc. For if discourse were as represented above, where would be the harm of each man fencing himself off in his own garden? In spite, however, of the persistence of the slogan "philosophy is analysis," we now realize that the atomistic conception of philosophy is a snare and a delusion. For "analysis" no longer connotes the definition of terms, but rather the clarification of the logical structure—in the broadest sense—of discourse, and discourse no longer appears as one plane parallel to another, but as a tangle of intersecting dimensions whose relations with one another and with extra-linguistic fact conform to no single or simple pattern. No longer can

the philosopher interested in perception say "let him who is interested in prescriptive discourse analyze its concepts and leave me in peace." Most if not all philosophically interesting concepts are caught up in more than one dimension of discourse, and while the atomism of early analysis has a healthy successor in the contemporary stress on journeyman tactics, the grand strategy of the philosophical enterprise is once again directed toward that articulated and integrated vision of man-in-the-universe—or, shall I say discourse-about-man-in-all-discourse—which has traditionally been its goal.

But the moral I wish specifically to draw is that no longer can one smugly say "Let the person who is interested in scientific discourse analyze scientific discourse and let the person who is interested in ordinary discourse analyze ordinary discourse." Let me not be misunderstood. I am not saying that in order to discern the logic—the polydimensional logic—of ordinary discourse, it is necessary to make use of the results or the methods of the sciences. Nor even that, within limits, such a division of labor is not a sound corollary of the journeyman's approach. My point is rather that what we call the scientific enterprise is the flowering of a dimension of discourse which already exists in what historians call the "prescientific stage," and that failure to understand this type of discourse "writ large"—in science—may lead, indeed, has often led to a failure to appreciate its role in "ordinary usage," and, as a result, to a failure to understand the full logic of even the most fundamental, the "simplest" empirical terms.

41. Another point of equal importance. The procedures of philosophical analysis as such may make no use of the methods or results of the sciences. But familiarity with the trend of scientific thought is essential to the *appraisal* of the framework categories of the common-sense picture of the world. For if the line of thought embodied in the preceding paragraphs is sound, if, that is to say, scientific discourse is but a continuation of a dimension of discourse which has been present in human discourse from the very beginning, then one would expect there to be a sense in which the scientific picture of the world *replaces* the common-sense picture; a sense in which the scientific account of "what there is" *supersedes* the descriptive ontology of everyday life.

Here one must be cautious. For there is a right way and a wrong way to make this point. Many years ago it used to be confidently said that science has shown, for example, that physical objects aren't really colored. Later it was pointed out that if this is interpreted as the claim that the sentence "Physical objects have colors" expresses an empirical proposition which, though widely believed by common sense, has been shown by science to be false, then, of course, this claim is absurd. The idea that physical objects aren't colored can make sense only as the (misleading) expression of one aspect of a philosophical critique of the very framework of physical objects located in Space and enduring through Time. In short, "Physical objects aren't really colored" makes sense only as a clumsy expression of the idea that there are no such things as the colored physical objects of the common-sense world, where this is interpreted, not as an empirical proposition—like "There are no nonhuman featherless bipeds"—*within* the common-sense frame, but as the expression of a rejection (in *some* sense) of this very framework itself, in favor of another built around different, if not unrelated, categories. This rejection need not, of course, be a *practical* rejection. It need not, that is, carry with it a proposal to brain-wash existing populations and train them to speak differently. And, of course, as long as the existing framework is used, it will be *incorrect* to say—otherwise than to make a philosophical point *about the framework*—that no object is really colored, or is located in Space, or endures through Time. But, *speaking as a philosopher*, I am quite prepared to say that the common-sense world of physical objects in Space and Time is unreal—that is, that there are no such things. Or, to put it less paradoxically, that in the dimension of describing and explaining the world, science is the measure of all things, of what is that it is, and of what is not that it is not.

43. There is a widespread impression that reflection on how we learn the language in which, in everyday life, we describe the world, leads to the conclusion that the categories of the common-sense picture of the world have, so to speak, an unchallengeable authenticity. There are, of course, different conceptions of just what this fundamental categorial framework is. For some it is sense contents and phenomenal relations between them; for others physical objects, persons, and processes in Space and Time. But whatever their points of difference, the philosophers I have in mind are united in the conviction that what is called the "ostensive tie" between our fundamental descriptive vocabulary and the world rules out of court as utterly absurd any notion that there are no such things as this framework talks about.

An integral part of this conviction is what I shall call (in an extended sense) the *positivistic conception of science,* the idea that the framework of theoretical objects (molecules, electromagnetic fields, etc.) and their relationships is, so to speak, an *auxiliary* framework. In its most explicit form, it is the idea that theoretical objects and propositions concerning them are "calculational devices," the value and status of which consist in their systematizing and heuristic role with respect to confirmable generalizations formulated in the framework of terms which enjoy a direct ostensive link with the world. One is tempted to put this by saying that according to these philosophers, the objects of ostensively linked discourse behave *as if* and *only as if* they were bound up with or consisted of scientific entities. But, of course, these philosophers would hasten to point out (and rightly so) that

X behaves as if it consisted of Y's

makes sense only by contrast with

X behaves as it does because it *does* consist of Y's

whereas their contention is exactly that where the Y's are *scientific* objects, no such contrast makes sense.

The point I am making is that as long as one thinks that there is a framework, whether of physical objects or of sense contents, the absolute authenticity of which is guaranteed by the fact that the learning of this framework involves an "ostensive step," so long one will be tempted to think of the authority of theoretical discourse as entirely derivative, that of a calculational auxiliary, an effective heuristic device. It is one of my prime purposes, in the following sections, to convince the reader that this interpretation of the status of the scientific picture of the world rests on two mistakes: (1) a misunderstanding (which I have already exposed) of the ostensive element in the learning and use of a language—the Myth of the Given; (2) a reification of the *methodological* distinction between theoretical and non-theoretical discourse into a *substantive* distinction between theoretical and non-theoretical existence.

44. One way of summing up what I have been saying above is by saying that there is a widespread impression abroad, aided and abetted by a naive interpretation of concept formation, that philosophers of science deal with a mode of discourse which is, so to speak, a peninsular offshoot from the mainland of ordinary discourse. The study of scientific discourse is conceived to be a worthy employment for those who

have the background and motivation to keep track of it, but an employment which is fundamentally a hobby divorced from the perplexities of the mainland. But, of course, this summing up won't quite do. For all philosophers would agree that no philosophy would be complete unless it resolved the perplexities which arise when one attempts to think through the relationship of the framework of modern science to ordinary discourse. My point, however, is not that any one would reject the idea that this is a proper task for philosophy, but that, by approaching the language in which the plain man describes and explains empirical fact with the presuppositions of *givenness*, they are led to a "resolution" of these perplexities along the lines of what I have called the positivistic or peninsular conception of scientific discourse—a "resolution" which, I believe, is not only superficial, but positively mistaken.

X. Private Episodes: the Problem

45. Let us now return, after a long absence, to the problem of how the similarity among the experiences of *seeing that an object over there is red, its looking to one that an object over there is red* (when in point of fact it is *not* red) and *its looking to one as though there were a red object over there* (when in fact there is *nothing* over there at all) is to be understood. Part of this similarity, we saw, consists in the fact that they all involve the idea—the proposition, if you please—that the object over there is red. But over and above this there is, of course, the aspect which many philosophers have attempted to clarify by the notion of *impressions* or *immediate experience*.

It was pointed out in Sections 21 ff. above that there are prima facie two ways in which facts of the form *x merely looks red* might be explained, in addition to the kind of explanation which is based on empirical generalizations relating the color of objects, the circumstances in which they are seen, and the colors they look to have. These two ways are (a) the introduction of impressions or immediate experiences as theoretical entities; and (b) the *discovery*, on scrutinizing these situations, that they contain impressions or immediate experiences as components. I called attention to the paradoxical character of the first of these alternatives, and refused, at that time, to take it seriously. But in the meantime the second alernative, involving as it does the Myth of the Given, has turned out to be no more satisfactory.

For, in the first place, how are these impressions to be described, if not by using such words as "red" and "triangular." Yet, if my argument, to date, is sound, physical objects alone can be literally red and triangular. Thus, in the cases I am considering, there is nothing to be red and triangular. It would seem to follow that "impression of a red triangle" could mean nothing more than "impression of the sort which is common to those experiences in which we either see that something is red and triangular, or something merely looks red and triangular or there merely looks to be a red and triangular object over there." And if we can never characterize "impressions" intrinsically, but only by what is logically a definite description, i.e., as the kind of entity which is common to such situations, then we would scarcely seem to be any better off than if we maintained that talk about "impressions" is a notational convenience, a code, for the language in which we speak of how things look and what there looks to be.

And this line of thought is reinforced by the consideration that once we give up the idea that we begin our sojourn in this world with any—even a vague, fragmentary, and undiscriminating—awareness of the logical space of particulars, kinds, facts, and resemblances, and recognize that even such "simple" concepts as those of colors are the fruit of a long process of publicly reinforced responses to public objects (including verbal performances) in public situations, we may well be puzzled as to how, even if there are such things as impressions or sensations, we could come to know that there are, and to know what sort of thing they are. For we now recognize that instead of coming to have a concept of something because we have noticed that sort of thing, to have the ability to notice a sort of thing is already to have the concept of that sort of thing, and cannot account for it.

Indeed, once we think this line of reasoning through, we are struck by the fact that if it is sound, we are faced not only with the question "How could we come to have the idea of an 'impression' or 'sensation?'" but by the question "How could we come to have the idea of something's looking red to us, or," to get to the crux of the matter, "of seeing that something is red?" In short, we are brought face to face with the general problem of understanding how there can be *inner episodes*—episodes, that is, which somehow combine *privacy*, in that each of us has privileged access to his own, with *intersubjectivity*, in that each of us can, in principle, know about the other's. We might try to put this more linguistically as the problem of how there can be a sentence (e.g. "S has a toothache") of which it is *logically* true that whereas anybody can use it to state a fact, only one person, namely S himself, can use it to make a report. But while this is a useful formulation, it does not do justice to the supposedly *episodic* character of the items in question. And that this is the heart of the puzzle is shown by the fact that many philosophers who would not deny that there are short-term hypothetical and mongrel hypothetical-categorical facts about behavior which others can ascribe to us on behavioral evidence, but which only *we* can *report*, have found it to be logical nonsense to speak of non-behavioral *episodes* of which this is true. Thus, it has been claimed by Ryle (17) that the very idea that there are such episodes is a category mistake, while others have argued that though there are such episodes, they cannot be characterized in intersubjective discourse, learned as it is in a context of public objects and in the 'academy' of one's linguistic peers. It is my purpose to argue that both these contentions are quite mistaken, and that not only are inner episodes *not* category mistakes, they are quite "effable" in intersubjective discourse. And it is my purpose to show, positively, *how* this can be the case. I am particularly concerned to make this point in connection with such inner episodes as sensations and feelings, in short, with what has—unfortunately, I think—been called "immediate experience." For such an account is necessary to round off this examination of the Myth of the Given. But before I can come to grips with these topics, the way must be prepared by a discussion of inner episodes of quite another kind, namely *thoughts*.

XI. Thoughts: the Classical View

46. Recent empiricism has been of two minds about the status of *thoughts*. On the one hand, it has resonated to the idea that insofar as there are *episodes* which are thoughts, they are *verbal* or *linguistic* episodes. Clearly, however, even if candid overt verbal behaviors by people who had learned a language were thoughts, there are not nearly enough of them to account for all the cases in which it would be argued that a person was thinking. Nor can we plausibly suppose that the remainder is accounted for by those inner episodes which are often very clumsily lumped together under the heading "verbal imagery."

On the other hand, they have been tempted to suppose that the episodes which are referred to by verbs pertaining to thinking include all forms of "intelligent behavior," verbal as well as nonverbal, and that the "thought episodes" which are supposed to be manifested by these behaviors are not really episodes at all, but rather hypothetical and mongrel hypothetical-categorical facts about these and still other behaviors. This, however, runs into the difficulty that whenever we try to explain what we mean by calling a piece of *nonhabitual* behavior intelligent, we seem to find it necessary to do so in terms of *thinking*. The uncomfortable feeling will not be downed that the dispositional account of thoughts in terms of intelligent behavior is covertly circular.

47. Now the classical tradition claimed that there is a family of episodes, neither overt verbal behavior nor verbal imagery, which are *thoughts*, and that both overt verbal behavior and verbal imagery owe their meaningfulness to the fact that they stand to these *thoughts* in the unique relation of "expressing" them. These episodes are introspectable. Indeed, it was usually believed that they could not occur without being known to occur. But this can be traced to a number of confusions, perhaps the most important of which was the idea that *thoughts* belong in the same general category as sensations, images, tickles, itches, etc. This mis-assimilation of thoughts to sensations and feelings was equally, as we saw in Sections 26 ff. above, a mis-assimilation of sensations and feelings to thoughts, and a falsification of both. The assumption that if there are thought episodes, they must be immediate experiences is common both to those who propounded the classical view and to those who reject it, saying that they "find no such experiences." If we purge the classical tradition of these confusions, it becomes the idea that to each of us belongs a stream of episodes, not themselves immediate experiences, to which we have privileged, but by no means either invariable or infallible, access. These episodes can occur without being "expressed" by overt verbal behavior, though verbal behavior is—in an important sense—their natural fruition. Again, we can "hear ourselves think," but the verbal imagery which enables us to do this is no more the thinking itself than is the overt verbal behavior by which it is expressed and communicated to others. It is a mistake to suppose that we must be having verbal imagery—indeed, any imagery—when we "know what we are thinking"—in short, to suppose that "privileged access" must be construed on a perceptual or quasi-perceptual model.

Now, it is my purpose to defend such a revised classical analysis of our common-sense conception of thoughts, and in the course of doing so I shall develop distinctions which will later contribute to a resolution, in principle, of the puzzle of *immediate experience*. But before I continue, let me hasten to add that it will turn out that the view I am about to expound could, with equal appropriateness, be represented as a modified form of the view that thoughts are *linguistic* episodes.

XII. Our Rylean Ancestors

48. But, the reader may well ask, in what sense can these episodes be "inner" if they are not immediate experiences? and in what sense can they be "linguistic" if they are neither overt linguistic performances, nor verbal imagery "*in foro interno*"? I am going to answer these and the other questions I have been raising by making a myth of my own, or, to give it an air of up-to-date respectability, by writing a piece of science fiction—anthropological science fiction. Imagine a stage in prehistory in which humans are limited to what I shall call a Rylean language, a language of which the fundamental descriptive vocabulary speaks of public properties of public objects located in Space and enduring through Time. Let me hasten to add that it is also Rylean in that although its basic resources are limited (how limited I shall be discussing in a moment), its total expressive power is very great. For it makes subtle use not only of the elementary logical operations of conjunction, disjunction, negation, and quantification, but especially of the subjunctive conditional. Furthermore, I shall suppose it to be characterized by the presence of the looser logical relations typical of ordinary discourse which are referred to by philosophers under the headings "vagueness" and "open texture."

I am beginning my myth *in medias res* with humans who have already mastered a Rylean language, because the philosophical situation it is designed to clarify is one in which we are not puzzled by how people acquire a language for referring to public properties of public objects, but are very puzzled indeed about how we learn to speak of inner episodes and immediate experiences.

There are, I suppose, still some philosophers who are inclined to think that by allowing these mythical ancestors of ours the use *ad libitum* of subjunctive conditionals, we have, in effect, enabled them to say anything that we can say when we speak of *thoughts*, *experiences* (seeing, hearing, etc.), and *immediate experiences*. I doubt that there are many. In any case, the story I am telling is designed to show exactly how the idea that an intersubjective language must be Rylean rests on too simple a picture of the relation of intersubjective discourse to public objects.

49. The questions I am, in effect, raising are "What resources would have to be added to the Rylean language of these talking animals in order that they might come to recognize each other and themselves as animals that *think*, *observe*, and have *feelings* and *sensations*, as we use these terms?" and "How could the addition of these resources be construed as reasonable?" In the first place, the language would have to be enriched with the fundamental resources of semantical discourse—that is to say, the resources necessary for making such characteristically semantical statements as " 'Rot' means red," and " 'Der Mond ist rund' is true if and only if the moon is round." It is sometimes said, e.g., by Carnap (6), that these resources can be constructed out of the vocabulary of formal logic, and that they would therefore already be contained, in principle, in our Rylean language. I have criticized this idea in another place (20) and shall not discuss it here. In any event, a decision on this point is not essential to the argument.

Let it be granted, then, that these mythical ancestors of ours are able to characterize each other's verbal behavior in semantical terms; that, in other words, they not only can talk about each other's predictions as causes and effects, and as indicators (with greater or less reliability) of other verbal and nonverbal states of affairs, but can also say of these verbal productions that they *mean* thus and so, that they say *that* such and such, that they are true, false, etc. And let me emphasize, as was pointed out in Section 31 above, that to make a semantical statement about a verbal event is not a shorthand way of talking about its causes and effects, although there is a sense of "imply" in which semantical statements about verbal productions do *imply* information about the causes and effects of these productions. Thus, when I say " '*Es regnet*' means it is raining," my statement "implies" that the causes and effects of utterances of "*Es regnet*" beyond the Rhine parallel the causes and effects of utterances of "It is raining" by myself and other members of the English-speaking community. And if it didn't imply this, it couldn't perform its role. But this is not to say that semantical statements are definitional shorthand for statements about the causes and effects of verbal performances.

310

50. With the resources of semantical discourse, the language of our fictional ancestors has acquired a dimension which gives considerably more plausibility to the claim that they are in a position to talk about *thoughts* just as we are. For characteristic of thoughts is their *intentionality, reference, or aboutness,* and it is clear that semantical talk about the meaning or reference of verbal expressions has the same structure as mentalistic discourse concerning what thoughts are about. It is therefore all the more tempting to suppose that the intentionality of *thoughts* can be traced to the application of semantical categories to overt verbal performances, and to suggest a modified Rylean account according to which talk about so-called "thoughts" is shorthand for hypothetical and mongrel categorical-hypothetical statements about overt verbal and nonverbal behavior, and that talk about the *intentionality* of these "episodes" is correspondingly reducible to semantical talk about the verbal components.

What is the alternative? Classically it has been the idea that not only are there overt verbal episodes which can be characterized in semantical terms, but, *over and above these,* there are certain inner episodes which are properly characterized by the traditional vocabulary of *intentionality.* And, of course, the classical scheme includes the idea that semantical discourse about overt verbal performances is to be analyzed in terms of talk about the intentionality of the mental episodes which are "expressed" by these overt performances. My immediate problem is to see if I can reconcile the classical idea of thoughts as inner episodes which are neither overt behavior nor verbal imagery and which are properly referred to in terms of the vocabulary of intentionality, with the idea that the categories of intentionality are, at bottom, semantical categories pertaining to overt verbal performances.*

XIII. Theories and Models

51. But what might these episodes be? And, in terms of our science fiction, how might our ancestors have come to recognize their existence? The answer to these questions is surprisingly straightforward, once the logical space of our discussion is enlarged to include a distinction, central to the philosophy of science, between the language of *theory* and the language of *observation.* Although this distinction is a familiar one, I

* An earlier attempt along these lines is to be found in (18) and (19).

shall take a few paragraphs to highlight those aspects of the distinction which are of greatest relevance to our problem.

Informally, to construct a theory is, in its most developed or sophisticated form, to postulate a domain of entities which behave in certain ways set down by the fundamental principles of the theory, and to correlate—perhaps, in a certain sense to identify—complexes of these theoretical entities with certain non-theoretical objects or situations; that is to say, with objects or situations which are either matters of observable fact or, in principle at least, describable in observational terms. This "correlation" or "identification" of theoretical with observational states of affairs is a tentative one "until further notice," and amounts, so to speak, to erecting temporary bridges which permit the passage from sentences in observational discourse to sentences in the theory, and vice versa. Thus, for example, in the kinetic theory of gases, empirical statements of the form "Gas g at such and such a place and time has such and such a volume, pressure, and temperature" are correlated with theoretical statements specifying certain statistical measures of populations of molecules. These temporary bridges are so set up that inductively established laws pertaining to gases, formulated in the language of observable fact, are correlated with derived propositions or theorems in the language of the theory, and that no proposition in the theory is correlated with a falsified empirical generalization. Thus, a good theory (at least of the type we are considering) "explains" established empirical laws by deriving theoretical counterparts of these laws from a small set of postulates relating to unobserved entities.

These remarks, of course, barely scratch the surface of the problem of the status of theories in scientific discourse. And no sooner have I made them, than I must hasten to qualify them—almost beyond recognition. For while this by now classical account of the nature of theories (one of the earlier formulations of which is due to Norman Campbell (5), and which is to be bound more recently in the writings of Carnap (8), Reichenbach (15, 16), Hempel (10), and Braithwaite (3)) does throw light on the logical status of theories, it emphasizes certain features at the expense of others. By speaking of the construction of a theory as the elaboration of a postulate system which is tentatively correlated with observational discourse, it gives a highly artificial and unrealistic picture of what scientists have actually done in the process of constructing theories. I don't wish to deny that logically sophisticated scientists today *might* and perhaps, on occasion, *do* proceed in true logistical style. I do, however, wish to emphasize two points:

(1) The first is that the fundamental assumptions of a theory are usually developed not by constructing uninterpreted calculi which might correlate in the desired manner with observational discourse, but rather by attempting to find a *model*, i.e. to describe a domain of familiar objects behaving in familiar ways such that we can see how the phenomena to be explained would arise if they consisted of this sort of thing. The essential thing about a model is that it is accompanied, so to speak, by a commentary which *qualifies* or *limits*—but not precisely nor in all respects—the analogy between the familiar objects and the entities which are being introduced by the theory. It is the descriptions of the fundamental ways in which the objects in the model domain, thus qualified, behave, which, transferred to the theoretical entities, correspond to the postulates of the logistical picture of theory construction.

(2) But even more important for our purposes is the fact that the logistical picture of theory construction obscures the most important thing of all, namely that the process of devising "theoretical" explanations of observable phenomena did not spring full-blown from the head of modern science. In particular, it obscures the fact that not all common-sense inductive inferences are of the form

All observed A's have been B, *therefore* (probably) all A's are B.

or its statistical counterparts, and leads one mistakenly to suppose that so-called "hypothetic-deductive" explanation is limited to the sophisticated stages of science. The truth of the matter, as I shall shortly be illustrating, is that science is continuous with common sense, and the ways in which the scientist seeks to explain empirical phenomena are refinements of the ways in which plain men, however crudely and schematically, have attempted to understand their environment and their fellow men since the dawn of intelligence. It is this point which I wish to stress at the present time, for I am going to argue that the distinction between theoretical and observational discourse is involved in the logic of concepts pertaining to inner episodes. I say "involved in" for it would be paradoxical and, indeed, incorrect, to say that these concepts are theoretical concepts.

52. Now I think it fair to say that some light has already been thrown

on the expression "inner episodes"; for while it would indeed be a category mistake to suppose that the inflammability of a piece of wood is, so to speak, a hidden burning which becomes overt or manifest when the wood is placed on the fire, not all the unobservable episodes we suppose to go on in the world are the offspring of category mistakes. Clearly it is by no means an illegitimate use of "in"—though it is a use which has its own logical grammar—to say, for example, that "in" the air around us there are innumerable molecules which, in spite of the observable stodginess of the air, are participating in a veritable turmoil of episodes. Clearly, the sense in which these episodes are "in" the air is to be explicated in terms of the sense in which the air "is" a population of molecules, and this, in turn, in terms of the logic of the relation between theoretical and observational discourse.

I shall have more to say on this topic in a moment. In the meantime, let us return to our mythical ancestors. It will not surprise my readers to learn that the second stage in the enrichment of their Rylean language is the addition of theoretical discourse. Thus we may suppose these language-using animals to elaborate, without methodological sophistication, crude, sketchy, and vague theories to explain why things which are similar in their observable properties differ in their causal properties, and things which are similar in their causal properties differ in their observable properties.

XIV. Methodological *versus* Philosophical Behaviorism

53. But we are approaching the time for the central episode in our myth. I want you to suppose that in this Neo-Rylean culture there now appears a genius—let us call him Jones—who is an unsung forerunner of the movement in psychology, once revolutionary, now commonplace, known as Behaviorism. Let me emphasize that what I have in mind is Behaviorism as a methodological thesis, which I shall be concerned to formulate. For the central and guiding theme in the historical complex known by this term has been a certain conception, or family of conceptions, of how to go about building a science of psychology.

Philosophers have sometimes supposed that Behaviorists are, as such, committed to the idea that our ordinary mentalistic concepts are *analyzable* in terms of overt behavior. But although behaviorism has often been characterized by a certain metaphysical bias, it is not a thesis about the *analysis* of *existing* psychological concepts, but one which concerns the construction of new concepts. As a methodological thesis, it involves no commitment whatever concerning the logical analysis of common-sense mentalistic discourse, nor does it involve a denial that each of us has a privileged access to our state of mind, nor that these states of mind can properly be described in terms of such common-sense concepts as believing, wondering, doubting, intending, wishing, inferring, etc. If we permit ourselves to speak of this privileged access to our states of mind as "introspection," avoiding the implication that there is a "means" whereby we "see" what is going on "inside," as we see external circumstances by the eye, then we can say that Behaviorism, as I shall use the term, does not deny that there is such a thing as introspection, nor that it is, on some topics, at least, quite reliable. The essential point about 'introspection' from the standpoint of Behaviorism is that *we introspect in terms of common sense mentalistic concepts*. And while the Behaviorist admits, as anyone must, that much knowledge is embodied in common-sense mentalistic discourse, and that still more can be gained in the future by formulating and testing hypotheses in terms of them, and while he admits that it is perfectly legitimate to call such a psychology "scientific," he proposes, for his own part, to make no more than a heuristic use of mentalistic discourse, and to construct his concepts "from scratch" in the course of developing his own scientific account of the observable behavior of human organisms.

54. But while it is quite clear that scientific Behaviorism is *not* the thesis that common-sense psychological concepts are *analyzable* into concepts pertaining to overt behavior—a thesis which has been maintained by some philosophers and which may be called 'analytical' or 'philosophical' Behaviorism—it is often thought that Behaviorism is committed to the idea that the concepts of a behavioristic psychology must be so analyzable, or, to put things right side up, that properly introduced behavioristic concepts must be built by explicit definition—in the broadest sense—from a basic vocabulary pertaining to overt behavior. The Behaviorist would thus be saying "Whether or not the mentalistic concepts of everyday life are definable in terms of overt behavior, I shall ensure that this is true of the concepts that I shall employ." And it must be confessed that many behavioristically oriented psychologists have believed themselves committed to this austere program of concept formation.

Now I think it reasonable to say that, *thus conceived*, the behavioristic program would be unduly restrictive. Certainly, nothing in the nature of sound scientific procedure requires this self-denial. Physics, the methodological sophistication of which has so impressed—indeed, overly impressed—the other sciences, does not lay down a corresponding restriction on its concepts, nor has chemistry been built in terms of concepts explicitly definable in terms of the observable properties and behavior of chemical substances. The point I am making should now be clear. The behavioristic requirement that all concepts should be *introduced* in terms of a basic vocabulary pertaining to overt behavior is compatible with the idea that some behavioristic concepts are to be introduced as *theoretical* concepts.

55. It is essential to note that the theoretical terms of a behavioristic psychology are not only *not* defined in terms of overt behavior, they are also *not* defined in terms of nerves, synapses, neural impulses, etc., etc. A behavioristic theory of behavior is not, as such, a physiological explanation of behavior. The ability of a framework of theoretical concepts and propositions successfully to explain behavioral phenomena is logically independent of the identification of these theoretical concepts with concepts of neurophysiology. What *is* true—and this is a logical point—is that each special science dealing with some aspect of the human organism operates within the frame of a certain regulative ideal, the ideal of a coherent system in which the achievements of each have an intelligible place. Thus, it is part of the Behaviorist's business to keep an eye on the total picture of the human organism which is beginning to emerge. And if the tendency to premature identification is held in check, there may be considerable heuristic value in speculative attempts at integration; though, until recently, at least, neurophysiological speculations in behavior theory have not been particularly fruitful. And while it is, I suppose, noncontroversial that when the total scientific picture of man and his behavior is in, it will involve some identification of concepts in behavior theory with concepts pertaining to the functioning of anatomical structures, it should not be assumed that behavior theory is committed *ab initio* to a physiological identification of *all* its concepts,—that its concepts are, so to speak, physiological from the start.

We have, in effect, been distinguishing between two dimensions of the logic (or 'methodologic') of theoretical terms: (a) their role in explaining the selected phenomena of which the theory is the theory; (b) their role as candidates for integration in what we have called the "total picture." These roles are equally part of the logic, and hence the "meaning," of theoretical terms. Thus, at any one time the terms in a theory will carry with them as part of their logical force that which it is reasonable to envisage—whether schematically or determinately— as the manner of their integration. However, for the purposes of my argument, it will be useful to refer to these two roles as though it were a matter of a distinction between what I shall call *pure theoretical concepts*, and hypotheses concerning the relation of these concepts to concepts in other specialties. What we *can* say is that the less a scientist is in a position to conjecture about the way in which a certain theory can be expected to integrate with other specialities, the more the concepts of his theory approximate to the status of pure theoretical concepts. To illustrate: We can imagine that Chemistry developed a sophisticated and successful theory to explain chemical phenomena before either electrical or magnetic phenomena were noticed; and that chemists developed as pure theoretical concepts, certain concepts which it later became reasonable to identify with concepts belonging to the framework of electromagnetic theory.

XV. The Logic of Private Episodes: Thoughts

56. With these all too sketchy remarks on Methodological Behaviorism under our belts, let us return once again to our fictional ancestors. We are now in a position to characterize the original Rylean language in which they described themselves and their fellows as not only a *behioristic* language, but a behioristic language which is restricted to the *non-theoretical* vocabulary of a behioristic psychology. Suppose, now, that in the attempt to account for the fact that his fellow men behave intelligently not only when their conduct is threaded on a string of overt verbal episodes—that is to say, as we would put it, when they "think out loud"—but also when no detectable verbal output is present, Jones develops a *theory* according to which overt utterances are but the culmination of a process which begins with certain inner episodes. *And let us suppose that his model for these episodes which initiate the events which culminate in overt verbal behavior is that of overt verbal behavior itself. In other words, using the language of the model, the theory is to*

the effect that overt verbal behavior is the culmination of a process which begins with "inner speech."

It is essential to bear in mind that what Jones means by "inner speech" is not to be confused with *verbal imagery*. As a matter of fact, Jones, like his fellows, does not as yet even have the concept of an image.

It is easy to see the general lines a Jonesean theory will take. According to it the true cause of intelligent nonhabitual behavior is "inner speech." Thus, even when a hungry person overtly says "Here is an edible object" and proceeds to eat it, the true—theoretical—cause of his eating, given his hunger, is not the overt utterance, but the "inner utterance of this sentence."

57. The first thing to note about the Jonesean theory is that, as built on the model of speech episodes, *it carries over to these inner episodes the applicability of semantical categories*. Thus, just as Jones has, like his fellows, been speaking of overt utterances as *meaning* this or that, or being *about* this or that, so he now speaks of these inner episodes as *meaning* this or that, or being *about* this or that.

The second point to remember is that although Jones' theory involves a *model*, it is not identical with it. Like all theories formulated in terms of a model, it also includes a *commentary* on the model; a commentary which places more or less sharply drawn restrictions on the analogy between the theoretical entities and the entities of the model. Thus, while his theory talks of "inner speech," the commentary hastens to add that, of course, the episodes in question are not the wagging of a hidden tongue, nor are any sounds produced by this "inner speech."

58. The general drift of my story should now be clear. I shall therefore proceed to make the essential points quite briefly:

(1) What we must suppose Jones to have developed is the germ of a theory which permits many different developments. We must not pin it down to any of the more sophisticated forms it takes in the hands of classical philosophers. Thus, the theory need not be given a Socratic or Cartesian form, according to which this "inner speech" is a function of a separate substance; though primitive peoples may have had good reason to suppose that humans consist of two separate things.

(2) Let us suppose Jones to have called these discursive entities *thoughts*. We can admit at once that the framework of thoughts he

has introduced is a framework of "unobserved," "nonempirical" "inner" episodes. For we can point out immediately that in these respects they are no worse off than the particles and episodes of physical theory. For these episodes are "in" language-using animals as molecular impacts are "in" gases, not as "ghosts" are in "machines." They are "nonempirical" in the simple sense that they are *theoretical*—not definable in observational terms. Nor does the fact that they are, *as introduced*, unobserved entities imply that Jones could not have good reason for supposing them to exist. Their "purity" is not a *metaphysical* purity, but, so to speak, a *methodological* purity. As we have seen, the fact that they are not introduced as physiological entities does not preclude the possibility that at a later methodological stage, they may, so to speak, "turn out" to be such. Thus, there are many who would say that it is already reasonable to suppose that these *thoughts* are to be "identified" with complex events in the cerebral cortex functioning along the lines of a calculating machine. Jones, of course, has no such idea.

(3) Although the theory postulates that overt discourse is the culmination of a process which begins with "inner discourse," this should not be taken to mean that overt discourse stands to "inner discourse" as *voluntary movements stand to intentions and motives.* True, overt linguistic events *can* be produced as means to ends. But serious errors creep into the interpretation of both language and thought if one interprets the idea that overt linguistic episodes *express* thoughts, on the model of the use of an instrument. Thus, it should be noted that Jones' theory, as I have sketched it, is perfectly compatible with the idea that the ability to have thoughts is acquired in the process of acquiring overt speech and that only after overt speech is well established, can "inner speech" occur without its overt culmination.

(4) Although the occurrence of overt speech episodes which are characterizable in semantical terms is explained by the theory in terms of *thoughts* which are *also* characterized in semantical terms, this does not mean that the idea that overt speech "has meaning" is being analyzed in terms of the intentionality of thoughts. It must not be forgotten that *the semantical characterization of overt verbal episodes is the primary use of semantical terms, and that overt linguistic events as semantically characterized are the model for the inner episodes introduced by the theory.*

(5) One final point before we come to the dénouement of the first

episode in the saga of Jones. It cannot be emphasized too much that although these theoretical discursive episodes or *thoughts* are introduced as *inner* episodes—which is merely to repeat that they are introduced as *theoretical* episodes—they are *not* introduced as *immediate* experiences. Let me remind the reader that Jones, like his Neo-Rylean contemporaries, does not as yet have this concept. And even when he, and they, acquire it, by a process which will be the second episode in my myth, it will only be the philosophers among them who will suppose that the inner episodes introduced for one theoretical purpose— thoughts—must be a subset of immediate experiences, inner episodes introduced for another theoretical purpose.

59. Here, then, is the *dénouement*. I have suggested a number of times that although it would be most misleading to say that concepts pertaining to thinking are theoretical concepts, yet their status might be illuminated by means of the contrast between theoretical and nontheoretical discourse. We are now in a position to see exactly why this is so. For once our fictitious ancestor, Jones, has developed the theory that overt verbal behavior is the expression of thoughts, and taught his compatriots to make use of the theory in interpreting each other's behavior, it is but a short step to the use of this language in self-description. Thus, when Tom, watching Dick, has behavioral evidence which warrants the use of the sentence (in the language of the theory) "Dick is thinking 'p'" (or "Dick is thinking that p"), Dick, using the same behavioral evidence, can say, in the language of the theory, "I am thinking 'p'" (or "I am thinking that p.") And it now turns out—need it have?—that Dick can be trained to give reasonably reliable self-descriptions, using the language of the theory, without having to observe his overt behavior. Jones brings this about, roughly, by applauding utterances by Dick of "I am thinking that p" when the behavioral evidence strongly supports the theoretical statement "Dick is thinking that p"; and by frowning on utterances of "I am thinking that p," when the evidence does not support this theoretical statement. Our ancestors begin to speak of the privileged access each of us has to his own thoughts. *What began as a language with a purely theoretical use has gained a reporting role.*

As I see it, this story helps us understand that concepts pertaining to such inner episodes as thoughts are primarily and essentially *intersubjective*, as intersubjective as the concept of a positron, and that the reporting role of these concepts—the fact that each of us has a privileged access to his thoughts—constitutes a dimension of the use of these concepts which is *built on* and *presupposes* this intersubjective status. My myth has shown that the fact that language is essentially an *intersubjective* achievement, and is learned in intersubjective contexts—a fact rightly stressed in modern psychologies of language, thus by B. F. Skinner (21), and by certain philosophers, e.g. Carnap (7), Wittgenstein (22)— is compatible with the "privacy" of "inner episodes." It also makes clear that this privacy is not an "absolute privacy." For if it recognizes that these concepts have a reporting use in which one is not drawing inferences from behavioral evidence, it nevertheless insists that the fact that overt behavior *is* evidence for these episodes *is built into the very logic of these concepts*, just as the fact that the observable behavior of gases is evidence for molecular episodes is built into the very logic of molecule talk.

XVI. The Logic of Private Episodes: Impressions

60. We are now ready for the problem of the status of concepts pertaining to immediate experience. The first step is to remind ourselves that among the inner episodes which belong to the framework of *thoughts* will be perceptions, that is to say, *seeing that the table is brown, hearing that the piano is out of tune*, etc. Until Jones introduced this framework, the only concepts our fictitious ancestors had of perceptual *episodes* were those of overt verbal *reports*, made, for example, in the context of looking at an object in standard conditions. *Seeing that something is the case* is an inner episode in the Jonesean theory which has as its model *reporting on looking that something is the case*. It will be remembered from an earlier section that just as when I say that Dick *reported* that the table is green, I commit myself to the truth of what he reported, so to say of Dick that he *saw* that the table is green is, in part, to ascribe to Dick the idea 'this table is green' and to endorse this idea. The reader might refer back to Sections 16 ff. for an elaboration of this point.

With the enrichment of the originally Rylean framework to include inner perceptual episodes, I have established contact with my original formulation of the problem of inner experience (Sections 22 ff.). For I can readily reconstruct in this framework my earlier account of the language of appearing, both *qualitative* and *existential*. Let us turn,

321

therefore to the final chapter of our historical novel. By now our ancestors speak a quite un-Rylean language. But it still contains no reference to such things as impressions, sensations, or feelings—in short, to the items which philosophers lump together under the heading "immediate experiences." It will be remembered that we had reached a point at which, as far as we could see, the phrase "impression of a red triangle" could only mean something like "that state of a perceiver—over and above the idea that there is a red and triangular physical object over there—which is common to those situations in which

(a) he sees that the object over there is red and triangular;
(b) the object over there looks to him to be red and triangular;
(c) there looks to him to be a red and triangular physical object over there."

Our problem was that, on the one hand, it seemed absurd to say that impressions, for example, are theoretical entities, while, on the other, the interpretation of impressions as theoretical entities seemed to provide the only hope of accounting for the positive content and explanatory power that the idea that there are such entities appears to have, and of enabling us to understand how we could have arrived at this idea. The account I have just been giving of *thoughts* suggests how this apparent dilemma can be resolved.

For we continue the myth by supposing that Jones develops, in crude and sketchy form, of course, a theory of sense perception. Jones' theory does not have to be either well-articulated or precise in order to be the first effective step in the development of a mode of discourse which today, in the case of some sense-modalities at least, is extraordinarily subtle and complex. We need, therefore, attribute to this mythical theory only those minimal features which enable it to throw light on the logic of our ordinary language about immediate experiences. From this standpoint it is sufficient to suppose that the hero of my myth postulates a class of inner—theoretical—episodes which he calls, say, *impressions*, and which are the end results of the impingement of physical objects and processes on various parts of the body, and, in particular, to follow up the specific form in which I have posed our problem, the eye.

61. A number of points can be made right away:

(1) The entities introduced by the theory are *states* of the perceiving subject, *not a class of particulars*. It cannot be emphasized too strongly that the particulars of the common-sense world are such things as books, pages, turnips, dogs, persons, noises, flashes, etc., and the Space and Time—Kant's *Undinge*—in which they come to be. What is likely to make us suppose that *impressions* are introduced as particulars is that, as in the case of thoughts, this ur-theory is formulated in terms of a model. This time the model is the idea of a domain of "inner replicas" which, when brought about in standard conditions, share the perceptible characteristics of their physical source. It is important to see that the model is the occurrence "in" perceivers of *replicas*, not of *perceivings of replicas*. Thus, the model for an impression of a red triangle is a *red and triangular replica*, not a *seeing of a red and triangular replica*. The latter alternative would have the merit of recognizing that impressions are not particulars. But, by misunderstanding the role of models in the formulation of a theory, it mistakenly assumes that if the entities of the model are particulars, the theoretical entities which are introduced by means of the model must themselves be particulars— thus overlooking the role of the commentary. And by taking the model to be *seeing a red and triangular replica*, it smuggles into the language of impressions the logic of the language of thoughts. For seeing is a *cognitive* episode which involves the framework of thoughts, and to take it as the model is to give aid and comfort to the assimilation of impressions to thoughts, and thoughts to impressions which, as I have already pointed out, is responsible for many of the confusions of the classical account of both thoughts and impressions.

(2) The fact that *impressions* are theoretical entities enables us to understand how they can be *intrinsically* characterized—that is to say, characterized by something more than a *definite description*, such as "entity of *the kind which* has as its standard cause looking at a red and triangular physical object in such and such circumstances" or "entity of *the kind which* is common to the situations in which there looks to be a red and triangular physical object." For although the predicates of a theory owe their meaningfulness to the fact that they are logically related to predicates which apply to the observable phenomena which the theory explains, the predicates of a theory are not shorthand for definite descriptions of properties in terms of these

observation predicates. When the kinetic theory of gases speaks of molecules as having *mass*, the term "mass" is not the abbreviation of a definite description of the form "the property which . . ." Thus, "impression of a red triangle" does not simply mean "impression such as is caused by red and triangular physical objects in standard conditions," though it is true—*logically* true—of impressions of red triangles that they are of that sort which *is* caused by red and triangular objects in standard conditions.

(3) If the theory of impressions were developed in true logistical style, we could say that the intrinsic properties of impressions are "implicitly defined" by the postulates of the theory, as we can say that the intrinsic properties of subatomic particles are "implicitly defined" by the fundamental principles of subatomic theory. For this would be just another way of saying that one knows the meaning of a theoretical term when one knows (a) how it is related to other theoretical terms, and (b) how the theoretical system as a whole is tied to the observation language. But, as I have pointed out, our ur-behaviorist does not formulate his theory in textbook style. He formulates it in terms of a model.

Now the model entities are entities which *do* have intrinsic properties. They are, for example, red and triangular wafers. It might therefore seem that the theory specifies the intrinsic characteristics of impressions to be the familiar perceptible qualities of physical objects and processes. If this were so, of course, the theory would be ultimately incoherent, for it would attribute to impressions—which are clearly not physical objects—characteristics which, if our argument to date is sound, only physical objects can have. Fortunately, this line of thought overlooks what we have called the commentary on the model, which qualifies, restricts and interprets the analogy between the familiar entities of the model and the theoretical entities which are being introduced. Thus, it would be a mistake to suppose that since the *model* for the impression of a red triangle is a red and triangular wafer, the impression itself is a red and triangular wafer. What can be said is that the impression of a red triangle is *analogous*, to an extent which is by no means neatly and tidily specified, to a red and triangular wafer. The *essential* feature of the analogy is that visual impressions stand to one another in a system of ways of resembling and differing which is structurally similar to the ways in which the colors and shapes of visible objects resemble and differ.

(4) It might be concluded from this last point that the concept of the impression of a red triangle is a "purely formal" concept, the concept of a "logical form" which can acquire a "content" only by means of "ostensive definition." One can see why a philosopher might want to say this, and why he might conclude that in so far as concepts pertaining to immediate experiences are *intersubjective*, they are "purely structural," the "content" of immediate experience being incommunicable. Yet this line of thought is but another expression of the Myth of the Given. For the theoretical concept of the impression of a red triangle would be no more and no less "without content" than any theoretical concept. And while, like these, it must belong to a framework which is logically connected with the language of observable fact, the logical relation between a theoretical language and the language of observable fact has nothing to do with the epistemological fiction of an "ostensive definition."

(5) The impressions of Jones' theory are, as was pointed out above, states of the perceiver, rather than particulars. If we remind ourselves that these states are not introduced as physiological states (see Section 55), a number of interesting questions arise which tie in with the reflections on the status of the scientific picture of the world (Sections 39-44 above) but which, unfortunately, there is space only to adumbrate. Thus, some philosophers have thought it obvious that we can expect that in the development of science it will become reasonable to identify *all* the concepts of behavior theory with definable terms in neurophysiological theory, and these, in turn, with definable terms in theoretical physics. It is important to realize that the second step of this prediction, at least, is either a *truism* or a *mistake*. It is a truism if it involves a tacit redefinition of "physical theory" to mean "theory adequate to account for the observable behavior of any object (including animals and persons) which has physical properties." While if "physical theory" is taken in its ordinary sense of "theory adequate to explain the observable behavior of physical objects," it is, I believe, mistaken.

To ask how *impressions* fit together with *electromagnetic fields*, for example, is to ask a mistaken question. It is to mix the framework of *molar* behavior theory with the framework of the *micro*-theory of physical objects. The proper question is, rather, "What would correspond in a *micro*-theory of sentient organisms to *molar* concepts per-

Wilfrid Sellars

taining to impressions?" And it is, I believe, in answer to this question that one would come upon the *particulars* which sense-datum theorists profess to find (by analysis) in the common-sense universe of discourse (cf. Section 23). Furthermore, I believe that in characterizing these particulars, the micro-behaviorist would be led to say something like the following: "It is such particulars which (from the standpoint of the theory) are being responded to by the organism when it looks to a *person* as though there were a red and triangular physical object over there." It would, of course, be incorrect to say that, in the ordinary sense, such a particular is red or triangular. What *could* be said,* however, is that whereas in the common-sense picture physical objects are red and triangular but the impression "of" a red triangle is neither red nor triangular, in the framework of this micro-theory, the theoretical counterparts of sentient organisms are Space-Time worms characterized by two kinds of variables: (a) variables which also characterize the theoretical counterparts of merely material objects; (b) variables peculiar to sentient things; and that these latter variables are the counterparts in this new framework of the perceptible qualities of the physical objects of the common-sense framework. It is statements such as these which would be the cash value of the idea that "physical objects aren't really colored; colors exist only in the perceiver," and that "to see that the facing surface of a physical object is red and triangular is to *mistake* a red and triangular sense content for a physical object with a red and triangular facing side." Both these ideas clearly treat what is really a speculative philosophical critique (see Section 41) of the common-sense framework of physical objects and the perception of physical objects in the light of an envisaged ideal scientific framework, as though it were a matter of distinctions which can be drawn *within* the common-sense framework itself.

62. This brings me to the final chapter of my story. Let us suppose that as his final service to mankind before he vanishes without a trace, Jones teaches his theory of perception to his fellows. As before in the case of *thoughts*, they begin by using the language of impressions to draw theoretical conclusions from appropriate premises. (Notice that the evidence for theoretical statements in the language of impressions

* For a discussion of some logical points pertaining to this framework, the reader should consult the essay, "The Concept of Emergence," by Paul E. Meehl and Wilfrid Sellars, on pp. 239–52 of this volume.

will include such introspectible inner episodes as *its looking to one as though there were a red and triangular physical object over there*, as well as overt behavior.) Finally he succeeds in training them to make a *reporting* use of this language. He trains them, that is, to say "I have the impression of a red triangle" when, and only when, according to the theory, they are indeed having the impression of a red triangle.

Once again the myth helps us to understand that concepts pertaining to certain inner episodes—in this case *impressions*—can be primarily and essentially *intersubjective*, without being resolvable into overt behavioral symptoms, and that the reporting role of these concepts, their role in introspection, the fact that each of us has a privileged access to his impressions, constitutes a dimension of these concepts which is *built on* and *presupposes* their role in intersubjective discourse. It also makes clear why the "privacy" of these episodes is not the "absolute privacy" of the traditional puzzles. For, as in the case of thoughts, the fact that overt behavior is evidence for these episodes is built into the very logic of these concepts as the fact that the observable behavior of gases is evidence for molecular episodes is built into the very logic of molecule talk.

Notice that what our "ancestors" have acquired under the guidance of Jones is not "just another language"—a "notational convenience" or "code"—which merely enables them to say what they can already say in the language of qualitative and existential looking. They have acquired another language, indeed, but it is one which, though it rests on a framework of discourse about public objects in Space and Time, has an autonomous logical structure, and contains an *explanation of*, not just a *code for*, such facts as that *there looks to me to be a red and triangular physical object over there*. And notice that while our "ancestors" came to *notice* impressions, and the language of impressions embodies a "discovery" that there are such things, the language of impressions was no more tailored to fit *antecedent* noticings of these entities than the language of molecules was tailored to fit antecedent noticings of molecules.

And the spirit of Jones is not yet dead. For it is the particulars of the micro-theory discussed in Section 61 (5) which are the solid core of the sense contents and sense fields of the sense-datum theorist. Envisaging the general lines of that framework, even sketching some of its regions, he has taught himself to play with it (in his study) as a report language. Unfortunately, he mislocates the truth of these con-

Wilfrid Sellars

ceptions, and, with a modesty forgivable in any but a philosopher, confuses his own creative enrichment of the framework of empirical knowledge, with an analysis of knowledge as it was. He construes as *data* the particulars and arrays of particulars which he has come to be able to observe, and believes them to be antecedent objects of knowledge which have somehow been in the framework from the beginning. It is in the very act of *taking* that he speaks of the *given*.

63. I have used a myth to kill a myth—the Myth of the Given. But is my myth really a myth? Or does the reader not recognize Jones as Man himself in the middle of his journey from the grunts and groans of the cave to the subtle and polydimensional discourse of the drawing room, the laboratory, and the study, the language of Henry and William James, of Einstein and of the philosophers who, in their efforts to break out of discourse to an *arché* beyond discourse, have provided the most curious dimension of all.

REFERENCES

1. Ayer, A. J. *Foundations of Empirical Knowledge.* London: Macmillan, 1940.
2. Ayer, A. J. "The Terminology of Sense Data," in *Philosophical Essays,* pp. 66–104. London: Macmillan, 1954. Also in *Mind,* 54, 1945, pp. 289–312.
3. Braithwaite, R. B. *Scientific Explanation.* Cambridge: Cambridge Univ. Pr., 1953.
4. Broad, C. D. *Scientific Thought.* London: Kegan Paul, 1923.
5. Campbell, Norman. *Physics: The Elements.* Cambridge: Cambridge Univ. Pr., 1920.
6. Carnap, Rudolf. *Introduction to Semantics.* Chicago: Univ. of Chicago Pr., 1942.
7. Carnap, Rudolf. "Psychologie in Physikalischer Sprache," *Erkenntnis,* 3:107–42 (1933).
8. Carnap, Rudolf. "The Interpretation of Physics," in H. Feigl and M. Brodbeck (eds.), *Readings in the Philosophy of Science,* pp. 309–18. New York: Appleton-Century-Crofts, 1953. This selection consists of pp. 59–69 of his *Foundations of Logic and Mathematics.* Chicago: Univ. of Chicago Pr., 1939.
9. Chisholm, Roderick. "The Theory of Appearing," in Max Black (ed.), *Philosophical Analysis,* pp. 102–18. Ithaca: Cornell Univ. Pr., 1950.
10. Hempel, C. G. *Fundamentals of Concept Formation in Empirical Science.* Chicago: Univ. of Chicago Pr., 1952.
11. Linnell, John. "Berkeley's Critique of Abstract Ideas." A Ph.D. thesis submitted to the Graduate Faculty of the University of Minnesota, June 1954.
12. Paul, G. A. "Is there a Problem about Sense Data?" in Supplementary Volume XV of the *Aristotelian Society Proceedings.* Also in A. G. N. Flew (ed.), *Logic and Language.* New York: Philosophical Lib., 1951.
13. Price, H. H. *Perception.* London: Methuen, 1932.
14. Price, H. H. *Thinking and Experience.* London: Hutchinson's Univ. Lib., 1953.
15. Reichenbach, H. *Philosophie der Raum-Zeit-Lehre.* Berlin: de Gruyter, 1928.
16. Reichenbach, H. *Experience and Prediction.* Chicago: Univ. of Chicago Pr., 1938.
17. Ryle, Gilbert. *The Concept of Mind.* London: Hutchinson's Univ. Lib., 1949.
18. Sellars, Wilfrid. "Mind, Meaning and Behavior," *Philosophical Studies,* 3:83–94 (1952).

19. Sellars, Wilfrid. "A Semantical Solution of the Mind-Body Problem," *Methodos*, 5:45–84 (1953).
20. Sellars, Wilfrid. "Empiricism and Abstract Entities," in *Paul A. Schlipp* (ed.), *The Philosophy of Rudolf Carnap*. Evanston (Ill.): Library of Living Philosophers (forthcoming). (Available in mimeograph form from the author.)
21. Skinner, B. F. "The Operational Analysis of Psychological Terms," *Psychological Review*, 52:270–77 (1945). Reprinted in H. Feigl and M. Brodbeck (eds.), *Readings in the Philosophy of Science*, pp. 585–94. New York: Appleton-Century-Crofts, 1953.
22. Wittgenstein, Ludwig. *Philosophical Investigations*. London: Macmillan, 1953.

A Possible Distinction between Traditional Scientific Disciplines and the Study of Human Behavior

I WISH to discuss what I believe to be a difference between subjects such as physics, chemistry, and astronomy on the one hand, and economics, anthropology, sociology, and psychology on the other. These groups of subjects have often been referred to as the physical (or natural) sciences and the social (or behavioral) sciences respectively. Many people, feeling that there is an essential difference between the groups, have wished to mark it by withholding the term "science" from the description of the latter group. Not wishing to prejudge the issue, I have formulated the title of this paper in such a way as to avoid the disputed terminology.

Let me begin by pointing out some respects in which it will not be possible to draw a categorical distinction. First, in nearly all studies of the world from bird-watching to biochemistry, there is a descriptive, non-explanatory aspect. This is exemplified in astronomy when we give the constituents of the planetary atmospheres or the approximate diameter of a spiral nebula, and in economics when we give a breakdown of the Swedish taxation revenue or the approximate value of the British national debt. It is certainly true that there are important connections between the units and descriptive terms used in giving such data and the accepted theories in the field. But even if it were granted that economic theories are scientifically disreputable, one could not deny the existence of an exact though perhaps incomplete descriptive language in which the data of an economic science can be formulated. Now, in some subjects this description forms the most important part of the material, while in others prediction and explanation are admittedly more important; but this distinction does not coincide with the one we seek. For astronomy (as opposed to celestial mechanics or cosmology) is mainly a descriptive science, and so is primitive anthropology, while thermodynamics and welfare economics are not.

Second, I cannot see any way in which one could establish the claim that human behavior is in principle undetermined and, hence, distinguish its study from that of the presumably determined inanimate world. No matter in how many respects two human state-descriptions are the same, if the ensuing behavior differs, we shall regard that as evidence that somewhere in the individual or genetic histories or in the current circumstances there must be a difference in the value of a parameter.* I regard this as an empirical (though meta-theoretical) belief because I can conceive circumstances which might lead us to abandon it, but not in a world that resembles the one we inhabit.

Third, I see no other reason to doubt that precise explanations and predictions are available or possible in the study of some behavioral phenomena, e.g., in the psychological field. I have in mind two types of behavior here: on the one hand, behavior under restraints or compulsions; and, on the other, choice-behavior with one heavily weighted alternative. It is not hard to predict or explain what is in one sense the behavior of a man chained hand and foot to a rotating wheel, nor that of a claustrophobe when he sees an exit from a confined space, nor that of a man needing an operation to save his life who is offered the money by a wealthy philanthropist.

These predictions or explanations are not based on anything which is referred to as a psychological theory, but merely on our observations and "common-sense" inference. One might wish to say that there is an implicit theory in our classifications and inference in these cases. If so, then my point can be rephrased to state that in the cases in which we feel most certain most often of our behavioral predictions and explanations, they are based on the theory implicit in common sense and not on theories developed by professional psychologists. Some obvious qualifications must be made; but I think most of them fall under the heading of special types of behavior which had not previously been observed in sufficient detail or with sufficient frequency to permit

---

* Making some allowance for the amplification of quantum effects does not affect this as a methodological principle but would require modification to it as a descriptive account.

generalization, e.g., neurosis, overlearning, parapsychology. Of course, the souls of all good psychologists will revolt at this claim. But if justified, it is not a reflection on their past achievements or present ability. It is a description of their difficulties. The difference between the scientific study of behavior and that of physical phenomena is thus partly due to the relatively greater complexity of the *simplest phenomena we are concerned to account for* in a behavioral theory. There are, I think, three related explanations of this difficulty.

1. The basic generalizations are more complex, in the sense that more standing conditions must be specified for a functional relationship of comparable simplicity, and consequently more variables must be measured in obtaining the basic data to which the basic generalizations refer.

2. The useful concepts, i.e., those occurring in observation-statements and theory, include many from physics and mathematics as a proper subset.

3. The ordinary procedures for explaining behavior that are embedded in our everyday language contain a considerable proportion of the low-level laws (albeit imprecisely formulated *) obtained simply as a result of long experience; thus, some of the cream has been skimmed from the subject in a way not possible in, e.g., spectrochemistry.

There are two important consequences of the preceding propositions.

A. Students of human behavior have to theoretically run before they can theoretically walk; i.e., they have to look for higher-order theories in order to get a lead on the variables to isolate for sound generalizations. This is not unique to, but is more common in, this area.

B. Practical problems of prediction, or explanation *at any level* (i.e., including theory-building), are more likely to be *insoluble* in the study of behavior.

Now, it is the latter point that I wish to recommend as a salutary point of distinction between the two groups of studies. It requires some expansion.

Must there be a theory or theories that explain the phenomena (meaning basic observational data and generalizations) in a given field? Naturally we do our very best to find one, and in many fields we have come very close to success or have completely succeeded in the attempt. Naturally, too, we can never absolutely prove that there is not one. And

---

* As Skinner has said (1), "If a reasonable order [in human behavior] was not discoverable, we could scarcely be effective in dealing with human affairs."

it is true that the longer we wait, the more material (or the more *reliable* material) we shall have on which to build one. But is there any reason—other than our past experience in some fields—to believe that the proliferation of evidence makes a theory any more possible? There is an obvious sense in which an increase in data may make the job of finding an adequate explanation more difficult. Now, a scientific theory is typically a system of propositions which organizes the evidence internally and in relation to other propositions of the system which concern certain (possibly hypothetical) entities or states; so that we can see it as a consistent and connected whole, where the connection consists of *explanation* (not necessarily deduction) in the direction

(propositions about [possibly hypothetical] entities or states)

to (propositions describing the phenomena)

and of *inference* (not necessarily induction in the narrow sense) in the other direction.

In what sense *must* there be such relations amongst a given set of statements and such inferable or actual entities or conditions? If our notion of what constitutes a satisfactory explanation were completely *a priori*, then it would indeed be surprising if we were always able to find explanations; and if that notion were so accommodating that any fresh observation-statement was acceptable as a new postulate (when not immediately explicable by some other accepted statement), then we should never be at a loss for an explanation. Compare the question: in what sense must there be a formula which gives us all the prime numbers? If the primes are like clues in a numerical crossword puzzle, we are quite right to assume there is a solution; if they are like the number of squares on a chessboard that have not been occupied prior to the nth move of a game, we are mistaken in thinking there is a solution—though, of course, we can establish certain limits. And the primes present a problem that is in certain ways very like each of these. It is not possible to conclude that there *must* be a formula. Is it possible even to say that, if it is true, there *must* be a proof of Goldbach's hypothesis (that any even number can be expressed in at least one way as the sum of two primes)? I do not think that even a convinced formalist impressed by proof-theoretic successes would be able to establish such a claim—though we may be justified in thinking it probably correct. How, then, could we support the view that there *must* be an explanation of, or a theory about, the phenomena in a given field?

Michael Scriven

In the field of the empirical disciplines, the concept of explanation is not, it seems to me, as precise as that of a prime-number function or a number-theoretic proof. If it were, then the analogy would be fairly close, and we could only assert "There must always be an explanation" as an empirically well-founded slogan. But it is also true that we occasionally admit new types of explanation, which makes the slogan more like a tautology, and that we impose certain restrictions on what constitute acceptable postulates and rules of inference, which makes the slogan more empirical. With these simple introductory remarks about the inevitability of explanations (and we can substitute "predictions" or "theory" throughout), let us return to consideration of the special thesis that new explanations will be less readily found in the field of behavior than they have been in the development of the first-born sciences (and may sometimes never be found). I wish to distinguish two arguments for this thesis. The first point I regard as moderately important, certainly true, and fairly obvious: it is that the student of behavior is, in general, faced with problems of explanation that are very much more difficult than those that faced the early physicists. This is apparent in the practical field for one reason already cited, viz., we already have common-sensical and well-supported explanations of nearly all the easy cases, and we are therefore left with the problems we haven't been able to solve exactly by common sense: how do pilots judge height? how can we predict a student's examination performances? what lighting suits a machine assembly-line best? what causes amnesia? Even here, we do have rough, untested, unquantified ideas about the answers. These problems can be approached in a perfectly scientific way and valuable answers produced, prior to the formalization of the theory of normal perception, problem-performance, etc. But even if it is thought possible to produce a precise general theory of basic behavior, it would be wrong to conclude that exact predictions and faultless explanations will be possible in the field of practical problems; for they are now very rarely achieved in this area by any sciences. The practical problems of physics today are engineering problems, meteorological problems, aerodynamical problems; and to these there are not often exact solutions, but only compromises and approximations. How far will a missile of this shape travel with this propellant? We cannot tell accurately from experiments with scale models because we cannot scale down the size of air molecules or the critical mass of

334

the propellant. Even a full-scale test does not yield exactly repeatable results, and there are no precise general formulas for air resistance. But we can give quite good answers or, as in fact we have done, produce radio-controls that circumvent the problem of prediction. In general, the psychologist (or economist, etc.) has to work with a larger number of critical variables and cannot run full-scale repeatable tests. So he is not even as successful as scientists in those fields; but my main point is that he has to deal with the hardest type of problem that they ever face.

Some theoretical psychologist will want to reply by saying that what remains to be done in psychology is the job that Galileo did—the mathematicizing of its basic theory. Given that, he might say, we shall be able to improve practical predictions until they are comparable with those made by physicists. However, the importance of my point rests on the fact that in the area of fundamental research the number of critical variables is absolutely crucial; or to put it another way, the degree of actualized approximation to the ideal case is important. Galileo wished to measure the rate at which bodies naturally fell. His ingenuity lay in transposing the problem to that of measuring the rate at which spheres roll down an inclined plane. His good fortune lay in the fact that the loss of energy due to rolling friction, elastic absorption, and air resistance was negligible; and that a comparatively simple law roughly relates any two of the remaining three variables (distance traveled along the plane [or vertically], the time taken, and the velocity attained). Furthermore, he had measuring instruments which were sufficiently sensitive to variations in the most recalcitrant variable (a waterclock reading to 1/10 of a "pulse-beat") to reveal the law, while not so sensitive that they would yield the progressively greater inaccuracy as the absolute size of any variable increased (due to the mounting energy losses). Galileo was indeed fortunate; no less so were Boyle, Charles, Gay-Lussac, Van der Waals, and the others who discovered the gas laws: no less so Kepler whose very favorite law about the planets, relating their orbits to the regular-solids, has not survived the test of more accurate measurements. Students of behavior are not so fortunate, and it would be misguided of them to labor at the task of proving otherwise.

I am not making the absurd claim that there will be no progress, but simply the claim that simple laws will very rarely be found even under the most idealized laboratory conditions. This is a claim based on the empirical evidence, not on any *a priori* necessity. If the evidence was simply that we have so far failed to discover any simple laws, then it would seem rash to claim that none will be found. I believe, however, that the evidence also suggests an explanation for the lack of such successes in terms of several factors, the most important of which has been discussed above, viz., the multiplicity of critical variables *in the simplest interesting cases.* I wish also to combine the basic fact of relative lack of success with what I shall call the finitude of the set of usable hypotheses to provide another, substantially weaker, reason. It seems to me that in the field of individual behavior, to restrict the area sharply, the talk of "another Newton" is inappropriate. I would venture to say that it is extremely improbable that anything remotely corresponding to the simplicity and importance of the concept of universal gravitation can possibly be found in the field of psychology. The apparent exception is Freud. His importance is, to me, tempered by the recognition that his work was not only nonquantitative but in other respects imprecise, even as now reformulated (cf. evolutionary theory, which does not require statistical genetics for precision), and applies most successfully to *abnormal* psychology and is irrelevant to, or only partly relevant to, e.g., perception and learning.* (Now of course, gravitation did not explain electromagnetic phenomena; I wish only to point out that important restrictions do exist and that they exclude most of the area from which our fund of common observation stems). I am sceptical that a basic concept or set of concepts that will provide a new and fundamental insight into *ordinary* human behavior is discoverable. Man might have been a simple creature, his behavior governed by the stars or by enlightened self-interest, but he is not.

If the arguments that I have previously given convince us that a new conceptual scheme or theory in terms of some behavioral construct is unlikely to prove revelatory, it may be on the grounds that we must look for our revelations in the brain, as Dalton sought the explanations of overt chemical behavior in the atom. But the comparison is unsound. Dalton was faced with a large number of precise laws of chemical com-

---

* The theory of dream-interpretation and the parapraxes in Freud are, I would think it clear, too simple to be correct *except* (a) occasionally in normal people or (b) generally in some abnormal people. The vagueness of the postulates in, e.g., the theory of slips does not make it any less true that they are simple in the sense that they exclude motor errors.

bination, and had precise data about the substances which thus interacted. Suppose that he had observed only the results of experiments with highly stable, highly heterogeneous mixtures labeled perhaps A, B, or C. His results would be inexplicable in terms of any simple theory. It is this situation which faces the student of behavior—and for him there can be no reduction of the macroscopic data to simple invariable regularities, whose existence could perhaps be explained by reference to a theory of the micro-structure. Why not? Because the fundamental experimental element is the human being, or his responses, enormously complex in structure and function and reared in an enormously complex environment. There can be no *practical* sense in which this element can be reduced to simpler ones. There is, of course, a *theoretical* sense in which we can analyze an individual's motivation in terms, say, of primary and acquired drives or his purchasing in terms of consumption, savings, or production. But these analyses are neither precise nor productive of simple laws, so we are not empirically justified in claiming that micro-concepts will be found that will yield simple laws. Here I do not intend "simple" to be very restrictive: the laws of radiation include fourth powers, those of electromagnetism vector differentials, those of elasticity tensor quantities, yet nothing as simple as these can be expected in behavior. This is not to deny that, under certain specified circumstances, the behavior of an organism can be precisely predicted, e.g., in a Skinner-box. This I earlier said was even possible with humans under nonexperimental conditions. I am denying that this possibility is more than an unimportant (though perhaps necessary) condition for developing a manageable *general* theory of behavior which will usefully predict the aspects of ordinary behavior that we need predictions about. The meteorologist is in the same position; he knows that under some circumstances he can predict rain with tremendous reliability, and he can always do quite well at predicting barometric pressure, and he can almost always see in retrospect how to explain his errors, i.e., can give a general account of weather. But the practical definition of his problems makes the long-range prediction of precipitation in all cases immensely important, and predicting morning rain in London for the next test match with Australia with the 51 per cent accuracy an insurance company would be interested in is just a pipe dream, whereas in astronomy it's child's-play. The practical problems in psychology are often worse than the meteorologist's.

Michael Scriven

The statistics of mathematical economics, perhaps the most highly formalized area in the study of behavior, is particularly interesting in this respect. It is quite true that if men always chose rationally, were equally well-informed, and had identical needs and desires, precise laws in economics could probably be found. And it is true that rationality, informedness, and requirements are dominating factors in the actual situation. It does not follow from this that a theory which describes the action of an agent or economic group in the ideal case is in the least valuable as a practical aid. It must also be proved that the variations from the ideal produce effects that are small compared with the total effects in the ideal case—or if the effects of the variations are large, they must themselves be predictable. I think that overlooking this point has led many mathematical economists to believe that, because they have a theory of the ideal case, they are therefore in as satisfactory a position as that of the theoretical chemist trying to predict the behavior of a mixture, granted a knowledge of the behavior of the ingredients: just a problem of measurement and calculation. Though it is true that scientific laws typically refer to an ideal case, and it is true that in the practical field they very often do not yield precise predictions, it does not follow that a theory which deals with an idealization of some or even all the factors involved in a behavior situation is properly called a theory of behavior. One might say that the essence of the success of the natural sciences is the possibility of finding simple laws referring to ideal cases that are or can be realized in empirical cases to an indefinitely high degree of approximation.

It is, I think, very important to distinguish two theses about the future of the behavioral sciences. First, there is the thesis that it will be possible to improve predictions and explanations indefinitely. Second, there is the thesis that it will be possible to improve predictions and explanations *in every case, and to an indefinitely high degree* of approximation. The first thesis I agree with; the second I think false for two reasons:

1. It is typical of problems in the field of behavior that we have limited access to data (extreme case: precise prediction of individual behavior may prove possible given certain data about values of neurological variables. But it would be dogmatic to insist that there must be a way to determine these that does not involve long study and perhaps surgery on that individual; therefore, the problem of prediction

338

given only limited observational access will probably never be precisely solved).

2. There is a great deal of difference between indefinite improvement in a field, i.e., continual progress with some aspects of some problems, and the attainment of indefinitely high approximations in solving a given aspect of a given problem. Science has not advanced by solving all problems but often by abandoning them; we never solved the problem of finding how the stars affected our lives; we never found a real philosopher's stone; we never found an elixir of life, nor the vital essence, nor the language of animals. Why then must there be laws in the social sciences that will enable us *in every case* to predict or explain? May we not here also come to see that the search is for something we may wish for but cannot expect?

There is a second reason for my main conclusion; and this one I regard as extremely important, not at all obvious, and only probably right. This is the existence of non-deductive explanations, which are the central type in the field of behavior, and it is connected with the requirements of universality and repeatability of effects. I shall discuss it elsewhere. The conclusion I hope then to establish more clearly, but which I have here tried to support, is not in general form a very exciting one, for we have all realized that in some sense psychological laws and theories have been harder to find than were the early physical ones. Its merit, if any, lies in the stress on the particular respects in which this is true and the reasons for these particular differences.

REFERENCE

1. Skinner, B. F. *Science and Human Behavior.* New York: Macmillan, 1953.

Name Index

Name Index

Hebb, D. O., 103, 133
Hegel, G. W. F., 224, 253
Hempel, C. G., 3, 4, 15, 39, 48, 53, 56, 132, 187, 312
Hilgard, E. R., 141
Holt, E. B., 236–38
Horney, K., 164n
Hovey, H. B., 191
Hull, C. L., 93, 98, 103, 104n, 133
Hume, D., 6, 9, 16, 25, 27, 28, 160n, 286, 288–89
Humphreys, L. G., 174

Jacoby, G., 16n
James, H., 327–28
James, W., 327–28
Jenkins, J. G., 175
Jevons, W. S., 25
Johnson, W. E., 25

Kant, I., 23, 24, 27, 34, 253, 272, 323
Kaplan, A., 4
Kaufmann, F., 4
Kelley, E. L., 193
Kendler, H. H., 102
Kepler, J., 334
Keynes, J. M., 23, 25, 28, 34
Kneale, W., 33, 35n, 134, 187
Koestler, A., 163n
Kraft, V., 10
Krech, D., 133
Kris, E., 155
Kubie, L. S., 141

Leibniz, G. W., 23
Lenzen, V., 24
Lewis, C. I., 24, 32, 35
Lindsay, R. B., 135
Lindzey, G., 133
Linnell, J., 286n
Locke, J., 284, 286–89
Lovejoy, A. O., 16n
Lucas, C. M., 185
Lundberg, G., 133, 134

McCandless, B. R., 133, 180
MacCorquodale, K., 73, 101, 132, 178
MacDougall, W., 159n
Macfarlane, J. W., 182
Mach, E., 5, 10, 16, 23
Margenau, H., 68
Marhenke, P., 15
Mates, B., 6n
Maxwell, J. C., 26, 33
Maze, J. R., 133

Meehl, P. E., 73, 101, 131n, 132, 134, 174, 176, 178, 326n
Mehlberg, H., 5
Michelson, A. A., 11
Mill, J. S., 25, 34
Miller, J. G., 223ff
Minkowski, H., 282
Mises, R. von, 3, 4, 23
Moore, G. E., 5, 27, 257
Mosier, C. I., 175

Nagel, E., 4
Neumann, J. von, 13
Neurath, D., 3
Newton, I., 10, 14, 26, 335
Nicod, J., 25
Noble, H. R., 12

Oppenheimer, R., 136

Pap, A., 4, 187
Paterson, D. G., 211
Pavlov, I., 101
Peak, H., 175
Peirce, C. S., 32
Pepper, S., 239–52 passim
Peters, R. S., 158n, 161, 162
Planck, M., 10
Plato, 161n
Poincarè, H., 10, 12
Popper, K., 4
Porteus, S. D., 185
Pratt, C. C., 133
Price, H. H., 268n, 291, 297
Pumpian-Mindlin, E., 141

Quine, W. V., 6ff

Rapaport, D., 133
Rappaport, A., 232
Rausch, H. L., 134
Reichenbach, H., 3, 4, 5, 6, 9, 10, 13, 14, 15, 22ff, 48, 53, 132, 134, 312
Reid, J., 131
Roessell, F. P., 191
Rosen, A., 210
Rudner, R., 135
Russell, B., 3, 16, 25, 167, 206
Ryle, G., 272, 289, 307, 309ff

Santayana, G., 27
Sarbin, T. R., 133, 134
Schlick, M., 3, 4, 6, 10, 14, 16, 17, 18, 53–54
Schofield, W., 131n

341

Scriven, M., 131, 132, 134, 174
Sears, R. R., 165
Seeger, R. J., 135
Seeman, W., 131
Sellars, R. W., 16n
Sellars, W. S., 18–19, 100, 131n, 174n, 187, 326n
Sitter, W. de, 11
Skinner, B. F., 88–130, 131, 133, 135, 141, 208, 321, 331n
Spiker, C. C., 133, 180
Spinoza, B., 284
Strawson, P. F., 35n
Sullivan, H. S., 131
Super, D. E., 174

Tarski, A., 5
Thistlethwaite, D. L., 174n
Thurstone, L. L., 176–77, 182

Tolman, E. C., 93, 103, 133
Toulmin, S. E., 160n, 161–63, 170
Trouton, F. T., 12

Verplanck, W. S., 89n, 103

Waals, J. D. van der, 334
Waismann, F., 8n, 108
Weinschenk, C., 16n
Wigner, E. P., 135
Will, F., 35n
Williams, D. C., 27
Winthrop, H., 131n
Wisdom, J. O., 35n, 159n
Wittgenstein, L., 4, 5, 14, 17, 18, 27, 321
Woodger, J. H., 4, 5

Zilsel, E., 4, 25
Zubin, J., 135

Subject Index

A priori, 9, 22, 23, 24, 31: synthetic, 8, 23, 24, 30, 33, 253; pragmatic, 10, 11, 24, 33; and emergence, 239
Abience, 236ff
Aboutness, 311: and semantical categories, 318, 319. *See also* Meaning
Abstraction: doctrine of, 16; and meaning, 18
Adience, 236ff
Ambiguity, systematic, 10
Analogy, in general systems theory, 224–32
Analysis, nature of, 5–6, 234–35, 301–2
Analytic statements, distinguished from synthetic, 6–14
Anxiety, concept of, 125, 177–78, 192

Barnum effect, 211–12, 218
Baye's rule, 209ff
Behavior: and perception, 82; unit of, 82; and learning, 83; and probability of response, 84; and self-observation, 85; and theories, 94; meaning of, 109–10; and motivation, 157; and dreams, 157n; and general systems theory, 223ff
Behaviorism, 70, 71, 72, 77–130, 133, 165, 168–69: and sensations, 250; methodological, 314ff; philosophical, 314ff
Binet scale, 182

Causality, 9, 25, 89: principle of, 8, 9; temporal structure of, 24. *See also* Determinism
Communication, in information theory, 233–34
Concept empiricism, 18
Concepts: network character of, 16–20 *passim*; dispositional, 18, 42, 53, 62–69, 71–74 *passim*, 113, 114, 121–22, 277; and laws, 18; theoretical, 38–76, 316ff; psychological, 69–75; significance of, 226; formation of, 257ff, 275ff, 306ff; coherence of, 275ff, 299. *See also* Constructs; Entities; Meaning

Conceptualism, 284ff
Confirmation, 13–33 *passim*, 122–23: successive, 13. *See also* Meaning, criterion of; Testability; Verifiability
Consciousness: concept of, 85; and emergence, 249–50; and sensing, 257
Construct validity, 174–204, 216
Constructivism, in the observation language, 41
Constructs
  HYPOTHETICAL, 17, 42, 73, 78–79, 117ff, 132–37 *passim*, 151, 178, 187: and implicit definition, 192
  IN PSYCHOLOGY: defined, 178; kinds of, 178
  SCIENTIFIC, *see* Constructs, hypothetical
  THEORETICAL, *see* Constructs, hypothetical
  See also Concepts; Entities
Contrary-to-fact conditionals, *see* Implication, subjunctive
Conventionalism, 10, 11
Correspondence rules, *see* Language, correspondence rules of
Cosmology, 22, 24, 34, 300
Counterfactuals, *see* Implication, subjunctive

Deduction: and induction, 7; theory of, 13
Definition, 8: contextual, 7, 256; recursive, 7; disguised, 9; by postulates, 9, 18, 93, 99; and laws, 10; ostensive, 18, 99, 325; coordinating, 20, 21; correlative, 48; conditional, 53–64; and necessary equivalence, 269ff; and analysis, 301–2
  EXPLICIT, 7, 9, 18, 21: in the observation language, 41; and theoretical terms, 42, 53; and disposition terms, 63, 64; and scientific concepts, 112; and Behaviorism, 315–16

343

Subject Index

and science, 300ff; and philosophy, 300ff

OBSERVATION, 19, 20, 21, 38–76 *passim*, 112, 127, 311ff: dichotomy with the theoretical language, 19, 99, 311ff; explained, 40–42

THEORETICAL, 19, 20, 21, 38–76, 304, 311ff: dichotomy with the observation language, 19, 99, 311ff; and sense data language, 265, 311ff

Law of Effect, 94, 97, 103

Laws: and inductive probability, 32; causal, 33; statistical, 33, 49, 52, 187; probabilistic, 49, 52, 71, 72; deterministic, 187; vagueness of in psychology, 192; and ideal cases, 337

Learning: and behavior, 83; theory of, 99–105; and sensing, 257ff; and language, 290ff

Logic: of science, 4, 32, 34; modal, 9, 33, 63–64; laws of, 13; many-valued, 13; two-valued, 13; probability, 28; of meaning, 290ff

Logical atomism, 275ff

Logical constructions, and the unconscious, 159–60

Logical reconstruction, 5, 8, 10, 13, 20, 34, 69

Looks: and relations, 269; analysis of, 269ff; qualitative and existential, 273–74; explanation of, 278ff, 305, 326

Mathematics, entities of, 43, 45, 46

Meaning, 19: as rules of language, 5, 18; criterion of, 13ff, 38–48 *passim*, 49–62; and abstraction, 18; and definitions, 18; changes in, 112, 113; logic of, 290ff. See also Aboutness; Definition; Language; Semantics

Metaphysics, 4, 22, 33, 39, 135: inductive, 15, 22; transcendent, 15; and science, 16, 17; and theoretical entities, 44, 46; and the meaning criterion, 54, 55, 56; and physicalism, 75; and introspection, 112; and general systems theory, 223ff; and emergence, 240; and Behaviorism, 314–15

Mind-body problem, 19ff, 80–82, 114, 117ff, 253–328 *passim*

Models, and theories, 311ff

Monism, 19ff

Morality, and the unconscious, 160–61

Motives, and the unconscious, 155–73

Necessity, 24: as causal connection, 9

Neurophysiology, see Psychology, and physiology

Nominalism: in the observation language, 41, 46; and empiricism, 259; psychological, 289ff

Nomological network, 16–20 *passim*, 178: and construct validity, 187ff; explained, 187–88

Occam's razor, 13ff

Ontology, 34, 300, 302: and theoretical entities, 44

Operationism, 16, 17, 34, 65, 66, 68, 70: and theoretical terms, 53; defined, 131–36; in psychoanalysis, 131–54; in psychological tests, 179–80, 201; and givenness, 267. See also Definition, operational

Parsimony, see Occam's razor; Simplicity

Perception, and behavior, 82. See also Sense data; Sense qualities

Personality, characterization of, 206–22

Phenomenalism, 16, 17, 19, 21, 34. See also Sense data

Physical$_1$, defined, 252

Physical$_2$, defined, 252

Physicalism, 18, 19, 21, 74–75: and purposes, 164; and psychoanalysis, 169–72

Physics, entities of, 43–44

Positivism, 17, 19, 22, 34: logical, 3; therapeutic, 5; and B. F. Skinner, 117

Positivistic conception of science, 304–5

Postulates, independence of, 12. See also Definition, by postulates; Systems; Theories

Pragmatism, 32

Prediction, 11, 29: clinical vs. statistical, 206ff

Privacy, 321, 327

Probability: theory of, 22–27 *passim*, 28ff; statistical, 49

Psychoanalysis, 77–87, 105ff, 155–73: and operationism, 131–54

Psychological nominalism, 289ff

Psychologism, 27

Psychology: entities of, 44, 74, 77–79, 84, 86, 99, 117ff, 128–29 (see also Impressions; Sense data; Thoughts); concepts of, 69–75; molar, 73–75, 97, 124–26, 151; micro, 74, 75; and physiology, 74, 77–130 *passim*, 133, 151, 171, 247ff, 316, 325, 327, 335–37; and purpose, 159n, 165, 171; tests in, 174–204, 209ff; vagueness in, 192; and physics, 236–38, 325, 334; and mathematics, 334

345